M000239467

Studies in Inductive Logic and Probability

VOLUME I

Studies in Inductive Logic and Probability

VOLUME I

Rudolf Carnap and Richard C. Jeffrey

EDITORS

UNIVERSITY OF CALIFORNIA PRESS

BERKELEY · LOS ANGELES · LONDON · 1971

216915

University of California Press
Berkeley and Los Angeles

University of California Press, Ltd.
London, England

Copyright © 1971 by The Regents of the University of California

ISBN: 0-520-01866-4
Library of Congress Catalog Card Number: 77-136025

Printed in the United States of America

Designed by Dave Comstock

Contents

Introduction

Carnap's *Logical Foundations of Probability* [1950] was planned as the first in a two-volume work, *Probability and Induction.* A summary of the system of inductive logic projected for Volume II, based on the function c^*, appeared as an appendix to Volume I; but two years later, with the publication of *The Continuum of Inductive Methods*, it became apparent that Volume II would not simply be the theory of c^*. The method based on that function appeared as a single point in the continuum, distinguished by a combination of plausibility and simplicity, but no longer the clearly chosen inductive method. During the following two years' work at the Institute for Advanced Study, Carnap's ideas changed still further, partly as a result of his work with John Kemeny: the continuum of inductive methods itself was seen as too narrow, e.g., because none of the c-functions in the continuum are adequately sensitive to analogy by similarity. These investigations resulted in a new axiom system for c-functions, which appeared as Appendix B in Carnap [1959]. (See the bibliography at the end of this volume.) But in the light of further work, this system, too, seemed too narrow: see Carnap [1964*a*] §§25 and 26.

Thus, in the decade following publication of Carnap [1950], an accumulation of small steps resulted in a change of perspective on past and future work. Volume II of *Probability and Induction* would be no mere elaboration of the outline at the end of Volume I, but the outcome of at least another decade's work, the shape of which could not yet be clearly seen. Furthermore, the technical apparatus elaborated in Volume I no longer seemed satisfactory, partly because of Carnap's extensive use of mathematical tools like de Finetti's representation theorem, which had not figured in his earlier work, and partly because of a desire to formulate inductive logic in terms that had come to be standard in mathematical probability theory and theoretical statistics, where probabilities are attributed to "events" (or "propositions") which are construed as sets of entities which can handily be taken to be *models*, in the sense in which that term is used in logic.

Then, in 1960, Carnap drew up a plan of articles for *Studies in Inductive Logic and Probability*—a surrogate for Volume II of the work projected in 1950, in the form of a nonperiodical journal in which various authors would report work in progress toward an adequate system of inductive logic. To begin, some twenty articles were projected, by Carnap, Kemeny, Jeffrey, and Gaifman. The first few were planned to be completed in the course of a year or two; but they are finally appearing only now. A version of Art. 1 has already been published (Carnap [1962*a*]), and an earlier version of the Basic System (Art. 2 here, with its continuation to follow in Volume 2) was distributed in dittographed form in 1959–61 under the title, "An Axiom System of Inductive Logic". Meanwhile, a number of important papers (by Gaifman, Krauss, and others) that bear on the project have appeared in various journals. Thus this volume appears too late to avoid dispersion and the generation of dittographed *arcana*, and to that extent it fails in its original purpose. But part of that original project was apparently unrealistic. The more important part is realized (in this volume and the next) in Carnap's detailed presentation of his basic system of inductive logic as it now exists. It is *basic* first in the sense that many issues requiring more thorough exploration are touched on here only lightly; notes for papers on these issues exist in Carnap's shorthand, and it is to he hoped that this material will begin to appear in print in later volumes. And it is basic, too, in the sense that what we have now is to be viewed as a foundation, not as a completed structure. Nor, of course, is the foundation immune from revision: difficulties may well appear in the upper stories which will force changes in the basics.

Rudolf Carnap and Richard C. Jeffrey
1969

Postscript

Carnap died in September, 1970, after a brief illness. He had finished revising all but the last two sections of the continuation of the Basic System (Art. 2) which will appear in Volume II. These last two sections are now being revised by Lary Kuhns and Gordon Matthews, who had been working with Carnap over the years, and with whom Carnap had discussed the two sections in detail.

The Introduction above is a draft, written by me and incompletely revised by Carnap, who approved it and sent me some additional notes, which are reproduced below essentially as he wrote them. They give some of the further facts he wanted mentioned.

Thanks are due to Carnap's assistant, Brooks Colburn, for proofreading Articles 1 and 2, and for other help; and to Hannaliese

Thost-Carnap, for keeping her father's working papers together and accessible to his collaborators.

Richard C. Jeffrey
February, 1971

Further Material for the Introduction

1952–1954: Carnap was at the Institute for Advanced Study, in Princeton.

First year: 1952–1953. Throughout this period Carnap collaborated regularly with John Kemeny. (Kemeny was teaching at the Department of Philosophy at Princeton University. He was also a very efficient mathematician; as such he had been an assistant to Einstein.) Kemeny and Carnap worked chiefly on the problem of several families of attributes. Carnap had found a solution for two families (see [1959] Anhang B, sec. VIII). They now extended this to a language with any (finite) number of families. Kemeny also studied de Finetti's work, especially his representation theorem, according to which any symmetric M-function can be represented by a distribution function in the structure space (see Art. 3, §10). Sometimes they also had talks with L. J. Savage. Among other things, Savage showed them that the use of a language L_N with a finite number N of individuals is not advisable, because a symmetric M-function in L_N cannot always be extended to an M-function in a language with a greater number of individuals.

Yehoshua Bar-Hillel was in Princeton for some time in April, 1953. Carnap told him about his ideas on a semantical concept of content measure or amount of information based on the logical concept of probability, in contrast to the statistical concept of amount of information (Shannon). This led to the Research Report: Carnap and Bar-Hillel [1952]. Frequently there is confusion between these two concepts. Only the second, not the first, is related to the physical concept of entropy. Bar-Hillel and Carnap also had some talks with John von Neumann. He asserted that the basic concepts of quantum theory are subjective and that this holds especially for entropy since this concept is based on probability and amount of information. They tried in vain to convince him of the existence of a difference in each of these two pairs of concepts (see Bar-Hillel [1964, p. 12]).

Second Year: 1953–1954. Kemeny was in England. Carnap worked mostly on the big manuscript on entropy (unpublished). He tried to clarify the nature of the entropy concept as it occurs in statistical mechanics (Boltzmann and Gibbs); and especially to show the difference between this physical concept and a corresponding logical concept.

Carnap had many talks with Hilary Putnam; also some talks with Kurt Gödel. [I hope to provide more material on the second year later, when I shall have read more of my diary.]

1954–1962: Carnap was teaching at UCLA. He had many talks with philosophers and others who came to Los Angeles for a time, often for work at the Rand Corporation.

Kemeny and Richard Jeffrey were Research Associates in Carnap's research grant NSF (2) for 1959–62. Jeffrey had written his doctoral dissertation on inductive logic with Hempel.

Research Assistants

Gordon Matthews and Lary John Kuhns (financed by Research Committee of UCLA 1957–63; later by NSF grants (3) and (4), see below).

Haim Gaifman, 1959–60 (NSF grant (2)).

Peter Krauss, 1962–63 (NSF grant (3)).

Institutions and Foundations

Institute for Advanced Study, Princeton, 1952–54. Stipend from the institute, supplemented in the first year by:

Bollingen Foundation, 1952–53, and NSF (1), and in the second year by:

John Simon Guggenheim Memorial Foundation, 1953–54.

UCLA Research Committee, 1957–62: yearly grants for Research Assistants Matthews and Kuhns.

Office of Naval Research: Contract Nonr-233(55). July 1, 1961–January 31, 1963, only for Research Assistant Krauss.

National Science Foundation:

(1) Grant G163.
(2) Grant G7585.
(3) Grant G22315.
(4) Grant GS550; this is a continuation of (3).

I wish to express my deep appreciation for the support of my research work by the Institute and the foundations listed above.

Rudolf Carnap
May 21, 1970

1

Inductive Logic and Rational Decisions

BY RUDOLF CARNAP

1
Decision Making[1]

By "inductive logic" I understand a theory of logical probability providing rules for inductive thinking. I shall try here to make clear the nature of inductive logic by showing how it can be used in determining rational decisions.

Decision theory involves the concepts of utility and probability. I shall try to show that, in this context, we must understand "probability" not as relative frequency, but as degree of belief. This is originally, in descriptive decision theory, a psychological concept, referring to actual beliefs of actual human beings. Later I shall go to normative decision theory by introducing some requirements of rationality. Up to that point I shall be in agreement with the representatives of a personal (or "subjective") conception of probability. But then I shall take a further step leading from a quasi-psychological to a logical concept of probability. By "inductive logic" I understand the theory of this concept.

Let us begin with the customary schema of decision making. A person X at a certain time T has to make a choice among possible acts $A_1, A_2, \ldots$. We assume the following. X knows that the possible states of nature (or of a part of nature relevant for his decision) at time T are $W_1, W_2, \ldots$; but he does not know which of them is the actual state. The number of possible acts and the number of possible states are finite. X knows the following: if he were to carry out the act A_m and if the state W_n were the actual state of nature, then the outcome would be $O_{m,n}$. This outcome $O_{m,n}$ is uniquely determined by A_m and W_n; and X knows how it is determined. We assume that there is a utility function U_X for the person X and that X knows his utility function so that he can use it in order to calculate values.

Now we define the (*subjective*) *value* (desirability) of a possible act A_m for X at time T:

(1) *Definition.* $V_{X,T}(A_m) = \sum_n [U_X(O_{m,n})P(W_n)]$, where $P(W_n)$ is the probability of the state W_n, and the sum covers all possible states W_n.

In other words, we take as the value of the act A_m for X the *expected utility* of the outcome of this act. (1) holds for the time T before any of the possible acts is carried out. It refers to the contemplated act A_m; therefore it uses the utilities for the possible outcomes

[1] This article is a modified and expanded version of my paper "The aim of inductive logic" which appeared in: *Logic, methodology and philosophy of science: Proceedings of the 1960 International Congress*, ed. E. Nagel, P. Suppes, and A. Tarski (Stanford University Press, 1962).

$O_{m,n}$ of act A_m in the various possible states W_n. [If the situation is such that the probability of W_n could possibly be influenced by the assumption that act A_m were carried out, we should take the conditional probability $P(W_n \mid A_m)$ instead of $P(W_n)$. Analogous remarks hold for our later forms of the definition of V.]

Now the customary *Bayesian rule* of decision making says:

(2) Choose an act so as to maximize the value V.

As a principle (statement) it may be stated in either of the following two forms, which are essentially different but are not always clearly distinguished:

(3a) Decisions are (usually, under normal conditions) made in such a way that the chosen act has the maximum value.

(3b) A *rational* decision consists in the choice of an act that has the maximum value.

The principle (3a) is an alleged psychological law belonging to *descriptive decision theory*, which is a part of psychology. In contrast, (3b) belongs to *normative decision theory*, which states conditions of rationality for decisions. This distinction will presently be discussed. But first we have to remove an ambiguity in the definition (1) of value, concerning the interpretation of the probability P. There are several conceptions of probability; thus the question arises which of them is adequate in the context of decision theory.

The main conceptions of probability are often divided into two kinds, statistical (or objective) and personal (or subjective) conceptions. As I see it, these are not two incompatible doctrines concerning the same concept, but rather two theories concerning two different probability concepts, both of them legitimate and useful. The concept of *statistical probability* is closely connected with relative frequencies in mass phenomena. It plays an important role in mathematical statistics, and it occurs in laws of various branches of empirical science, especially physics.

The second concept is *personal probability*. It is the probability assigned to a proposition or event H by a person X, in other words, the *degree of belief of X in H*. Now it seems to me that we should clearly distinguish two versions of personal probability, one representing the *actual* degree of belief and the other the *rational* degree of belief.

Which of these two concepts of probability, the statistical or the personal, ought to be used in the definition of value and thereby in the decision principle? At the present time, the great majority of those who work in mathematical statistics still regard the statistical concept of probability as the only legitimate one. This concept refers, however, to an objective feature of nature, a feature that holds whether or not the observer X knows about it. And in fact, the numerical values of statistical probability are in general not known to *X*. Therefore this concept is unsuitable for a decision principle. It seems that for this reason a number of those who work in decision theory, be it descriptive or normative, incline toward the view that some version of the personal concept of probability must be used here. I agree with this view.

The statistical concept of probability remains, of course, a legitimate and important concept both for mathematical statistics and for many branches of empirical science. And in the special case that *X* knows the statistical probabilities for the relevant states W_n but does not know which is the actual state, the decision principle would use these probabilities. There is general agreement on this point. And this is not in conflict with the view that the decision principle should refer to personal probability, because in this special situation the personal probability for *X* would be equal to the statistical probability.

Once we recognize that decision theory needs the personal concept of probability, it is clear that the theory of *actual* decisions involves the first version of this concept, i.e., the *actual* degree of belief, and the theory of *rational* decisions involves the second version, the *rational* degree of belief.

2
Actual Decisions

Let us first discuss descriptive decision theory, the theory of *actual* decisions. The concept of probability in the sense of the *actual* degree of belief is a psychological concept; its laws are empirical laws of psychology, to be established by the investigation of the behavior of persons in situations of uncertainty, e.g., behavior with respect to bets or games of chance. I shall use for this psychological concept the technical term *degree of credence* or *credence* for short. In symbols, I write '$\mathrm{Cr}_{X,T}(H)$' for "the [degree of] credence of the proposition H for the person X at the time T." Different persons X and Y may have different credence functions $\mathrm{Cr}_{X,T}$ and $\mathrm{Cr}_{Y,T}$. And the same person X may have different credence functions Cr_{X,T_1} and Cr_{X,T_2} at different times T_1 and T_2; e.g., if X observes between T_1 and T_2 that H holds, then $\mathrm{Cr}_{X,T_1}(H) \neq \mathrm{Cr}_{X,T_2}(H)$. (Let the ultimate possible cases be represented by the points of a logical space, usually called the probability space. Then a proposition or event is understood, not as a sentence, but as the range or truth set of a sentence, i.e., the set of points representing those possible cases in which the sentence holds. To the conjunction of two sentences corresponds the intersection of the propositions.)

On the basis of credence, we can define *conditional credence*, "the credence of H with respect to the proposition E" (or " . . . given E"):

(4) *Definition.* $\mathrm{Cr}'_{X,T}(H \mid E) = \dfrac{\mathrm{Cr}_{X,T}(E \cap H)}{\mathrm{Cr}_{X,T}(E)}$, provided that $\mathrm{Cr}_{X,T}(E) > 0$. $\mathrm{Cr}'_{X,T}(H \mid E)$ is the credence that H would have for X at T if X ascertained that E holds.

Using the concept of credence, we now replace the definition of value (1) by the following:

(5) *Definition.* $V_{X,T}(A_m) = \sum_n [U_X(O_{m,n})\mathrm{Cr}_{X,T}(W_n)]$.

As was pointed out by Frank P. Ramsey, we can determine X's credence function by his betting behavior. A bet is a contract of the following form: X pays into the pool the amount u, his partner Y pays the amount v; they agree that the total stake $u + v$ goes to X if the hypothesis H turns out to be true, and to Y if it turns out to be false. If X accepts this contract, we say that he bets on H with the total stake $u + v$ and with the betting quotient $q = u/(u + v)$ (or, at odds of u to v). If we apply the decision principle with the definition (5) to the situation in which X may either accept or reject an offered bet on H with the betting quotient q, we find that X will accept the bet if q is not larger than his credence for H. Thus we may interpret $\mathrm{Cr}_{X,T}(H)$ as the highest betting quotient at which X is willing to bet on H. (As is well known, this holds only under certain conditions and only approximately.)

Utility and credence are psychological concepts. The utility function of X represents the system of valuations and preferences of X; his credence function represents his system of beliefs (not only the content of each belief, but also its strength). Both concepts are theoretical concepts which characterize the state of mind of a person; more exactly, the nonobservable microstate of his central nervous system, not his consciousness, let alone his overt behavior. But since his behavior is influenced by his state, we can indirectly determine characteristics of his state from his behavior. Thus experimental methods have been developed for the determination of some values and some general characteristics of the utility function and the credence function ("subjective probability") of a person on the basis of his behavior with respect to bets and similar situations. Interesting investigations of this kind have been made among others by F. C. Mosteller and P. Nogee, and more recently by D. Davidson, P. Suppes, and S. Siegel [1957] (see the Bibliography at the end of this volume).

3
Rational Decisions

Now we go from descriptive to normative decision theory. The latter is of greater interest to us, not so much for its own sake (its methodological status is in fact somewhat problematic), but because it is the connecting link between descriptive decision theory and inductive logic. Normative decision theory is concerned not with actual credence, but with *rational* credence. (We should also distinguish here between actual utility and rational utility; but we omit this.) The statements of a theory of this kind are not found by experiments but are established on the basis of requirements of rationality. The formal procedure usually consists in deducing theorems from axioms that are justified by general considerations of rationality, as we shall see. It seems fairly clear that the probability concepts used by the following authors are meant in the sense of rational credence (or of rational credibility, which I shall explain presently): John Maynard Keynes [1921], Frank P. Ramsey [1931*a*], Harold Jeffreys [1957], B. O. Koopman [1940*b*], Georg Henrik von Wright [1957], I. J. Good [1950], Leonard J. Savage [1954].

It is now clear that the probability concept of Bruno de Finetti ([1937] (English translation [1964])) belongs to the same kind. His earlier formulations were sometimes misleading, e.g., when he said that his probability concept refers not to rational, but to actual beliefs. He made his view clear in a lengthy footnote on p. 111 of Kyburg-Smokler [1964]. At the end of this note he says: "In order to avoid frequent misunderstandings it is essential to point out that probability theory is not an attempt to describe actual behavior; its subject is coherent behavior, and the fact that people are only more or less coherent is inessential."

[Some remarks on *terminology*. Instead of "statistical" and "personal" as characterizing adjectives attached to "probability," the terms "objective" and "subjective" are frequently used. Now the concept of statistical probability can indeed be correctly characterized as being objective. But the use of "subjective" for the concept of personal probability seems to me highly questionable. We might still apply it to the concept of *actual* degree of belief, but its use for the *rational* degree of belief in normative decision theory would seem to me inappropriate, and still more for the *logical* concept of probability to be discussed later. (See my remarks in [1950], p. 238; and *ibid.*, p. 43, with a quotation from J. M. Keynes [1921], p. 4.) I agree with Keynes in the view that the concept of logical probability is just as objective as the concept of logical implication in deductive logic. (This logical objectivity is, of course, quite different from the factual objectivity of concepts in physics and of statistical probability.) The term "personal probability" was introduced by L. J. Savage [1954]; for the reasons mentioned above, it seems to me preferable to "subjective probability," especially in normative decision theory.]

I now give some examples of rationality requirements that I regard as valid. There is no general agreement in the question of validity. Each author regards as "rational credence functions" those that satisfy the rationality requirements accepted by him. Sometimes, to make the picture more lively, one speaks of a "completely rational" person X; this means an (imaginary) person whose credence function is assumed to be perfectly rational.

Suppose that X makes n simultaneous bets; let the ith bet ($i = 1, \ldots, n$) be on the proposition H_i with the betting quotient q_i and the total stake s_i. Before we observe which of the propositions H_i are true and which are false, we can consider the *possible* cases. For any possible case, i.e., a logically possible assignment of truth values to the n propositions H_i, we can calculate the gain or loss for each bet and hence the total balance of gains and losses from the n bets. If in *every* possible case X suffers a net loss, i.e., his total balance is negative, it is obviously unreasonable for X to make these n bets. Let X's credence function at a given time be Cr. By a (finite) betting system in accordance with Cr we mean a finite system of n bets on n arbitrary propositions H_i ($i = 1, \ldots, n$) with n arbitrary (positive) stakes s_i, but with the betting quotients $q_i = \mathrm{Cr}(H_i)$.

(6) *Definition.* A function Cr is *coherent* if and only if there is no betting system in accordance with Cr such that there is a net loss in every possible case.

For X to make bets of a system of this kind would obviously be unreasonable. Therefore we lay down the *first requirement* as follows:

R1. In order to be rational, Cr must be *coherent*.

Now the following important result holds:

(7) A function Cr from propositions to real numbers is coherent if and only if Cr is a probability measure, i.e., satisfies the basic axioms of the calculus of probability. (7) was first proved by de Finetti [1931].

Let Cr′ be the conditional credence function defined on the basis of Cr by (4). As ordinary bets are based on Cr, conditional bets are based on Cr′. The concept of coherence can be generalized so as to be applicable also to conditional credence functions. (7) can then easily be extended by the result that a conditional credence function Cr′ is coherent if and only if Cr′ satisfies the customary basic axioms of conditional probability, including the general multiplication axiom.

Following Shimony [1955], we introduce now a concept of coherence in a stronger sense, for which I use the term "strict coherence":

(8) *Definition.* A function Cr is *strictly coherent* if and only if Cr is coherent and there is no (finite) system of bets in accordance with Cr on molecular propositions such that the result is a net loss in at least one possible case, but not a net gain in any possible case.

It is clear that it would be unreasonable to accept the bets of a system of the kind just specified. Therefore we lay down the *second requirement:*

R2. In order to be rational, a credence function must be *strictly coherent*.

We define *regular credence function* (essentially in the sense of Carnap [1950, §55*A*]):

(9) *Definition.* A function Cr is *regular* if and only if Cr is a probability measure and, for any molecular proposition H, $\text{Cr}(H) = 0$ only if H is impossible.

By analogy with (7), we have now the following important theorem (10); its first part ("... regular if...") is attributable to Shimony [1955], its second part ("... only if...") was proved by John Kemeny [1955] and by R. Sherman Lehman [1955] independently of each other.

(10) A function Cr is strictly coherent if and only if Cr is regular.

Most of the authors of systems for personal or logical probability adopt only the basic axioms; they thus require nothing but coherence. A few go one step further by including an axiom for what I call regularity; they thus require in effect strict coherence, but nothing more. Axiom systems of both kinds are extremely weak; they yield no result of the form "$P(H \mid E) = r$," except in the trivial cases where r is 0 or 1. In my view, inductive logic should accomplish much more.

The two preceding requirements apply to any credence function that holds for X at any time T of his life. We now consider two of these functions, Cr_n for the time T_n and Cr_{n+1} for a time T_{n+1} shortly after T_n. Let the proposition E represent the observation data obtained by X between these two time points. The *third requirement* refers to the transition from Cr_n to Cr_{n+1}:

R3 (a) The transformation of Cr_n into Cr_{n+1} depends only on the proposition E.

(b) More specifically, Cr_{n+1} is determined by Cr_n and E as follows: for any H, $\text{Cr}_{n+1}(H) = \text{Cr}_n(E \cap H)/\text{Cr}_n(E)$ (hence $= \text{Cr}'_n(H \mid E)$ by definition (4)).

Part (a) is of course implied by (b). I have separated part (a) from (b) because X's function Cr might satisfy (a) without satisfying (b). Part (a) requires merely that X be rational to the extent that changes in his credence function are influenced only by his observational results, but not by any other factors, e.g., feelings like his hopes or fears concerning a possible future event H, feelings that in fact often influence the beliefs of all actual human beings. Part (b) specifies exactly the transformation of Cr_n into Cr_{n+1}; the latter is the conditional credence Cr'_n with respect to E. The rule (b) can be used only if $\mathrm{Cr}_n(E) \neq 0$; this condition is fulfilled for any possible observational result, provided that Cr_n satisfies the requirement of strict coherence.

4
Credibility

Let the proposition E_{n+2} represent the data obtained between T_{n+1} and a later time point T_{n+2}. Let Cr_{n+2} be the credence function at T_{n+2} obtained by R3(b) from Cr_{n+1} with respect to E_{n+2}. It can easily be shown that the same function Cr_{n+2} results if R3(b) is applied to Cr_n with respect to the combined data $E_{n+1} \cap E_{n+2}$. In the same way we can determine any later credence function Cr_{n+m} from the given function Cr_n either in m steps, applying the rule R3(b) in each step to one datum of the sequence $E_{n+1}, E_{n+2}, \ldots, E_{n+m}$, or in one step to the intersection $\bigcup_{p=1}^{m} E_{n+p}$. If m is large so that the intersection contains thousands of single data, the objection might be raised that it is unrealistic to think of a procedure of this kind, because a man's memory is unable to retain and reproduce at will so many items. Since, however, our goal is not the psychology of actual human behavior in the field of inductive reasoning, but rather inductive logic as a system of rules, we do not aim at realism. We may make the further idealizing assumption that X is not only perfectly rational but has also an infallible memory. Our assumptions deviate from reality very much if the observer X is a natural human being, but not so much if we think of X as a robot with organs of perception, memory, data processing, decision making, and acting. Thinking about the design of a robot might help us in finding rules of rationality. Once found, these rules can be applied not only in the construction of a robot but also in advising human beings in their effort to make their decisions as rational as their limited abilities permit.

Consider now the whole sequence of data obtained by X up to the present time T_n: $E_1, E_2, \ldots, E_n$. Let K_{X,T_n} or, for short, K_n be the proposition representing the combination of all these data:

(11) *Definition.* $K_n = \bigcap_{i=1}^{n} E_i$.

Thus K_n represents, under the assumption of infallible memory, the total observational knowledge of X at the time T_n. Now consider the sequence of X's credence functions. In the case of a human being we would hesitate to ascribe to him a credence function at a very early time point, before his abilities of reason and deliberate action are sufficiently developed. But again we disregard this difficulty by thinking either of an idealized human baby or of a robot. We ascribe to him a credence function Cr_1 for the time point T_1; Cr_1 represents X's personal probabilities based upon the datum E_1 as his only experience. Going even one step further, let us ascribe to him an *initial credence function*

Cr_0 for the time point T_0 before he obtains his first datum E_1. Any later function Cr_n for a time point T_n is uniquely determined by Cr_0 and K_n:

(12) For any H, $\mathrm{Cr}_n(H) = \mathrm{Cr}_0'(H \mid K_n)$, where Cr_0' is the conditional function based on Cr_0.

$\mathrm{Cr}_n(H)$ is thus seen to be the *conditional initial credence* of H given K_n.

How can we understand the function Cr_0? In terms of the robot, Cr_0 is the credence function that we originally build in and that he transforms step for step, with regard to the incoming data, into the later credence functions. In the case of a human being X, suppose that we find at the time T_n his credence function Cr_n. Then we can, under suitable conditions, reconstruct a sequence $E_1, \ldots, E_n$, the proposition K_n, and a function Cr_0 such that (a) $E_1, \ldots, E_n$ are possible observation data, (b) K_n is defined by (11), (c) Cr_0 satisfies all requirements of rationality for initial credence functions, and (d) the application of (12) to the assumed function Cr_0 and K_n would lead to the ascertained function Cr_n. We do not assert that X actually experienced the data $E_1, \ldots, E_n$, and that he actually had the initial credence function Cr_0, but merely that, under idealized conditions, his function Cr_n *could* have evolved from Cr_0 by the effect of the data $E_1, \ldots, E_n$.

For the conditional initial credence function (Cr_0') we shall also use the term "credibility function" and the symbol 'Cred'. As an alternative to defining 'Cred' on the basis of 'Cr_0', we could introduce it as a primitive term. In this case we may take the following universal statement as the main postulate for the theoretical primitive term 'Cred':

(13) Let Cred be any function from pairs of propositions to real numbers, satisfying all requirements which we have laid down or shall lay down for credibility functions. Let H and A be any propositions (A not empty). Let X be any observer and T any time point. If X's credibility function is Cred and his total observational knowledge at T is A, then his credence for H at T is $\mathrm{Cred}(H \mid A)$.

Note that (13) is much more general than (12). There the function Cred (or Cr_0') was applied only to those pairs H, A, in which A is a proposition of the sequence $K_1, K_2, \ldots$, and thus represents the actual observational knowledge of X at some time point. In (13), however, A may be any nonempty proposition. Let A_1 be a certain nonempty proposition that does not occur in sequence $K_1, K_2, \ldots$, and H_1 some proposition. Then the statement

$$\mathrm{Cr}_T(H_1) = \mathrm{Cred}(H_1 \mid A_1)$$

is to be understood as a counterfactual conditional as follows:

(14) Let X's credibility function be 'Cred'. If his total observational knowledge at some time point T *had been* A_1, then his credence for H_1 at T *would have been* equal to $\mathrm{Cred}(H_1 \mid A_1)$.

This is a true counterfactual based on the postulate (13), analogous to ordinary counterfactuals based on physical laws.

Applying (13) to X's actual total observational knowledge $K_{X,T}$ at time T, we have:

(15) For any H, $\mathrm{Cr}_{X,T}(H) = \mathrm{Cred}_X(H \mid K_{X,T})$.

Now we can use credibility instead of credence in the definition of the value of an act A_m, and thereby in the decision rule. Thus we have instead of (5):

(16) *Definition.* $V_{X,T}(A_m) = \sum_n [U_X(O_{m,n})\mathrm{Cred}_X(W_n \mid K_{X,T})]$.

[If the situation is such that the assumption of A_m could possibly change the credence of W_n, we have to replace '$K_{X,T}$' by '$K_{X,T} \cap A_m$'; see the remark in the paragraph following (1).]

If Cred is taken as primitive, Cr_0 can be defined as follows:

(17) *Definition.* For any H, $\mathrm{Cr}_0(H) = \mathrm{Cred}(H \mid Z)$, where Z is the necessary proposition (the tautology).

This is the special case of (13) for the initial time T_0, when X's knowledge K_0 is the tautology.

While $\mathrm{Cr}_{X,T}$ characterizes the *momentary state* of X at time T with respect to his beliefs, his function Cred_X is *a trait of his underlying permanent intellectual character*, namely his permanent disposition for forming beliefs on the basis of his observations.

5
Permanent Dispositions

Since each of the two functions Cr_0 and Cred is definable on the basis of the other, there are two alternative equivalent procedures for specifying a basic belief-forming disposition, namely, either by Cr_0 or by Cred.

Most of those who have constructed systems of subjective probability (in the narrower sense, in contrast with logical probability), e.g., Ramsey, de Finetti, and Savage, have concentrated their attention on what we might call "adult" credence functions, i.e., those of persons sufficiently developed to communicate by language, to play games, make bets, and so on, hence persons with an enormous amount of experience. In descriptive decision theory it has many practical advantages to take adult persons as subjects of investigation, since it is relatively easy to determine their credence functions on the basis of their behavior with games, bets, and the like. When I propose to take as a basic concept, not adult credence but either initial credence or credibility, I must admit that these concepts are less realistic and remoter from overt behavior and may therefore appear as elusive and dubious. On the other hand, when we are interested in normative decision theory, these concepts have important methodological advantages. Only for these concepts, not for credence, can we find a sufficient number of requirements of rationality as a basis for the construction of a system of inductive logic.

If we look at the development of theories and concepts in various branches of science, we find frequently that it was possible to arrive at powerful laws of widespread generality only when the development of concepts, beginning with directly observable properties, had progressed step by step to more abstract concepts, connected only indirectly with observables. Thus, physics proceeds from concepts describing visible motion of bodies to the concept of a momentary electric force, and then to the still more abstract concept of a permanent electric field. In the sphere of human action we have first concepts describing overt behavior, say of a boy who is offered the choice of an apple or an ice cream cone and takes the latter; then we introduce the concept of an underlying momentary inclination, in this case the momentary preference of ice cream over apple; and finally we form the abstract concept of an underlying permanent disposition, in our example the general utility function of the boy.

What I propose to do here is simply to take the same step—from momentary inclination to the permanent disposition for forming momentary inclinations—also with the second concept occurring in the decision principle, namely, personal probability or degree of belief. Here it is the step from credence to credibility.

When we wish to judge the morality of a person, we do not simply look at some of his acts; we study rather his character, the system of his moral values, which is part of his utility function. Observations of single acts without knowledge of motives give little basis for judgment. Similarly, if we wish to judge the rationality of a person's beliefs, we should not look simply at his present beliefs. Information on his beliefs without knowledge of the evidence out of which they arose tells us little. We must rather study the way in which the person forms his beliefs on the basis of evidence. In other words, we should study his credibility function, not simply his present credence function. For example, let X have the evidence E that from an urn containing white and black balls ten balls have been drawn, with replacement, two of them white and eight black. Let Y have the evidence E' which is similar to E, but with seven balls white and three black. Let H be the prediction that the next ball drawn will be white. Suppose that for both X and Y the credence of H is 2/3. Then we would judge this same credence value 2/3 of the proposition H as unreasonable for X, but reasonable for Y. We would condemn a credibility function Cred as nonrational if $\mathrm{Cred}(H \mid E) = 2/3$; while the result $\mathrm{Cred}(H \mid E') = 2/3$ would be no ground for condemnation.

Suppose X has the credibility function Cred, which leads him, on the basis of his knowledge K_n at time T_n, to the credence function Cr_n, and thereby, with his utility function U, to the act A_m. If this act seems to us unreasonable in view of his evidence K_n and his utilities, we shall judge that Cred is nonrational. But for such a judgment on Cred it is not necessary that X is actually led to an unreasonable act. Suppose that for E and H as in the above example, K_n contains E and otherwise only evidence irrelevant for$H$. Then we have $\mathrm{Cr}_n(H) = \mathrm{Cred}(H \mid K_n) = \mathrm{Cred}(H \mid E) = 2/3$; and this result seems unreasonable on the given evidence. If X bets on H with betting quotient 2/3, this bet is unreasonable, even if he wins it. But his credence 2/3 is anyway unreasonable, no matter whether he acts on it or not. It is unreasonable because there are possible situations, no matter whether real or not, in which the result $\mathrm{Cred}(H \mid E) = 2/3$ would lead him to an unreasonable act. Furthermore, it is not necessary for our condemnation of the function Cred that it actually leads to unreasonable Cr-values. Suppose that another man X' has the same function Cred but is not led to the unreasonable Cr-value in the example, because he has an entirely different life history, and at no time is his total knowledge either E or a combination of E with data irrelevant for H. Then we would still condemn the function Cred and the man X' characterized by this function. Our argument would here, as frequently in an intellectual or moral condemnation, be expressed in a counterfactual conditional as follows: if the total knowledge of X' had at some time been E, or E together with irrelevant data, then his credence for H would have had the unreasonable value 2/3. The same considerations hold, of course, for the initial credence function Cr_0 corresponding to the function Cred; for, on the basis of any possible knowledge proposition K, Cr_0 and Cred would lead to the same credence function.

The following is an example of a requirement of rationality for Cr_0 (and hence for Cred) which has no analogue for credence functions. As we shall see later, this requirement leads to one of the most important axioms of inductive logic. (The term "individual" means "element of the universe of discourse", or "element of the population" in the terminology of statistics.)

R4. Requirement of symmetry. Let a_i and a_j be two distinct individuals. Let H and H' be two propositions such that H' results from H by taking a_j for a_i and vice versa. Then Cr_0 should be such that $Cr_0(H) = Cr_0(H')$. (In other words, Cr_0 should be invariant with respect to any finite permutation of individuals.)

This requirement seems indispensable. H and H' have exactly the same logical form; they differ merely by their reference to two distinct individuals. These individuals may happen to be quite different. But since their differences are not known to X at time T_0, they cannot have any influence on the Cr_0-values of H and H'. Suppose, however, that at a later time T_n, X's knowledge K_n contains information E relevant to H and H', say information making H more probable than H' (as an extreme case, E may imply that H is true and H' is false). Then X's credence function Cr_n at T_n will have different values for H and for H'. Thus it is clear that R4 applies only to Cr_0, but is not generally valid for other credence functions Cr_n ($n > 0$).

Suppose that X is a robot constructed by us. Since the propositions H and H' are alike in all their logical properties, it would be entirely arbitrary and therefore unreasonable for us to assign to them different Cr_0-values in the construction of X.

A function Cr_0 is suitable for being built into a robot only if it fulfills the requirements of rationality; and most of these requirements apply only to Cr_0 (and Cred) but not generally to other credence functions.

6
Inductive Logic

Now we are ready to take the step from normative decision theory to inductive logic. This step consists in the transition from the concepts of a rational Cr_0-function and a rational Cred-function to corresponding purely logical concepts. The former concepts are quasi-psychological; they are assigned to an imaginary subject X supposed to be equipped with perfect rationality and an unfailing memory; the logical concepts, in contrast, have nothing to do with observers and agents, whether natural or constructed, real or imaginary. For a logical function corresponding to Cr_0, I shall use the symbol '$\mathscr{M}$' and I call such functions (inductive) measure functions or $\mathscr{M}$-functions; for a logical function corresponding to Cred, I shall use the symbol '$\mathscr{C}$', and I call these functions (inductive) confirmation functions or $\mathscr{C}$-functions. I read '$\mathscr{C}(H \mid E)$' as "the degree of confirmation (or briefly "the confirmation") of H with respect to E" (or: ". . . given E"). An $\mathscr{M}$-function is a function from propositions to real numbers. Any $\mathscr{M}$-function $\mathscr{M}$ or $\mathscr{C}$-function $\mathscr{C}$ is supposed to be defined in a purely logical way, i.e., on the basis of concepts of logic (in the wide sense, including set theory and hence the whole of pure mathematics). Therefore the values of $\mathscr{M}$ or of $\mathscr{C}$ for given propositions depend merely on the logical (set-theoretic) properties of these propositions (which are sets in a probability space) but not on any contingent facts of nature (e.g., the truth of the propositions).

Inductive logic studies those $\mathscr{M}$-functions that correspond to rational Cr_0-functions, and those $\mathscr{C}$-functions that correspond to rational Cred-functions. Suppose $\mathscr{M}$ is a logically defined $\mathscr{M}$-function. Let us imagine a subject X whose function Cr_0 corresponds to $\mathscr{M}$, i.e., for every proposition H, $\mathrm{Cr}_0(H) = \mathscr{M}(H)$. If we find that Cr_0 violates one of the rationality requirements, say R4, then we would reject this function Cr_0, say for a robot we plan to build. Consequently we also exclude the corresponding function $\mathscr{M}$ from those treated as admissible in the system of inductive logic we plan to construct. Therefore, we set up axioms of inductive logic about $\mathscr{M}$-functions so that these axioms correspond to the requirements of rationality which we find in the theory of rational decision making about Cr_0-functions.

For example, we may lay down as the basic axioms of inductive logic for $\mathscr{M}$ the usual axioms of the calculus of probability. These axioms correspond to the requirement R1 of coherence, by virtue of theorem (7). Further we may have an axiom saying that $\mathscr{M}$ is regular. This axiom corresponds to the requirement R2 of strict coherence by theorem (10).

Then we shall have in inductive logic, in analogy to the requirement R4 of symmetry, the following:

(18) *Axiom of Symmetry.* $\mathcal{M}$ is invariant with respect to any finite permutation of individuals.

There is another alternative: we may state axioms for $\mathcal{C}$, instead of those for $\mathcal{M}$. (This method is used in [Art. **2**].)

All axioms of inductive logic state relations among values of $\mathcal{M}$ or $\mathcal{C}$ as dependent only upon the logical properties and relations of the propositions involved (with respect to language systems with specified logical rules). Inductive logic is the theory based upon these axioms. It may be regarded as a part of logic in view of the fact that the concepts occurring are logical concepts. (Exactly speaking, this holds only for *pure* inductive logic, not for *applied* inductive logic. The distinction between these two fields is discussed in [Art. **2**, §4A].) It is an interesting result that this part of normative decision theory, namely, the logical theory of the $\mathcal{M}$-functions and the $\mathcal{C}$-functions, can thus be separated from the rest. We should note, however, that this logical theory deals only with the abstract, formal aspects of probability, and that the full meaning of (personal) probability can be understood only in the wider context of decision theory through the connections between probability and the concepts of utility and rational action.

It is important to notice clearly the following distinction. While the *axioms* of inductive logic themselves are formulated in purely logical terms and do not refer to any contingent matters of fact, the *reasons* for our choice of the axioms are not purely logical. For example, when asked why I accept the axiom of symmetry (18), I would point out that if X has a Cr_0-function corresponding to an $\mathcal{M}$-function violating (18), then his function Cr_0 would violate R4, and I show that therefore X, in a certain possible knowledge situation, would be led to an unreasonable decision. Thus, in order to give my reasons for the axiom, I move from pure logic to the context of decision theory and speak about beliefs, actions, possible losses, and the like. However, these considerations are not in the field of descriptive, but of normative decision theory. Therefore, in giving my reasons, I do not refer to particular empirical results concerning particular agents or particular states of nature and the like. Rather, I refer to a *conceivable* series of observations by X, to conceivable sets of possible acts, to possible states of nature, to possible outcomes of the acts, and the like. These features are characteristic for an analysis of *reasonableness* of a given function Cr_0, in contrast with an investigation of the *successfulness* of the (initial or later) credence function of a given person in the real world. Success depends upon the particular contingent circumstances, rationality does not.

There is a class of axioms of inductive logic which I call *axioms of invariance*. The axiom of symmetry is one of them. Another axiom says that, under certain conditions, $\mathscr{M}$ is invariant with respect to any finite permutation of attributes belonging to a family of attributes, e.g., colors, provided these attributes are alike in their logical properties. These and other invariance axioms may be regarded as representing the valid core of the old *principle of indifference* (or principle of insufficient reason). The principle in its original form, as used by Laplace and other authors in the classical period of the theory of probability, was certainly too strong. It was later correctly criticized by showing that it led to absurd results.[2] I believe, however, that the basic idea of the principle is sound. Our task is to restate it by specific restricted axioms.

It seems that for personal probability most authors do not accept any axioms of invariance. In the case of those authors who take credence as their basic concept, e.g., Ramsey, de Finetti, and Savage, this is inevitable, since the invariance axioms do not generally hold for credence functions. In order to obtain a stronger system, it is necessary to take as the basic concept either initial credence or credibility (or other concepts in terms of which these are definable).

When we construct an axiom system for $\mathscr{M}$, then the addition of each new axiom has the effect of excluding certain $\mathscr{M}$-functions. We accept an axiom if we recognize that the $\mathscr{M}$-functions excluded by it correspond to nonrational Cr_0-functions. Even on the basis of all axioms that I would accept at the present time for a simple qualitative language (with one-place predicates only, without physical magnitudes), the number of admissible $\mathscr{M}$-functions, i.e., those that satisfy all accepted axioms, is still infinite; but their class is immensely smaller than that of all coherent $\mathscr{M}$-functions. There will presumably be further axioms, justified in the same way by considerations of rationality. We do not know today whether in this future development the number of admissible $\mathscr{M}$-functions will always remain infinite or will become finite and possibly even be reduced to one. Therefore, at the present time I do not assert that there is only one rational Cr_0-function.

---

[2] On this question, compare my [1953*b*, pp. 193 f.] reprinted in [1955, pp. 21 f.].

7
The Question of Acceptance

I think that the theory of the $\mathscr{M}$- and $\mathscr{C}$-functions deserves the often misused name of "inductive logic". Earlier I gave my reasons for regarding this theory as a part of logic. The term "inductive" seems appropriate because this theory provides the foundation for inductive reasoning (in a wide sense). I agree in this view with John Maynard Keynes and Harold Jeffreys. It is important, however, that we recognize clearly the essential form of inductive reasoning. My view on this point differs from that of almost all writers on induction in the past and the great majority of contemporary writers. They regard inductive reasoning as an *inference* leading from some known propositions, called the premisses or evidence, to a new proposition, called the conclusion, usually a law or a singular prediction. From this point of view the result of any particular inductive reasoning is the *acceptance* of a new proposition (or its rejection, or its suspension until further evidence is found, as the case may be). I have serious doubts about this view. If we hold it, we are unable to refute Hume's dictum that there are no rational reasons for induction. Suppose that we find in earlier weather reports that a weather situation like the one we have today has occurred one hundred times and that it was followed each time by rain the next morning. (If someone objects that the number one hundred is too small, let him take one hundred thousand or any number he regards as sufficiently large.) According to the customary view, on the basis of this evidence the "inductive method" entitles us *to accept* the prediction that it will rain tomorrow morning. But then Hume is certainly right in protesting that we have no rational reason for the acceptance of this prediction, since, as everyone will agree, it is still possible that it will not rain tomorrow.

In contrast with this view, it seems to me that the result of a paradigmatic piece of inductive reasoning with respect to a hypothesis H, starting from the evidence E, consists in an assignment of a probability to H, namely the value of $\mathscr{C}(H \mid E)$.

I do not regard it as generally wrong to accept or reject propositions. For the purpose of a special investigation, an investigator will usually accept some general assumptions (see my discussion of basic assumptions in [Art. **2**, §5]), or specific assumptions, for example about the reliability of his measuring instruments. But I would not say that such assumptions are conclusions obtained by "inductive inference". For further discussion on acceptance compare my discussion remarks "On rules of acceptance" [1968, pp. 146 ff.] and Jeffrey [1956].

Let us apply this new view of the essential task of inductive reasoning to the earlier example. Let H be the prediction of rain for tomorrow. According to the new view, X does not assert the prediction H, but merely the following statements (where the value 0.99 serves simply as an example):

(19) (a) At the present moment T_n, the totality of X's observation results is K_n.

(b) $\mathscr{C}(H \mid K_n) = 0.99$.
(c) $\text{Cred}_X(H \mid K_n) = 0.99$.
(d) $\text{Cr}_{X,T_n}(H) = 0.99$.

(a) is the statement of the evidence at hand, the same as in the first case. But now, instead of accepting H, X asserts the statement (c) of the Cred-value for H on his evidence. (c) is the result of X's inductive reasoning. Against this result Hume's objection does not hold, because X can give rational reasons for it. (c) is derived from (b) because X has chosen a mathematically defined function $\mathscr{C}$ as his credibility function. (b) is an analytic statement based on the definition of $\mathscr{C}$. X's choice of $\mathscr{C}$ was guided (though not uniquely determined) by the axioms of inductive logic. And for each of the axioms we can give a reason, namely, a rationality requirement for credibility functions. Thus $\mathscr{C}$ represents a reasonable credibility function. Finally, X's credence value (d) is derived from (c) and (a) by (15).

Now some philosophers, including some of my empiricist friends, would raise the following objection. If the result of inductive reasoning is merely an analytic statement (like (b) or (c)), then induction cannot fulfill the task of guiding our practical decisions. As a basis for a decision we need a statement with factual content. If we do not wish to *accept* the prediction H itself, then, they say, we must use a statement of the *statistical* probability of H, which is a factual statement. In answer to this objection I would first point out that X *does have* a factual basis in his evidence, as stated in (a). And for the determination of a rational decision neither the acceptance of H nor knowledge of the statistical probability of H is needed. The rational personal probability, i.e., the credence as stated in (d), is sufficient for determining first the rational value of each possible act by (16), and then a rational decision. Thus, in our example, in view of (b), X would decide to make a bet on rain tomorrow if it were offered to him at odds of ninety-nine to one or less, but not more.

The old puzzle of induction consists in the following dilemma. On the one hand we see that inductive reasoning is used by the scientist and the man in the street every day without apparent scruples; and we have the feeling that it is valid and indispensable. On the other hand, once Hume awakens our intellectual conscience, we recognize that here is a serious difficulty. Who is right, the man of common sense or the critical philosopher? We see here, as so often, that both are partially right. Hume's criticism of the customary forms of induction was correct. But still the basic idea of common sense thinking is vindicated: induction, if properly reformulated, can be shown to be valid by rational criteria.

2

A Basic System of Inductive Logic Part I

BY RUDOLF CARNAP

1
Basic Concepts and Basic Axioms

A. BASIC CONCEPTS

"Inductive logic" is here understood as the theory of probability in the logical or inductive sense, in distinction to probability in the statistical sense, measured by frequencies. This and the subsequent articles are based on the conception of the nature of inductive logic as explained in [Art. **1**] (i.e., Article **1** in this volume) and treated in greater detail in my book [1950] (see the Bibliography at the end of this volume). (Knowledge of the book is not presupposed in the present article.)

In my book the functions *m* (measure function, absolute probability) and *c* (confirmation function, relative probability) were applied to *sentences* in some language. However, in the case of more complex conceptual systems, e.g., those involving real numbers and real-valued functions, no language can express all possible cases by sentences (or even by classes of sentences). Therefore, I have here chosen to take as arguments of the probability functions not sentences, but *events* or *propositions*. I use the latter two terms as synonymous. In probability theory the term "event" is more customary, in logic the term "proposition". The term "event" has here, of course, a much wider sense than in ordinary language. It refers not only to actual events, but also to merely possible events. Further, in our sense, the series of all eclipses of the moon is one event; likewise Newton's law of gravitation, no matter whether true or false. And there is even one impossible event. (We shall, however, not use formulations like "two successive occurrences of the same event"; we shall say instead "two successive events of the same kind" or "two successive individuals having the same attribute".) The term "proposition" is often used in logic for certain intensional entities, regarded with suspicion by some philosophers. Here, however, we shall represent propositions in an extensional way (namely, by sets of models, §3B).

Instead of the functions *m* and *c* applied to sentences we shall use corresponding functions $\mathcal{M}$ and $\mathcal{C}$ applied to propositions. Nevertheless, each discussion of inductive logic in these articles will refer to some language or class of languages, and in particular to the set of descriptive (i.e., nonlogical) constants of the language. For any language $\mathcal{L}$, $\mathcal{E}_{\mathcal{L}}$ is the class of events or propositions on $\mathcal{L}$. $\mathcal{E}_{\mathcal{L}}$ contains all events described by sentences in $\mathcal{L}$, but in general it contains also others. For any language form that we shall discuss, we shall define the corresponding class $\mathcal{E}_{\mathcal{L}}$. (We shall often omit the subscript "$\mathcal{L}$" in these and similar notations, if only one language is talked about.)

We use 'E', 'H', 'A', 'B', etc., for propositions. Thus '$\mathscr{C}(H \mid E)$' takes the place of the earlier '$c(h, e)$', where h and e were sentences. Since propositions will be defined as certain sets, set connectives will be used instead of sentence connectives. Thus the complement $-E$ corresponds to the negation $\sim e$, the intersection $E \cap H$ corresponds to the conjunction $e \,.\, h$, and the union $E \cup H$ corresponds to the disjunction $e \vee h$. The necessary proposition **Z** (the set of all models, §3) corresponds to any tautological sentence; the empty (or impossible) proposition $\varnothing$ corresponds to any self-contradictory sentence. Inclusion, e.g., $E \subset H$, corresponds to logical implication, e.g., $\vdash e \supset h$.

Other set-theoretic notations: $\{x\}$ is the set whose only element is x; analogously, $\{x, y\}$, $\{x_1, \ldots, x_n\}$. $\{x: \ldots x \ldots\}$ is the set A such that $x \in A$ if-if x satisfies the condition $\ldots x \ldots$. (I write 'if-if' for 'if and only if'.) If $\mathscr{A}$ is a class of sets, $\bigcup \mathscr{A}$ is the union of $\mathscr{A}$, $\bigcap \mathscr{A}$ is the intersection of $\mathscr{A}$. $\langle x, y\rangle$ is the ordered pair with x as the first member and y as the second; analogously, $\langle x, y, z\rangle$ is an ordered triple, $\langle x_1, \ldots, x_n\rangle$ an ordered n-tuple. $A \times B =_{\text{Df}} \{\langle x, y\rangle: x \in A$ and $y \in B\}$; the Cartesian product $A \times B$ is the set of all ordered pairs whose first member belongs to A and whose second member to B.

We shall use the terms "class" and "set" as synonyms. We sometimes, however, prefer "class of sets" to "set of sets" (and therefore also "class of functions", since functions may be regarded as sets of pairs or of n-tuples).

We use '**I**' for the set of all integers; '**N**' for the set of the natural numbers (the positive integers), and $^0\mathbf{N}$ for $\mathbf{N} \cup \{0\}$. A set A is said to be **denumerable** if-if it has the same cardinal number as **N** (namely, aleph-zero). A is said to be **countable** if-if A is finite or denumerable.

D1-1. **a.** Two sets A, B are **disjoint** $=_{\text{Df}}$ A and B have no common element (in other words, $A \cap B = \varnothing$).

b. $\mathscr{A}$ is a **disjoint class** of sets $=_{\text{Df}}$ any two distinct sets $A, B \in \mathscr{A}$ are disjoint.

c. The class $\mathscr{A}$ is a **covering** of the set $A =_{\text{Df}} A \subset \bigcup \mathscr{A}$.

d. The class (or sequence) $\mathscr{A}$ is a **partition** of the set $A =_{\text{Df}} \mathscr{A}$ is a disjoint class of one or more sets, and $\bigcup \mathscr{A} = A$.

D1-2. Let X be a nonempty set and $\mathscr{A}$ be a class of subsets of X.

a. $\mathscr{A}$ is a **field** on $X =_{\text{Df}}$

(i) $X \in \mathscr{A}$;

(ii) if $A \in \mathscr{A}$, $X - A \in \mathscr{A}$;

(iii) if $A, B \in \mathscr{A}$, $A \cup B \in \mathscr{A}$.

b. $\mathscr{A}$ is a **σ-field** on $X =_{\text{Df}} \mathscr{A}$ is a field on X, and for any countable subclass $\mathscr{B}$ of $\mathscr{A}$, $\bigcup \mathscr{B} \in \mathscr{A}$.

A field is closed under all finite sequences of Boolean operations (union, intersection, difference). A σ-field is closed under all countable sequences of such operations.

The intersection of any class of fields [σ-fields] on X is again a field [σ-field] on X. We define:

D1-3. Let X be a nonempty set, and $\mathscr{A}$ be a class of subsets of X. $\mathscr{B}$ is (a) **the field** [(b) **the σ-field**] **on** X **generated** by $\mathscr{A}$ $=_{\mathrm{Df}}$ $\mathscr{B}$ is the intersection of all those fields [σ-fields] on X which include $\mathscr{A}$.

T1-1. Let $\mathscr{A}$ be any class of subsets of X, and $\mathscr{B}$ be (a) the field [(b) the σ-field] on X generated by $\mathscr{A}$. Then $\mathscr{B}$ is the only class that satisfies the following three conditions:

a. $\mathscr{A} \subset \mathscr{B}$,

b. $\mathscr{B}$ is a field [a σ-field] on X,

c. $\mathscr{B}$ is the smallest class satisfying (a) and (b); that is to say, if any class $\mathscr{B}'$ satisfies (a) and (b), then $\mathscr{B} \subset \mathscr{B}'$.

We shall assume that for any language $\mathscr{L}$, the class of sentences in $\mathscr{L}$ and the class of propositions $\mathscr{E}_{\mathscr{L}}$ satisfy the following conditions.

(1-1) **(i)** The class of sentences is closed with respect to the following sentence-forming operations: negation, disjunction, and conjunction.

(ii) For every sentence S in $\mathscr{L}$, there is a proposition $E_S \in \mathscr{E}$ *corresponding to* S; we say then also that S *designates* or describes E_S.

(iii) $\mathscr{E}$ is a σ-field.

For any language $\mathscr{L}$ to be used we shall proceed as follows. We shall specify a certain class $\mathbf{Z}_{\mathscr{L}}$ of functions, called the model-functions or simply the **models** of $\mathscr{L}$. (The models are the "points" of our "probability space".) $\mathscr{E}$ will be defined as a certain σ-field on **Z**. In most cases we shall define first a subclass of $\mathscr{E}$, namely $\mathscr{E}^{\text{bas}}$, the class of the basic propositions on $\mathscr{L}$ (sometimes defined as the propositions corresponding to certain sentences, called the basic sentences of $\mathscr{L}$). Then we shall define $\mathscr{E}$ as the σ-field generated by $\mathscr{E}^{\text{bas}}$ on **Z**.

Each model represents a most specific possible case with respect to $\mathscr{L}$. The two extreme propositions are the *necessary proposition*, holding in every possible case, and the *empty* event or the *impossible proposition*, holding in none of the possible cases. We define these and related concepts as follows:

D1-4. Let E and E' be propositions (events).

a. E is *necessary* $=_{\mathrm{Df}} E = \mathbf{Z}$.

b. E is *impossible* (or *empty*) $=_{\mathrm{Df}} E = \varnothing$.

c. E is *possible* (or *nonempty*) $=_{\mathrm{Df}} E \neq \varnothing$.

d. E is *contingent* (or factual) $=_{\mathrm{Df}} E$ is neither necessary nor impossible.

e. E is *included in* E' (or E strictly implies E') $=_{\mathrm{Df}} E \subset E'$.

B. THE BASIC AXIOMS

In inductive logic, the $\mathscr{C}$-functions are more important than the $\mathscr{M}$-functions, since some $\mathscr{C}$-values represent rational degrees of belief and thus help in determining rational decisions. The $\mathscr{M}$-functions serve mainly as convenient means for defining $\mathscr{C}$-functions and for determining their values. An $\mathscr{M}$-function is an (absolute) probability function in the sense of the axiomatic probability calculus (which is neutral with respect to interpretations); a $\mathscr{C}$-function is a conditional (or relative) probability function. In some systems, $\mathscr{M}$ is taken as primitive and $\mathscr{C}$ is defined on its basis. Some $\mathscr{C}$-functions, however, cannot be defined on the basis of corresponding $\mathscr{M}$-functions by the customary definition in form of a quotient (e.g., ${}^{\lambda}\mathscr{C}$ for $\lambda = 0$, my [1952*a*] §14]). Therefore we take here $\mathscr{C}$ as primitive and $\mathscr{M}$ as defined, and we state axioms only for $\mathscr{C}$. In the following it is always assumed that the second argument of $\mathscr{C}$ is nonempty.

A1. *Axiom of the lower bound:* $\mathscr{C}(H \mid E) \geqq 0$.

A2. *Axiom of self-confirmation:* $\mathscr{C}(E \mid E) = 1$.

A3. *Axiom of the complement:* $\mathscr{C}(H \mid E) + \mathscr{C}(-H \mid E) = 1$.

A4. *General multiplication principle:* If $E \cap H$ is possible,

$$\mathscr{C}(H \cap H' \mid E) = \mathscr{C}(H \mid E)\mathscr{C}(H' \mid E \cap H).$$

The first three axioms are here given in forms weaker than the customary ones (A1 instead of a combination of A1 with the subsequent theorem T2a; A2 instead of T2b; A3 instead of the special addition principle T2h). Von Wright ([1957], see the Bibliography at the end of this volume) proposed these weaker forms and showed that the customary forms are provable on this basis. The end of a proof is marked by '■'.

T1-2. Some consequences of the axioms.

a. $\mathscr{C}(H \mid E) \leq 1$. (The principle of the upper bound.)

Proof. From A3: $\mathscr{C}(H \mid E) = 1 - \mathscr{C}(-H \mid E)$.
From A1: $\mathscr{C}(-H \mid E) \geqq 0$. Hence the assertion. ■

b. If $E \subset H$, $\mathscr{C}(H \mid E) = 1$.

Proof. Let $E \subset H$. Then $E \cap H = E$. Hence

$$\mathscr{C}(E \mid E) = \mathscr{C}(E \cap H \mid E) = \mathscr{C}(E \mid E)\mathscr{C}(H \mid E) \quad \text{(A4)}.$$

Hence the assertion with A2. ■

c. If $E \subset -H$, $\mathscr{C}(H \mid E) = 0$. (From (b) and A3.)
d. $\mathscr{C}(\mathbf{Z} \mid E) = 1$. (From (b).)
e. $\mathscr{C}(\varnothing \mid E) = 0$. (From (c).)
f. $\mathscr{C}(H \mid E) = \mathscr{C}(H \cap H' \mid E) + \mathscr{C}(H \cap -H' \mid E)$.

Proof. 1. If $E \cap H = \varnothing$, this follows from (c).—2. Let $E \cap H \neq \varnothing$. Then from A3: $\mathscr{C}(H' \mid E \cap H) + \mathscr{C}(-H' \mid E \cap H) = 1$. By multiplying with $\mathscr{C}(H \mid E)$ on both sides and exchanging the sides, we obtain:

$$\mathscr{C}(H \mid E) = \mathscr{C}(H \mid E)\mathscr{C}(H' \mid E \cap H) + \mathscr{C}(H \mid E)\mathscr{C}(-H' \mid E \cap H).$$

Transforming both products by A4 yields the assertion. ■

g. $\mathscr{C}(H \cup H' \mid E) = \mathscr{C}(H \mid E) + \mathscr{C}(H' \mid E) - \mathscr{C}(H \cap H' \mid E)$.

Proof. From (f):

$$\begin{aligned}\mathscr{C}(H \cup H' \mid E) &= \mathscr{C}((H \cup H') \cap H' \mid E) + \mathscr{C}((H \cup H') \cap -H' \mid E) \\ &= \mathscr{C}(H' \mid E) + \mathscr{C}(H \cap -H' \mid E).\end{aligned}$$

Again from (f): $C(H \cap -H' \mid E) = \mathscr{C}(H \mid E) - \mathscr{C}(H \cap H' \mid E)$.
Hence the assertion. ■

+h. Special addition principle. If $E \cap H \cap H' = \varnothing$,

$$\mathscr{C}(H \cup H' \mid E) = \mathscr{C}(H \mid E) + \mathscr{C}(H' \mid E).$$

Proof. Under the condition stated, $\mathscr{C}(H \cap H' \mid E) = 0$ (from (c)). Hence the assertion with (g). ■

Thus the four axioms are equivalent to most of the customary axiom systems for conditional probability. Some systems contain another axiom, which we shall give later in a restricted form (the axiom of regularity, A5). [For *c* with *sentences* as arguments, another axiom is necessary to effect that the value of $c(h, e)$ remains unchanged if either *h* or *e* is replaced by a logically equivalent sentence.]

D1-5. A function $\mathscr{C}$ is a **conditional probability function** or a **confirmation function** (briefly, a **$\mathscr{C}$-function**) on $\mathscr{E}'$ for the language $\mathscr{L}$ $=_{\text{Df}}$

(a) the domain of $\mathscr{C}$ is $\mathscr{E}' \times \mathscr{E}''$ where $\mathscr{E}' \subset \mathscr{E}_{\mathscr{L}}$, $\mathscr{E}'$ is a field on **Z**, and $\mathscr{E}''$ is $\mathscr{E}' - \{\varnothing\}$;

(b) the range of $\mathscr{C}$ is a set of real numbers;

(c) $\mathscr{C}$ satisfies the axioms A1–A4.

[I use the term "conditional probability" because it is customary. In inductive logic, however, one must not be misled by this term into formulating a sentence of the form "$\mathscr{C}(H \mid E) = r$" as a conditional sentence: "If E holds (or: is true), the probability of H is r". This formulation would be incorrect; see my [1950] p. 32. A correct formulation would be: "The probability of H, given E (or ". . . with respect to E") is r". Thus for inductive probability, in contrast with statistical probability, the term "relative probability" would be more appropriate.]

We shall now give the definition of the general concept of a probability measure as used in the abstract theory of probability. (This theory is abstract in the sense that it does not specify the nature of the sets to which the measure is applied; and it is neutral with respect to various possible interpretations of the term "probability", say, as statistical probability or logical probability, or personal probability.)

D1-6. A function f is a **measure-function** or briefly a **measure on** $\mathscr{A}$ $=_{\text{Df}}$

a. $\mathscr{A}$ is a field;

b. the domain of f is $\mathscr{A}$;

c. the values of f are nonnegative real numbers;

d. if A, B are disjoint sets in $\mathscr{A}$, $f(A \cup B) = f(A) + f(B)$.

D1-7. A measure f on $\mathscr{A}$ is a **probability measure (PM)** $=_{\text{Df}}$ f is **normalized,** i.e., $f(\bigcup \mathscr{A}) = 1$.

Every measure f is **finitely additive** in this sense: if $\mathscr{B}$ is any finite class of disjoint sets in $\mathscr{A}$, then $f(\bigcup \mathscr{B}) = \sum_{B \in \mathscr{B}} f(B)$. The following definition refers to the case that the additivity holds also for denumerable unions.

D1-8. A measure f on $\mathscr{A}$ is **σ-additive** (or completely additive) $=_{\text{Df}}$ for any countable, disjoint sequence $\mathscr{B} = \{B_1, B_2, \ldots\}$ such that $\mathscr{B} \subset \mathscr{A}$ and $\bigcup \mathscr{B} \in \mathscr{A}$, $f(\bigcup \mathscr{B}) = \sum_{n=1}^{\infty} f(B_n)$.

[Note that my definition of "measure" (D6) is wider than the customary one; it requires only finite additivity, not σ-additivity.]

D1-9. Let $\mathscr{C}$ be a $\mathscr{C}$-function on $\mathscr{E}' \subset \mathscr{E}$. For any nonempty E in $\mathscr{E}'$, we define the one-place function $\mathscr{C}_E$ (sometimes called the **relativization** of $\mathscr{C}$ with respect to E) thus:

For any $A \in \mathscr{E}'$, $\mathscr{C}_E(A) =_{\text{Df}} \mathscr{C}(A \mid E)$.

T1-3. Let $\mathscr{C}$ and E be as in D9. Then $\mathscr{C}_E$ is a PM on $\mathscr{E}'$.

D1-10. Let $\mathscr{E}' \subset \mathscr{E}_{\mathscr{L}}$ be a field. $\mathscr{M}$ is an $\mathscr{M}$-function on $\mathscr{E}'$ for $\mathscr{L} =_{\text{Df}} \mathscr{M}$ is a PM on $\mathscr{E}'$.

D1-11. Let $\mathscr{C}$ be a $\mathscr{C}$-function and $\mathscr{M}$ an $\mathscr{M}$-function, both on $\mathscr{E}' \subset \mathscr{E}$ for $\mathscr{L}$. $\mathscr{C}$ and $\mathscr{M}$ are **related** *to each other* $=_{\text{Df}}$ for any H and nonempty E in $\mathscr{E}'$,

$$\mathscr{M}(E \cap H) = \mathscr{M}(E)\mathscr{C}(H \mid E).$$

T1-4. If $\mathscr{C}$ and $\mathscr{M}$ are related, then for any E with positive $\mathscr{M}$, and any H,

$$\mathscr{C}(H \mid E) = \frac{\mathscr{M}(E \cap H)}{\mathscr{M}(E)}.$$

T1-5. Let $\mathscr{C}$ be a $\mathscr{C}$-function and $\mathscr{M}$ an $\mathscr{M}$-function, both on $\mathscr{E}' \subset \mathscr{E}$. $\mathscr{M}$ and $\mathscr{C}$ are *related* if-if $\mathscr{M} = \mathscr{C}_{\mathbf{Z}}$ (i.e., for any $H \in \mathscr{E}'$, $\mathscr{M}(H) = \mathscr{C}(H \mid \mathbf{Z})$).

Proof. 1. Let $\mathscr{M}$ and $\mathscr{C}$ be related and let $H \in \mathscr{E}'$. Then (D1, with $\mathbf{Z}$ for E) $\mathscr{M}(\mathbf{Z} \cap H) = \mathscr{C}(H \mid \mathbf{Z})\mathscr{M}(\mathbf{Z})$. Since $\mathscr{M}(\mathbf{Z}) = 1$, $\mathscr{M}(H) = \mathscr{C}(H \mid \mathbf{Z})$.—2. Suppose that $\mathscr{M} = \mathscr{C}_{\mathbf{Z}}$. Let $E \in \mathscr{E}'$ be nonempty. We distinguish two cases, (a) and (b).

(a) Let $\mathscr{M}(E) > 0$. Then $\mathscr{C}(E \mid \mathbf{Z}) > 0$. By A4: $\mathscr{C}(E \cap H \mid \mathbf{Z}) = \mathscr{C}(E \mid \mathbf{Z})\mathscr{C}(H \mid E)$. Hence:

$$(*) \quad \mathscr{M}(E \cap H) = \mathscr{M}(E)\mathscr{C}(H \mid E).$$

(b) Let $\mathscr{M}(E) = 0$. Then $\mathscr{M}(E \cap H) = 0$. Hence (*) is again fulfilled. Thus (*) holds for any E. Therefore, $\mathscr{M}$ and $\mathscr{C}$ are related. ■

We see from this theorem that for any $\mathscr{C}$-function on $\mathscr{E}'$ there is one and only one related $\mathscr{M}$-function on $\mathscr{E}'$, namely, $\mathscr{C}_{\mathbf{Z}}$. (We shall see later that the converse holds under certain conditions.)

From now on, unless otherwise indicated, '$\mathscr{C}$' refers always to a $\mathscr{C}$-function, and '$\mathscr{M}$' to an $\mathscr{M}$-function. If '$\mathscr{C}$' and '$\mathscr{M}$' occur in the same context, they refer to related functions.

2
Individuals and Attributes

A. MONADIC PREDICATE LANGUAGES

The **individuals,** i.e., the objects that the sentences of our languages $\mathcal{L}$ describe, are denoted by **individual constants** (or names) 'a_1', 'a_2', ... $\text{Ind}_{\mathcal{L}}$ is the set of individuals; it is sometimes called "*domain of individuals*" or "*universe* (*of discourse*)" and in statistics "*population*". In our languages, the set $\text{Ind}_{\mathcal{L}}$ is always countable, and usually denumerable. (If no misunderstanding is possible, we often omit the subscript '$\mathcal{L}$' in '$\text{Ind}_{\mathcal{L}}$' and in other symbols.) $\mathcal{L}$ contains for every individual exactly one name. Therefore '$a_2 = a_5$' is taken as logically false.

A language must furthermore contain constants for the concepts to be ascribed to the individuals by the sentences of the language. The languages considered in this article contain only monadic (i.e., one-place) **predicates** designating **attributes** (properties) of the individuals. Therefore we characterize the languages as *monadic predicate languages.*

We assume that the **primitive attributes** in $\mathcal{L}$, i.e., those designated by primitive predicates in $\mathcal{L}$, are observable properties of observable objects (e.g., a continuing body, a body-moment, i.e., a body at a certain time, a continuing process, e.g., a flame). The primitive attributes of $\mathcal{L}$ are classified into **families**; the attributes of a family are related to each other by belonging to the same general kind. Examples for these kinds, which we shall call "**modalities**" (this term is here not meant in the sense of the logic of modalities): the modality of colors (attributes: red, blue, etc.), the modality of shapes (spherical, cubical, etc.), the modality of substances (iron, stone, wood, etc.), and the like. In addition to these **qualitative modalities,** $\mathcal{L}$ may also contain **quantitative modalities;** e.g., for person-moments, the modalities of age, weight, height, and the like. The quantitative modalities will soon be discussed in greater detail.

We assume that the class $\mathcal{F} = \{F^1, F^2, \ldots, F^n\}$ of the families occurring in $\mathcal{L}$ is finite. But the number n of families in $\mathcal{L}$ need not be specified. Whenever we work with some family F^m in $\mathcal{L}$, it is useful to consider its **attribute space** $\mathbf{U}^m$. This is an abstract, logical space whose points represent the elementary (i.e., most specific) properties of the modality in question, e.g., specific shades of color or specific pitches of sound. The attributes belonging to F^m, in contrast, are less specific; hence they are represented, not by points, but by extended **regions** in $\mathbf{U}^m$. These regions are the parts of a countable (mostly finite) **partition** of $\mathbf{U}^m$, say, $\{X_1^m, X_2^m, \ldots\}$. The assignment of points in $\mathbf{U}^m$ to elementary properties is assumed to be such that the more similar two qualities P and P' are to each other (in their subjective appearance, not with respect to their physical substrata, e.g., frequencies of electromagnetic waves or sound waves), the nearer to each other are their representative points u and u' in $\mathbf{U}^m$. *Quantitative* properties of individuals may be based upon a measurable magnitude G^m (which is itself not designated by a sign in $\mathscr{L}$), e.g., the length (of iron rods, or of the wings of bees) or the weight (of persons, or of grains of wheat) or the like. In this case the points of $\mathbf{U}^m$ represent the possible numerical values of the magnitude G^m in question; therefore, we call an attribute space of this kind also a **value space**. (The set of the possible values of G^m is supposed to be given by the rules of the language.) Here again, the attributes of F^m are represented by the parts of a countable partition of $\mathbf{U}^m$. Suppose that $\mathbf{U}^m$ is the set of all real numbers or of an interval. Here we choose a partition of (equal or unequal) subintervals $X_1^m, X_2^m, \ldots, X_k^m$; these intervals in $\mathbf{U}^m$ represent here the primitive attributes $P_1^m, P_2^m, \ldots, P_k^m$ of F^m. P_j^m is the property of an individual of having a G^m-value lying in the interval X_j^m.

Now we shall consider one example for a qualitative and one for a quantitative family.

(2-1) Example: Color Space. Suppose that F^1, the first family in $\mathscr{L}$, contains the six color attributes Red, Orange, Yellow, Green, Blue, Violet, designated (in the given order) by the six predicates, 'P_1^1', 'P_2^1', . . . , 'P_6^1'. This family corresponds to a six-part partition of the color space $\mathbf{U}^1$; the points of this space represent the possible shades of color.

Since each family is based on some partition of some attribute space, it is clear that two distinct attributes of a family are incompatible. Every individual has exactly one attribute of each family.

The following example has to do with a *quantitative* modality, namely, age.

(2-2) Example: Family F^2, based on **age** (in years). Let the individuals be the inhabitants of Los Angeles at noon, January 1, 1966. We take as possible values the nonnegative real numbers up to 200. Thus $\mathbf{U}^2$ is a value space, namely, the interval [0, 200]. Suppose we decide to take into consideration only the age rounded to full years (either because the data at hand are not more precise, or because we decide that for the purposes of our statistical investigation higher precision is unnecessary). This means that we base the family F^2 on the partition of $\mathbf{U}^2$ into 200 intervals of length one, which represent the 200 attributes of F^2. The attribute P_j corresponds to the interval $[j-1, j)$. $P_8 a_{20}$ is the proposition that the age of the person a_{20} is at least seven, but under eight years. If we wish a higher precision, we take another partition where the length of the intervals is, say, a month, or a day, or a minute.

The intervals of the partition of a value space need not be of the same length. If it is found in a statistical investigation that very low and very high values of the magnitude occur only rarely, then often larger intervals are used in the low and high parts of the value space.

(2-3) Example: Age (cont.). In example (2), we might take a partition of the value space into eleven unequal intervals with the following upper bounds (in years): 20, 30, 35, 40, 45, 50, 55, 60, 70, 90, 110, 200.

Similarly, our languages admit families of qualitative attributes corresponding to a partition of the attribute space into parts of unequal sizes (called "widths").

(2-4) Example: Color Space (cont.). The family specified in example (1) may be regarded as represented by a partition of the color space into six parts of equal width. In another language, we might instead use a family based on the same attribute space, but represented by a coarser partition into three parts. For example, we might take as the first attribute Red-or-Violet-or-Blue, as the second Green, and as the third Yellow-or-Orange.

In the case of families of this kind the rules of inductive logic must, of course, take into account the different widths of the attributes. (This question will be discussed in detail in a later section dealing with the attribute space.)

As mentioned before, we assume that, in any given language $\mathscr{L}$, the class $\mathfrak{F}$ of families is finite. This seems justified in view of the fact that the class of families considered in any given scientific investigation is finite; and hence the same holds for the totality of all scientific investigations going on at any time or having been made on our planet up to any given time point. The modalities on which the families are based are either qualitative (modalities of sense perception) or quantitative, namely, primitive measurable magnitudes. (The number of quantitative magnitudes *definable* on this finite basis is, of course, infinite.)

Here it is relevant to mention the following property of the system of inductive logic dealt with in this article. If we wish to determine the numerical value of $\mathscr{C}(H \mid E)$ for given propositions H and E, based upon the language $\mathscr{L}$, this language must obviously contain all those families of which some attributes are involved in H or E. (This concept of involvement will be defined in §3.) The important point is that it is irrelevant for the determination of the $\mathscr{C}$-value whether or not $\mathscr{L}$ contains any additional families. Thus we may at any time in the course of a certain investigation add new families for other modalities to our language $\mathscr{L}$ and thereby extend it to a new language $\mathscr{L}'$. The previously determined $\mathscr{C}$-values for $\mathscr{L}$ remain valid in $\mathscr{L}'$. (This principle of the invariance of $\mathscr{C}$ with respect to the introduction of additional families will be discussed in §6 on sublanguages; see T6-1b.)

[The invariance just explained did not hold in the system in my book [1950]. Therefore in that system, a requirement of the completeness of the language was needed; before determining a $\mathscr{C}$-value, it was necessary to have a complete list of all families and all attributes. This bothersome requirement is now abolished. On the other hand, our present system, which admits denumerable families, but assumes that the number of families is finite without fixing any upper bound, seems in agreement with Keynes's principle of limited variety (if we may interpret his term "independent groups" as meaning modalities). He says [1921, p. 258]: "We seem to need some such assumption as that the amount of variety in the universe is limited in such a way that there is no one object so complex that its qualities fall into an infinite number of independent groups." But our assumption is weaker than Keynes; it does not say anything about the world, but merely assumes that the number of modalities is finite within any one investigation (which may be the investigation consisting of all special investigations carried on in all fields of science at the present time).]

For any set A, let Ix(A) be the **index set** of A. For the sets Ind, $\mathscr{F}$, and any family, say, F^m, which may contain k_m attributes or be denumerable, the index sets are as follows (either finite or denumerable):

(2-5) *Index Sets;*

Set	Elements	Index set	If finite	If in-finite	Index variable
Ind	The individuals: $a_1, a_2, \ldots, a_i, \ldots$	Ix(Ind) $= D =$	$\mathbf{N}_N$	$\mathbf{N}$	'i'
$\mathscr{F}$	The families: $F^1, F^2, \ldots, F^m, \ldots, F^n$	Ix($\mathscr{F}$) $=$	$\mathbf{N}_n$	——	'm'
F^m	The attributes of F^m: $P^m_1, P^m_2, \ldots, P^m_j, \ldots$	Ix(F^m) $=$	$\mathbf{N}_{k_m}$	$\mathbf{N}$	'j'

Since in the languages here considered the sets Ind and all sets F^m ($m = 1, 2, \ldots$) are countable, we call them "*countable languages*". If in a language all those sets are finite, we call it a "*finite language*" (since $\mathscr{F}$ was assumed to be finite); otherwise an "*infinite language*", and, among countable languages, more specifically a "*denumerable language*".

A language $\mathscr{L}$ of the kind here used is a first-order language with identity. We shall now specify the *primitive signs*, the *formulas*, and the *sentences* occurring in $\mathscr{L}$. The *individual constants* and the *predicates* have earlier been discussed. There is a denumerable set of *individual variables* ('x_1', 'x_2', etc.). An *individual sign* is either an individual constant or an individual variable. An *identity formula* consists of the *sign of identity* '=' flanked by two individual signs.

An *atomic formula* consists of a predicate followed by an individual sign. Further formulas are built out of atomic and identity formulas with the help of connectives and quantifiers (and parentheses as auxiliary signs) in the customary way. A formula without the identity sign and quantifiers is called a "*molecular formula*". A formula with at least one quantifier is called a "*general formula*".

These are all the kinds of signs and formulas occurring in $\mathscr{L}$. Any formula without free variables is called a *sentence*. Thus we have among others *atomic*, *identity*, *molecular*, and *general sentences*. (A nongeneral sentence is one without variables; it is either molecular or contains the identity sign.)

In this article the signs, formulas, and sentences do not play an essential role; we shall deal mostly with nonlinguistic entities like individuals, attributes, models, propositions, and the like. Our class of propositions, $\mathscr{E}$, contains for every sentence of the language the proposition designated by it; but $\mathscr{E}$ is immensely more comprehensive. (This will later be made clear; see the remarks following T3-4.) At some occasions a reference to linguistic entities is made in order to facilitate understanding. For example, a certain proposition may be specified by the corresponding sentence; instead of "the proposition designated by the sentence '$P_2^1 a_5$' ", we shall often write simply "the proposition $P_2^1 a_5$" (thus taking sentences of the symbolic language as names of propositions).

Instead of saying that any particular system of inductive logic applies to a certain language, we might just as well say that it applies to a certain **conceptual system**, namely, a universe of objects and a system of descriptive concepts that characterize the objects; and, further, a class of *propositions* of various forms, involving these individuals and characterizing concepts.

(2-6) A synopsis of the **conceptual system:**

(1) The *individuals*: Ind $= \{a_1, a_2, \ldots\}$.

(2) The *attribute spaces*: $\mathbf{U} = \{\mathbf{U}^1, \mathbf{U}^2, \ldots, \mathbf{U}^n\}$.

(3) The *families*: $\mathscr{F} = \{F^1, F^2, \ldots, F^n\}$.

In a nutshell, our *system of the basic entities* consists of a finite sequence of $n + 1$ countable sets: {ind; $F^1, F^2, \ldots, F^n$}.

For each space $\mathbf{U}^m$, there is a family F^m (a countable partition of $\mathbf{U}^m$ into regions). Thus for $\mathbf{U}^1$ (the color space):

(4a) the family of *regions*: $F^1_{\text{reg}} = \{X^1_1, X^1_2, \ldots\}$,

(4b) the family of *attributes*: $F^1_{\text{att}} = \{P^1_1, P^1_2, \ldots\}$
$= \{\text{Red, Orange}, \ldots\}$.

[The corresponding **signs** in the language:

(1) The *individual constants*: 'a_1', 'a_2', ...

(4c) The family of *predicates* $F^1_{\text{pred}} = \{\text{'}P^1_1\text{'}, \text{'}P^1_2\text{'}, \ldots\}$.]

[I now use the subscripts 'reg', 'att', and 'pred' attached to 'F^1' to make clear the distinction between the three sets. But further on, I shall use these subscripts hardly ever, since it is always clear from the context whether the discussion is about regions, attributes, or predicates.]

B. STRONGER LANGUAGES

We have restricted the present system of inductive logic to monadic predicate languages. Let us now look at a few kinds of *stronger languages* and see which of them would introduce essentially new kinds of propositions and therefore require radical changes in the system of inductive logic. First, a new language might contain p-adic predicates with $p > 1$; thus, in addition to attributes, we would have two- or more-place relations, and atomic propositions ascribing a p-adic relation to an ordered p-tuple of individuals. For this we would need new inductive methods. (A first, simple method for a dyadic relation will be proposed in a later article.) This change would not be a radical one. There are two other more important restrictions of our present language $\mathscr{L}$. The first is the restriction of every family of attributes to a *countable partition* of the attribute (or value) space $\mathbf{U}$. Another language $\mathscr{L}'$ may take instead the noncountable partition of $\mathbf{U}$ into unit sets of points. Thus here a family may contain *a continuum of attributes*. For example, an atomic proposition might say that the length (in centimeters, at a fixed time point) of the rod a_5 is (exactly) $\sqrt{2}$. This language $\mathscr{L}'$ would be essentially different from $\mathscr{L}$. A still more radical change would lead to a language $\mathscr{L}''$ in which the set of *individuals* is not countable but a *continuum*, for example, the time continuum, or the four-dimensional space-time-system. The individual indices (here called "coordinates") are real numbers or quadruples of real numbers, respectively.

We might call languages of the kind $\mathscr{L}'$ "*value-continuous*", and those of the kind $\mathscr{L}''$ "*individual-continuous*". The latter ones are usually also value-continuous. These *continuous languages* are in contrast with the countable languages; the latter may be called noncontinuous or *discrete languages*.

Any continuous language makes, within its conceptual system, certain distinctions that are much too fine to be decided empirically even with the most precise measuring instruments. Let L be the length in centimeters of bodies at a fixed time point. A scientist is interested in a certain rod, a_5, at the present time. He knows that $L(a_5)$ is a positive real number, and that certainly one and only one of the following two cases holds: either (1) $L(a_5) \leq 3$, or (2) $L(a_5) > 3$. But every measuring instrument has a limited accuracy. Even for the best instrument available to the scientist, there is a small but positive real number δ such that, if $L(a_5)$ happens to lie in the interval $3 \pm \delta$, it is not possible to decide, with the help of that instrument, whether (1) or (2) holds.

If we wish to have a language that does not go beyond what can be empirically and intersubjectively decided—by direct observation or simple measuring operations—then we must take a countable language, or even a finite language. Such an *observational language* may take the logical form of the monadic predicate language $\mathscr{L}$ we have discussed here. But the choice of Ind must be made such that the individuals are observable things or thing-moments or processes, and the primitive attributes are either perceptible sense qualities or intervals of the scales of simply measurable magnitudes, intervals large enough to correspond to differences detectable by our measuring instruments. Among physical magnitudes we might think here of such examples as spatial distance (or length), duration, volume, weight; further, for a body at a given time point: temperature, electric charge, and the like.

Thus we are led to the distinction between two parts of the total language of science (or of a special field of science), the *observational language* $\mathscr{L}_O$ and the *theoretical language* $\mathscr{L}_T$. This distinction has been found to be useful for the discussion of some problems in the methodology of empirical science.[1]

Previously I thought it preferable not to include in the observational language any quantitative magnitudes. I think my main reason was the continuous value scale. If we use, not the points of this scale, but only

[1] Compare, e.g., R. Carnap, "The methodological character of theoretical concepts," in H. Feigl, M. Scriven, and G. Maxwell (editors), *Minnesota Studies in Philosophy of Science*, Vol. I (1956); R. Carnap, *Philosophical Foundations of Physics* (New York, 1966), chap. xiii.

intervals of a finite partition and of sufficient size as indicated above, then I do not see any reason against the admission of these magnitudes to $\mathscr{L}_O$. With respect to the admission of objects as individuals, I would regard from my present point of view the property of direct visibility of objects no longer as essential. After all, there is a gradual transition from objects I can see with the naked eye, to those for which I (but not younger men) need glasses, to those for which all of us need an optical microscope, or an electron microscope, finally to those particles of which we can see only the track in the Wilson cloud chamber. The essential difference is rather in the logical structure, as we shall see.

From our previous characterization of the languages $\mathscr{L}$ considered in this article, it is clear that the observational language $\mathscr{L}_0$, both in its structure and in its interpretation, must be a language of that kind (possibly extended by including primitive *n*-adic relations).

The *theoretical language* $\mathscr{L}_T$ differs from $\mathscr{L}_O$ chiefly in two respects. *First*, it contains concepts not definable in terms of observables, but introduced as primitives by postulates of two kinds: the theoretical postulates, which contain as descriptive signs only theoretical terms, and the correspondence postulates, which contain both theoretical and observational terms and thus convey a partial interpretation to the theoretical terms. *Second*, $\mathscr{L}_T$ may differ from $\mathscr{L}_O$ not only in the kinds of concepts, but also in its logical structure. When this is the case, it makes a decisive difference for inductive logic.

The structure of $\mathscr{L}_T$ varies with the special field of science, and, within some fields, with the nature of the special investigation. Each of the three main kinds of structure we have distinguished, does occur:

(1) a countable, discrete language,
(2) a language with a *value continuum*,
(3) a language with a *continuum of individuals* (usually combined with a value continuum).

It would be of interest to explore the frequency of the use of these three kinds (or a larger number of subkinds) in special investigations in various fields of science, investigations that make use of theoretical concepts. Not having made such a study, I can only indicate a vague, superficial impression. It seems to me that in all fields outside of physics, in practically all investigations using theoretical concepts, the language has still a structure of the first kind, and in the great majority of cases, it is even finite. This seems clear for all behavioral sciences, even including mathematical economics. In any one investigation within these sciences, the number of objects is certainly finite. And it seems to me that for the measurable magnitudes used in these fields, a countable interval partition would be sufficient.

In some investigations, a value-continuous language will be

desirable. (This would presumably be the case where some theoretical laws have the form of differential equations, chiefly in physics.) I think the construction of a system of inductive logic for a language of this kind will not meet difficulties of a fundamental nature. [The general approach for such a language is outlined by Jeffrey in [Art. 3], at the end of §2. Instead of $Z(m, i) = j$, with a positive integer j in our present languages, we would have $Z(m, i) = x$, with a real number x, in order to say that, in the model Z, the value of the mth magnitude (say, length) for the individual a_1 is x. Jeffrey indicates how the propositions in the σ-field are generated by basic propositions, each of which states for a finite number n of individuals n intervals for the values of the magnitude. He further indicates how probability measures can be defined for the propositions of the original field (or ring) and then for those of the σ-field, by the Lebesgue-Stieltjes method. It will be the task of inductive logic to propose intuitively acceptable probability functions of the kind here needed.]

In the third kind of language, the set of individuals is a continuum, e.g., the space-time points in the four-dimensional space-time continuum. I think that, even in physics, in most investigations based on experimental results a countable space-time-cell system is sufficient. But in some contexts the full continuum is needed, e.g., in field theories and in phase spaces like those for the ψ-functions in quantum theory (not for phase-spaces like Gibbs's in statistical mechanics, where a countable partition into "cells" is used). The construction of an inductive logic for languages of this kind is a task for the future.

Once we have not only a theoretical language $\mathscr{L}_T$, but also an inductive logic IL_T for $\mathscr{L}_T$, then there are, of course, great advantages in changing over from IL_O to IL_T. The great amount of factual information found by science and formulated in $\mathscr{L}_T$ becomes now available as additional evidence. More important, the general laws and theories developed in the more advanced branches of science are now at hand and give more reliable probability values for predictions of observable events. The basic laws of the theories are incorporated into the language $\mathscr{L}_T$ as theoretical postulates. However, I think the $\mathscr{M}$-value 1 should not be assigned to these postulates T, still less to the correspondence postulates C, which connect the theoretical concepts with observational concepts. It should rather be assigned to the analytic A-postulates of the theory TC.[2]

The transition from IL_O to IL_T is not a slow, step-by-step development. One important point in the transition is not much

[2] I have proposed as the one analytic postulate for a theory TC the conditional sentence ${}^RTC \supset TC$, where ${}^RTC$ is the so-called Ramsey sentence of TC. See my [1964*a*, p. 965]; for the Ramsey sentence, see *ibid.* p. 962.

influenced by the amount of factual knowledge and general laws acquired. This is the transition to a new basis for the determination of $\mathcal{M}$-values. Suppose, the observer, a botanist, has so far used IL_O. A physicist instructs him in IL_T; he explains to him the basic physical magnitudes, among them the frequency of light waves. He tells him that the colors are no longer primitive attributes, as they were in IL_O, but are now defined in terms of frequencies of light waves. In IL_O, equal $\mathcal{M}$-values were given to regions of equal width in the color space; but in IL_T, they are given to equal intervals of the frequency scale. Further, let P_1 and P_6 be two attributes of the same family. Other things being equal, $\mathcal{M}(P_1a_1 \cap P_6a_2)$—and therefore also $\mathcal{C}(P_6a_2 \mid P_1a_1)$—is the greater, the smaller the distance between the regions of P_1 and P_6 in the attribute space, in other words, the stronger the similarity between the attributes. (This "similarity influence" will be discussed in detail in §16B, which will appear in Part II in Volume II.) Let P_1 be the color Red, and P_6 Violet. In IL_O, these attributes are represented by neighboring regions, because to men on earth with "normal" vision, these colors appear similar. In contrast, the corresponding attributes in IL_T have maximum distance, hence minimum similarity, because on the frequency scale, the corresponding attributes P_1' and P_6' are represented by intervals near the low and the high end, respectively, of the visible spectrum. Thus, in the transition from IL_O to IL_T, some $\mathcal{M}$- and $\mathcal{C}$-values are abruptly changed. Suppose the botanist has discovered three specimens of a new plant species whose flowers had slightly different shades of pure red; he is interested in the probability that, among the next hundred specimens he will find, there will be at least one with violet-colored flowers. According to IL_O, this chance, though small, is noticeable; but according to IL_T, it is negligible.

Note that this discrepancy in $\mathcal{C}$-values occurs even if there is no change in the relevant evidence. The example was chosen so that the relevant evidence is very meager; if it is more comprehensive, then the numerical change would be small and mostly negligible. But it is important to realize that, quite aside from the change in the evidence (by the factual information transmitted by the physicist), there is a change in the very basis of the system of inductive logic.

The fact that in IL_T the primary $\mathcal{M}$-values for atomic propositions are based, not on the features of subjective sense-qualities but on a system of theoretical physics, is certainly a great advantage of IL_T. The basis of IL_O is different for a person of normal color vision and one with a specific color blindness, and again for others with various kinds of color blindness (not to speak of rational beings on other planets with whom we might have radio communication). In contrast, theoretical physics supplies an intersubjective basis.

3

Models and Propositions

A. THE SPACE OF MODELS

We shall now introduce for every family F^m a special function $^*Z^m$. (We shall use these functions chiefly for informal discussions, for example, in connection with the model functions Z.) A function of this kind specifies for every individual a_i (the index of) that attribute in F^m which a_i actually possesses. Therefore we define:

(3-1). For any family F^m, any attribute P^m_j in F^m, and any individual a_i,

$$^*Z^m(i) = j \text{ if-if the individual } a_i \text{ has the attribute } P^m_j.$$

For example, '$^*Z^1(20) = 3$' says that, as a matter of actual fact, the individual a_{20} has the attribute P^1_3 (in the earlier example (2-1), this is the color Yellow).

(3-2) Example. Let us use the example (2-1) of the family F^1 of six colors. Let us assume that the domain of individuals contains only four individuals a_1, a_2, a_3, a_4, say, a sequence of specimens in a collection. Suppose we have found by observation that these four objects have the following colors, respectively: Blue, Red, Blue Green. These are the following attributes in F^1: P^1_5, P^1_1, P^1_5, P^1_4. Then the function $^*Z^1(i)$ has, for $i = 1, 2, 3, 4$, the values 5, 1, 5, 4, respectively.

For this finite domain of four individuals, it is possible to determine all values of $^*Z^1(i)$ by observations. If, however, the domain of individuals is denumerable, as we usually assume in our languages, then we are never in a position to know all values of $^*Z^1(i)$. But the function $^*Z^1$ is convenient when we want to speak about the unknown colors of objects; e.g., the hypothesis that the (unknown) colors of a_{1000} and a_{1001} are the same, can be formulated by the equation "$^*Z^1(1{,}000) = {}^*Z^1(1{,}001)$".

In order to apply probability concepts, say, our functions $\mathscr{C}$ and $\mathscr{M}$, to a language $\mathscr{L}$, we need a *possibility space* for $\mathscr{L}$, that is to say, a system of all possible cases of the totality of individuals with respect to the families of $\mathscr{L}$. Let us go back to the example (3-2) with the family F^1 and the domain of four individuals. By observation, we found for the four individuals the attributes P^1_5, P^1_1, P^1_5, P^1_4, respectively. Thus we could give the description of the *actual* state of the universe by the four atomic sentences '$P^1_5a_1$', '$P^1_1a_2$', '$P^1_5a_3$', and '$P^1_4a_4$'; or by their conjunction. And we could define the set of *all possibilities* for this universe of four individuals with respect to F^1 as the set of all conjunctions of four atomic sentences of the following kind: the first sentence contains 'a_1', the second 'a_2', the third 'a_3', the fourth 'a_4', and every sentence contains one of the six predicates in F^1. (There are 6^4 possibilities.) For the denumerable domain, however, we cannot form such a conjunction (unless we admit languages with expressions of infinite length). But here we could take the infinite sequence of the true atomic sentences (which we do not know) as the complete description of the *actual* state of the universe with respect to F^1, and analogously all sequences of atomic sentences with predicates of F^1 and with the *i*th sentence in each sequence containing the *i*th individual constant, as descriptions of the *possible* states of the universe. (I used this method in [1950, §18A and C]; I called these sequences "state descriptions," and denoted their class by "$\mathfrak{Z}$' (from the German term "*Zustandsbeschreibung*").)

In our present system, we prefer to speak, not of *signs* of the language but instead of the corresponding *entities*, especially individuals and attributes. Therefore, we take as representatives of the possible cases with respect to a given language, not state-descriptions but **models**, as is customary today in the (semantical) theory of logical language-systems and axiom systems.

The concept of *model* in the indicated sense was originally introduced by A. Tarski; compare his "Contributions to the theory of models", *Koninklijke. Akademie van Wetenschappen, Amsterdam, Proceedings*, Series A, 57 (1954) and 58 (1955); *Indagationes Mathematicae*, 16 (1954) and 17 (1955). The use of models instead of state-descriptions in inductive logic was first suggested to me by John G. Kemeny in [1952] and carried out in [1953]; compare also his "Models of logical systems", *J. Symb. Logic*, 13 (1948), 16–30.

This sense of the term "model" is quite different from that used in some branches of empirical science like physics (e.g., Bohr's model of the atom), mathematical economics (e.g., the model of an economic society with free competition), and the like. In this use, the model of a theory is a schema or simplified picture of the system, serving as a basis for the theory. On the various meanings of the term 'model', compare P. Suppes [1960].

A model for a predicate language is often specified by assigning to each (primitive) predicate of the language one possible extension. Since in our languages $\mathscr{L}$ the predicates are monadic, we could here represent a model by a function that assigns to every predicate (or to every attribute) a set of individuals such that the k sets assigned to the k predicates of a family form a partition of Ind. Another procedure would consist in assigning, with respect to every family F^m, to every individual exactly one attribute of F^m. We shall adopt essentially this procedure;

but for reasons of convenience we represent families, individuals, and attributes by their indexes. Hence we take a model as consisting of n **model-components**, one for each of the n families; and we take a model-component for the family F^m as assigning to every individual index i exactly one attribute index in F^m; in other words, as a function $Z^{(m)}$ from Ix(Ind) to Ix(F^m). Hence we define:

D3-1. For any family index m in $\mathscr{L}$, $\mathbf{Z}_{\mathscr{L}}^{(m)}$ **(the set of the model-components for** F^m) $=_{\mathrm{Df}}$ the set of all functions $Z_{\mathscr{L}}^{(m)}$ such that the domain of $Z_{\mathscr{L}}^{(m)}$ is Ix(Ind) and its range of values is Ix(F^m).

(We shall usually omit the subscript '$\mathscr{L}$'.)

For any given family, say, the family F^1 in example (2-1), every; model component $Z^{(1)} \in \mathbf{Z}^{(1)}$ is analogous to the earlier function $*Z^{(1)}$; but $Z^{(1)}$ may have arbitrary values different from those of $*Z^{(1)}$. Usually, we shall think of the functions in $\mathbf{Z}^{(m)}$ as purely mathematical concepts (although no language restricted to expressions of finite length is strong enough to define all these functions). But since the actual case is certainly one of the possible cases, the function $*Z^{(1)}$ belongs also to $\mathbf{Z}^{(1)}$. [If we were to use a language of logical modalities, in which we distinguish between extensional identity '$\equiv$' and intensional identity '$\underline{\equiv}$' (compare my [1956, §39] and [1964*a*, §9.II]), then we could describe the situation more exactly as follows: there is in $\mathbf{Z}^{(1)}$ a mathematical function, say, $Z_\alpha^{(1)}$, such that $*Z^{(1)} \equiv Z_\alpha^{(1)}$; but not $*Z^{(1)} \underline{\equiv} Z_\alpha^{(1)}$. (Remember that $*Z^{(1)}$ was descriptively defined and hence is not a mathematical function in the strict sense of being purely logical.) In the language used in this article, which is a nonmodal, extensional language, essentially that of set theory, we have only one identity sign, '$=$', whose sense is that of '$\equiv$', not that of '$\underline{\equiv}$'. Therefore, here we assert simply the identity sentence "$*Z^{(1)} = Z_\alpha^{(1)}$", and hence also '$*Z^{(1)} \in \mathbf{Z}^{(1)}$'. But note that the identity sentence just mentioned is not mathematically valid but only factually true, just like "The number of planets = 9".]

We can now define **the set $\mathbf{Z}_{\mathscr{L}}$ of all models** of the language $\mathscr{L}$, which represent tht total possibilities with respect to the individuals and the families in $\mathscr{L}$. We might define any model as a sequence $\{Z^{(1)}, Z^{(2)}, \ldots, Z^{(n)}\}$ such that, for every m, $Z^{(m)} \in \mathbf{Z}^{(m)}$. It seems preferable, however, to represent a model, not by such a sequence of functions, but rather by *one two*-place function $Z(m, i)$, defined in terms of those sequences:

D3-2. $\mathbf{Z}_{\mathscr{L}} =_{\mathrm{Df}}$ the set of all two-place functions $Z_{\mathscr{L}}$ satisfying the following condition: there is a sequence $\{Z_{\mathscr{L}}^{(1)}, Z_{\mathscr{L}}^{(2)}, \ldots, Z_{\mathscr{L}}^{(n)}\}$ such that, for any family index m, $Z_{\mathscr{L}}^{(m)} \in \mathbf{Z}_{\mathscr{L}}^{(m)}$, and $Z_{\mathscr{L}}(m, i) = Z_{\mathscr{L}}^{(m)}(i)$.

The set of models is also called the **possibility space;** and its elements, the models, are sometimes called the *points* of the space.

For abstract mathematical theories, a slightly different form of models is customary, one in which the specification of a model includes a specification of a domain of individuals. In such theories, not only the kinds of individuals may vary from model to model, but even the cardinal number of the domain. Thus different models may be finite with various cardinal numbers, others may be denumerable, and still others noncountable. This seems useful for abstract (uninterpreted) axiom systems like group theory, topology, and similar ones. But it seems to me that in inductive logic it is more useful to specify for each investigation, once for all, the domain of individuals and the families of qualitative attributes or the partition of the value space to be used, so that these specifications hold for all models, that is, for all possibilities considered. This is the customary procedure in mathematical statistics. Each statistical investigation refers to a specified "population," e.g., the inhabitants of Los Angeles on January 1, 1966, or the light bulbs produced by a specified factory, beginning tomorrow. Further, the qualitative or quantitative characteristics of individuals to be observed and registered (usually called the "variables") are specified. Thus each of the possibilities considered involves the same characteristics.

It is important to make a clear *distinction between models and interpretations.* This distinction is often disregarded, even by good authors. (I have pointed out the necessity of the distinction in [1964*a*, p. 902].) For any investigation applying inductive logic, we assume that a language $\mathscr{L}$ is specified with a fixed interpretation, which is the same for all models. In example (2-1), we fixed the interpretation of the predicate 'P_1^1' as the color Red; this predicate keeps this meaning in all models. While an interpretation assigns a *meaning* (intension) to a predicate, the models assign merely various possible *extensions* (sets of individuals) to the predicate, without changing its meaning.

B. PROPOSITIONS

As mentioned earlier, our functions $\mathscr{C}$ and $\mathscr{M}$ will be applied, not to sentences in $\mathscr{L}$ but to propositions on $\mathscr{L}$. For every sentence there is a corresponding proposition, but the converse is not true; most of the propositions on $\mathscr{L}$ are not expressible in $\mathscr{L}$. Therefore, for the purposes of our system of inductive logic, it is not necessary to speak about sentences. But I think it is sometimes useful to do so, especially for those who are more familiar with logical language systems than with the set-theoretic system of models and propositions (events).

Since every model represents a totally specific possible case, for any model Z in $\mathbf{Z}$ and any sentence S in $\mathscr{L}$, either S is satisfied in Z or else its negation $\sim S$ is. If S is satisfied in Z, one says also that S is "true in Z". [Note that this concept of *truth relative to a model* Z, in contrast with the simple (absolute) concept "S is true", is a purely logical concept. If we are in a position to find out whether S is or is not true in Z, then this is done by a purely logical analysis of S and Z, without any use of factual information.] For any sentence S, we shall call (in this section only) the set of those models Z in which S is true, the **truth set** of S, Tr(S). We shall now give a recursive definition of this concept. (It will hardly ever be used in later sections.)

D3-3. Let S and S' be sentences in $\mathscr{L}$, and S'' a sentential formula in $\mathscr{L}$.

- **a.** For any indexes m, i, j in $\mathscr{L}$, if S is the *atomic sentence* with the ith individual constant and the jth predicate of the family F^m, then $\mathrm{Tr}(S) =_{\mathrm{Df}} \{Z : Z \in \mathbf{Z}, \text{ and } Z(m, i) = j\}$.
- **b.** For any S, $\mathrm{Tr}(\sim S) =_{\mathrm{Df}} -\mathrm{Tr}(S)$.
- **c.** $\mathrm{Tr}(S \vee S') =_{\mathrm{Df}} \mathrm{Tr}(S) \cup \mathrm{Tr}(S')$.
- **d.** $\mathrm{Tr}(S\,.\,S') =_{\mathrm{Df}} \mathrm{Tr}(S) \cap \mathrm{Tr}(S')$.
- **e.** If S is an *identity sentence* with two occurrences of the same individual constant, $\mathrm{Tr}(S) =_{\mathrm{Df}} \mathbf{Z}$.
- **f.** If S is an *identity sentence* with two distinct individual constants, $\mathrm{Tr}(S) =_{\mathrm{Df}} \varnothing$.
- **g.** If S consists of a *universal quantifier* followed by the formula S'' as an operand, $\mathrm{Tr}(S) =_{\mathrm{Df}} \bigcap_i \mathrm{Tr}(S''_i)$ (with i running through all individual indexes) where S''_i is the substitution instance of S'' with the ith individual constant.

[It follows from (g) that, if S consists of an *existential quantifier* followed by the operand S'', $\mathrm{Tr}(S) = \bigcup_i \mathrm{Tr}(S''_i)$, with S''_i as in (g).]

These rules determine Tr(S) for any sentence S in $\mathscr{L}$. Tr(S) is analogous to what was called the range of S in my [1950] §18D, i.e., the class of state-descriptions in which S holds. Therefore, theorems about truth sets and models hold here in analogy to those on ranges and state-descriptions in *ibid.*, §§18D and 19.

It is easily seen that two sentences have the same truth set if-if they are logically equivalent, as, e.g., '$\sim(\sim S \vee S')$' and '$S \sim S'$'. Now two sentences are logically equivalent if-if they express the same proposition. Hence all sentences expressing a given proposition have the same truth set. It seems natural to assign this common truth set of those sentences also to the proposition as its truth set. As an example, consider the atomic sentence 'P_1a_8'. Suppose that its truth set is A. Then we assign A also to the proposition expressed by 'P_1a_8' as its truth set. We shall regard as propositions on $\mathscr{L}$ those whose truth sets belong to a certain, very comprehensive class $\mathscr{E}_{\mathscr{L}}$ (which we shall presently define as a σ-field constructed in a certain way). Thus there is a one-to-one correspondence between the propositions on $\mathscr{L}$ and their truth sets, the sets in $\mathscr{E}_{\mathscr{L}}$. Now we go one step further in simplifying our way of speaking. We have mostly to do, not with the propositions themselves but rather with their truth sets. These are the arguments of the functions $\mathscr{C}$ and $\mathscr{M}$. When we speak about $\mathscr{C}(H \mid E)$, instead of saying "the truth set $\mathscr{E}$ of the evidence proposition" we shall simply say "the evidence proposition E". Thus we identify propositions with truth sets. While in philosophy and in semantics the term "proposition" is used for intensions or meanings of sentences, we now use it for the truth sets in the class $\mathscr{E}$. In fact, we have already done so in §1.

(3-3) Example. Let $\mathscr{L}$ contain only the family F^1 in example (2-1). Let us consider the proposition (possible event) that every seventh individual (i.e., a_7, a_{14}, a_{21}, etc.) is red and all others are yellow. Its truth set is $A =_{\text{Df}} \{Z$: for every i, if i is divisible by 7, $Z(1, i) = 1$, and otherwise $Z(1, i) = 3\}$. The proposition mentioned is not expressible in $\mathscr{L}$ or in any other monadic predicate language (because it would require arithmetical concepts or, at least, the two-place relation "immediate successor" among natural numbers). Instead of saying now that the set A represents the proposition mentioned, we shall say that the set A *is* the proposition. This way of speaking is generally used in set-theoretic probability theory (but with the term "event" instead of our "proposition", and with "set of points of the possibility space" instead of our "set of models").

In the definition of a set of models we are free to make use of any mathematical concepts we like; not only of elementary arithmetic, as in the above example, but also of higher mathematics. If, however, we wish to apply our functions $\mathscr{C}$ and $\mathscr{M}$ to such sets, we must show that the defined sets belong to the class $\mathscr{E}_{\mathscr{L}}$. For the set defined in the above example, this condition is satisfied. The definition specifies for every value of i exactly one value of j; hence the set contains just one model; therefore the set belongs to $\mathscr{E}_{\mathscr{L}}$, as we shall see (T1h).

The following definitions lead to the class of the propositions on $\mathscr{L}$, $\mathscr{E}_{\mathscr{L}}$.

D3-4. **+a**. For any index numbers m, i, j, the **atomic proposition** $P^m_j a_i =_{\text{Df}} \{Z: Z \in \mathbf{Z}$, and $Z(m, i) = j\}$.

b. The class of *the atomic propositions with the number pair* (m, i), $\mathscr{E}^{\mathrm{at}}_{m,i} =_{\mathrm{Df}} \{P^m_j a_i : j \in \mathrm{Ix}(F^m)\}$.

+c. The class of the atomic propositions on $\mathscr{L}$,

$$\mathscr{E}^{\mathrm{at}}_{\mathscr{L}} =_{\mathrm{Df}} \bigcup \{\mathscr{E}^{\mathrm{at}}_{m,i} : i \in \mathrm{Ix}(\mathrm{Ind}), m \in \mathrm{Ix}(\mathscr{F})\}.$$

+d. The class of molecular propositions on $\mathscr{L}$, $\mathscr{E}^{\mathrm{mol}}_{\mathscr{L}} =_{\mathrm{Df}}$ the field generated by $\mathscr{E}^{\mathrm{at}}_{\mathscr{L}}$ on **Z**. (See T1-1.)

+e. The class of the propositions (events) on $\mathscr{L}$, $\mathscr{E}_{\mathscr{L}} =_{\mathrm{Df}}$ the σ-field generated by $\mathscr{E}^{\mathrm{at}}_{\mathscr{L}}$ on **Z**.

The terms "atomic proposition" and "molecular proposition" were chosen because these propositions correspond to the atomic and the molecular sentences, respectively. But note that the definitions do not refer to the corresponding sentences.

We explain a few customary terms and notations, applicable to any function f. Let f be a function from A to B.

(3-4) B' is the **image** of A' under f $(B' = f^*(A')) =_{\mathrm{Df}} A' \subset A$ and $B' = \{y\colon$ for some x, $x \in A'$ and $f(x) = y\}$. In this case, $B' \subset B$.

(3-5) A'' is the **inverse image** of B'' $(A'' = f^{-1}(B'')) =_{\mathrm{Df}} B'' \subset B$ and $A'' = \{x : f(x) \in B''\}$. (If $B'' = \{y\}$, A'' is also called the inverse image of y; $A'' = f^{-1}(y)$.)

(3-6) *The closure of a class A* under certain operations is the intersection of all classes B such that $A \subset B$ and B is closed under those operations.

Theorems:

T3-1. **a.** If $E \in \mathscr{E}$, then $E \subset$ **Z**.

b. $\mathscr{E}^{\mathrm{at}} \subset \mathscr{E}^{\mathrm{mol}} \subset \mathscr{E}$.

c. $\mathscr{E}$ is closed under all countable sequences of Boolean operations, i.e., formation of complement with respect to **Z**, difference, union, or intersection.

d. Lemma. Let S be a universal sentence with operand S', and C be the set of substitution instances of S' with all individual constants. If $\mathrm{Tr}^*(C) \subset \mathscr{E}$, then $\mathrm{Tr}(S) \in \mathscr{E}$.

Proof. $\mathrm{Tr}(S) = \bigcap \mathrm{Tr}^*(C)$. Hence assertion by (c). ■

+e. For any sentence S in $\mathscr{L}$, $\mathrm{Tr}(S) \in \mathscr{E}$; for every sentence in $\mathscr{L}$, there is a corresponding proposition on $\mathscr{L}$.

Proof. The assertion follows from (b), (c), and (d), by mathematical induction with respect to the number of connectives and quantifiers in S. ∎

+f. For any class of sentences in $\mathscr{L}$ (with the customary conjunctive interpretation), there is a corresponding proposition. (From (e) and (c).)

g. For any given $Z \in \mathbf{Z}$, let $\mathscr{E}^{\mathrm{at}}_{(Z)}$ be $\{P^m_j a_i : m \in \mathrm{Ix}(\mathscr{F}),\ i \in \mathrm{Ix}(\mathrm{Ind}),\ \text{and}\ j = Z(m, i)\}$. This is the class of all atomic propositions containing Z. Let $A_Z = \bigcap \mathscr{E}^{\mathrm{at}}_{(Z)}$. Then $A_Z = \{Z\}$.

Proof. For any index numbers m and i, the following holds. $Z \in P^m_j a_i$ if-if $j = Z(m, i)$ (D4a). For any Z' in A_Z, $Z'(m, i) = Z(m, i)$, hence Z' is the same function as Z. Therefore $A_Z = \{Z\}$. ∎

+h. For any $Z \in \mathbf{Z}$, $\{Z\} \in \mathscr{E}$.

Proof. Since $\mathscr{F}$ is finite, $\mathscr{E}^{(\mathrm{at})}_{(Z)}$ is countable. Hence $A_Z \in \mathscr{E}$ (by (c)); and likewise $\{Z\}$ (by (g)). ∎

i. For any countable subset $\mathbf{Z}'$ of $\mathbf{Z}$, $\bigcap \mathbf{Z}' \in \mathscr{E}$. (From (h) and (c).)

We have defined $\mathscr{E}^{\mathrm{at}}_{m,i}$, for given m and i, as the class of *the atomic propositions with the number pair* (m, i), i.e., those concerning the individual a_i and (an attribute of) the family F^m. The following theorems are about this class.

T3-2. Let m and i be two given index numbers.

a. The class $\mathscr{E}^{\mathrm{at}}_{m,i}$ is disjoint.

Proof. For the given m and i, let $P^m_j a_i$ and $P^m_{j'} a_i$ be two distinct propositions in $\mathscr{E}^{\mathrm{at}}_{m,i}$; hence $j \neq j'$. Let $Z \in P^m_j a_i$ and $Z' \in P^m_{j'} a_i$. We have to show that Z and Z' are distinct functions. By D4a, $Z(m, i) = j$ and $Z'(m, i) = j'$. Thus Z and Z' are distinct. ∎

b. $\bigcup \mathscr{E}^{\mathrm{at}}_{m,i} = \mathbf{Z}$.

Proof. Let $Z \in \mathbf{Z}$. Then there is a number $j \in \mathrm{Ix}(F^m)$ such that $Z(m, i) = j$. Therefore, by D4a, $Z \in P^m_j a_i$, and, by D4b, $P^m_j a_i \in \mathscr{E}^{\mathrm{at}}_{m,i}$. Hence $Z \in \bigcup \mathscr{E}^{\mathrm{at}}_{m,i}$. ∎

c. $\mathscr{E}^{\mathrm{at}}_{m,i}$ is a countable partition of $\mathbf{Z}$. (From (a) and (b), since F^m is countable.)

We shall say that a proposition E **"involves"** an individual a_i and a family F^m if-if, roughly speaking, E has to do (possibly among other things) with the individual a_i with regard to (attributes of) the family F^m. The subsequent definition is intended to explicate this concept. But first I will explain my reason for *not* trying to explicate the concept of E involving a specific attribute, say the attribute P_5^1 of the family F^1 of six colors in example (2-1). It is doubtful whether such a concept has a clear sense, since the attributes of a family are not independent of each other. Let A_j $(j = 1, 2, \ldots, 6)$ be the atomic proposition $P_j^1 a_3$. First, we might perhaps be inclined to think that the attribute P_1^1 is involved by the proposition A_1, and also by $E = A_1 \cup A_2 \cup A_3$, but not by A_4, nor by $E' = A_4 \cup A_5 \cup A_6$, and hence also not by $-E'$ (since, if a proposition involves something, its negation [complement] involves it, too). But $-E'$ is the same proposition as E. Since a family is a partition of the whole attribute space, the union of all six atomic propositions is the necessary proposition $\mathbf{Z}$; hence $E \cup E' = \mathbf{Z}$, and $-E' = E$. Therefore we shall not speak of a single attribute, but only of the whole family as being involved by a proposition. Before defining this concept (in D5b), we shall first define the concept of involving a pair consisting of a family and an individual, say F^1 and a_3, represented by the number pair $(1, 3)$. According to D4a and D1-3b, the propositions in $\mathscr{E}$ are constructed out of atomic propositions by the operations of complement (with respect to $\mathbf{Z}$) and countable union. Now the basic idea leading to our definition D5a is this: the proposition E involves the pair $(1, 3)$ if-if every possible way of constructing E is bound to use at least one atomic proposition with the pair $(1, 3)$; in other words, if-if E cannot be constructed on a basis excluding these atomic propositions.

D3-5. Let $E \in \mathscr{E}$.

a. E **involves** the number pair (m, i) $=_{\text{Df}}$ $m \in \text{Ix}(\mathscr{F})$, $i \in \text{Ix}(\text{Ind})$, and E does not belong to the σ-field generated by $\mathscr{E}^{\text{at}} - \mathscr{E}^{\text{at}}_{m,i}$. (See D4b.)

b. E involves the index number m (or the family F^m) $=_{\text{Df}}$ for some i, E involves (m, i).

c. E involves the index number i (or the individual a_i) $=_{\text{Df}}$ for some m, E involves (m, i).

T3-3. Let (m, i) be a pair of index numbers. (We assume here that Ind contains at least two individuals.)

a. $\mathbf{Z}$ does not involve (m, i).

Proof. Let $i' \in \text{Ix}(\text{Ind})$ be distinct from i. For some j, let A be the atomic proposition $P_j^m a_{i'}$. Then A belongs to $\mathscr{E}^{\text{at}}_{m,i'}$, but not to $\mathscr{E}^{\text{at}}_{m,i}$, hence to $\mathscr{E}^{\mathrm{at}} - \mathscr{E}^{\mathrm{at}}_{m,i}$ and thus to the σ-field generated by this class. Since $A \cup -A = \mathbf{Z}$, $\mathbf{Z}$ belongs also to this σ-field. Hence the assertion by D5a. ■

b. $\varnothing$ does not involve (m, i). (The proof is like that for (a), with $A \cap -A = \varnothing$.)

These results show that *only contingent propositions can involve something.*

C. SAMPLE PROPOSITIONS AND RANDOM VARIABLES

(3-7) Some notations.

a. ${}^0\mathbf{N}$ is the set of nonnegative integers;
${}^0\mathbf{N}_n$ is the subset of ${}^0\mathbf{N}$ restricted to numbers $\leq n$;
${}^0\mathbf{N}^k$ is the set of all k-tuples of integers in ${}^0\mathbf{N}$;
${}^0\mathbf{N}^{k,s}$ is the subset of ${}^0\mathbf{N}^k$ containing the k-tuples with the sum s.

b. We use '$\mathbf{s}$' for a *k-tuple*. If $\mathbf{s} = \langle s_1, s_2, \ldots, s_j, \ldots, s_k \rangle$ in ${}^0\mathbf{N}^{k,s}$ then $\mathbf{s}^j =_{\mathrm{Df}} \langle s_1, s_2, \ldots, s_j + 1, \ldots, s_k \rangle$ in ${}^0\mathbf{N}^{k,s+1}$.

c. $\mathbf{s}_0 =_{\mathrm{Df}} (0, \ldots, 0)$ in ${}^0\mathbf{N}^{k,0}$.

By a **sample** we understand an arbitrary nonempty subset Ind′ of Ind, with index set D'. The samples we shall deal with will practically always be finite; a finite sample of s individuals will be called an *s-sample*. For any given $s > 0$, we call the set of the first s individuals (with index set $\mathbf{N}_s$) the *initial s-sample*. By an (individual) **sample proposition** (often abbreviated 's.p.') of a given sample with respect to one or more given families we understand a most specific proposition involving the individuals of the sample and the families; the technical definition will be given in D6b.

D3-6. Let Ind′ $\subset$ Ind, and $\mathscr{F}' \subset \mathscr{F}$. Let Ix(Ind′) $= D'$, and Ix($\mathscr{F}'$) $= I'$.

a. *The class of atomic propositions for* Ind′ *with respect to* $\mathscr{F}'$,

$$\mathscr{E}^{\mathrm{at}}_{I',D'} =_{\mathrm{Df}} \bigcup_{m \in I'} \bigcup_{i \in D'} \mathscr{E}^{\mathrm{at}}_{m,i}.$$

b. E is a **sample proposition** (s.p.) for Ind′ with respect to $\mathscr{F}'$ $=_{\mathrm{Df}}$ there is a class $\mathscr{A} \subset \mathscr{E}^{\mathrm{at}}_{I',D'}$ such that for every pair $(m, i) \in I' \times D'$, $\mathscr{A}$ contains exactly one atomic proposition of $\mathscr{E}^{\mathrm{at}}_{m,i}$, and $E = \bigcap \mathscr{A}$.

c. Let E be any countable intersection ($\neq \varnothing$) of atomic propositions (e.g., a sample state). *The class of the atomic* *propositions for* E, $\mathscr{E}^{\text{at}}_{(E)} =_{\text{Df}} \{A: A \in \mathscr{E}^{\text{at}}$, and $E \subset A\}$. (In the special case of an s.p. as in (b), $\mathscr{E}^{\text{at}}_{(E)}$ is the class $\mathscr{A}$ mentioned there.)

d. For any given $s > 0$, we take $\mathscr{B}^{(s)}$ to be *the class of all possible sample propositions for the s-sample* Ind′ with respect to $\mathfrak{F}'$. [In the case of the initial s-sample, these sample propositions correspond to the state-descriptions in $\mathscr{L}_N$ (for $N = s$) in my [1950] D18-1a. Therefore theorems analogous to those on state-descriptions in $\mathscr{L}_N$ given in *ibid.*, §§19 through 21 hold for the propositions in $\mathscr{B}^{(s)}$.]

e. Let $A \in \mathscr{E}$ be nonempty and such that every pair (m, i) involved by A is in $I' \times D'$. Then for any $B \in \mathscr{B}^{(s)}$, either $B \subset A$ or $B \subset -A$. We define:

$$\mathscr{B}^{(s)}_A =_{\text{Df}} \{B: B \in \mathscr{B}^{(s)} \textit{ and } B \subset A\}.$$

f. Let E be a s.p. as in (b), for an s-sample Ind′ and for $\mathfrak{F}'$ containing only *one finite family* F^m of k attributes. We say that E *has the cardinal numbers* $s_1, \ldots, s_k$, or that E *has the k-tuple* (or k-vector) $\mathbf{s} = \langle s_1, \ldots, s_k \rangle$ in ${}^0\mathbf{N}^{k,s}$ if-if, for every $j \leq k$, s_j (the jth number in $\mathbf{s}$) is the number of atomic propositions in the class $\mathscr{E}^{\text{at}}_{(E)}$ with the attribute index j (thus of the form $P^m_j a_i$ for some i).

Here some theorems about the concepts just defined.

T3-4. For a given $s > 0$, let $\mathscr{B}^{(s)}$, A, and $\mathscr{B}^{(s)}_A$ be as in D6d and e. Then the following holds. '$\sum\limits_B$' covers all B in $\mathscr{B}^{(s)}$, '$\sum\limits_{B(A)}$' covers all B in $\mathscr{B}^{(s)}_A$. (Compare my [1950] T21-8a, b, c.)

a. $\varnothing$ does not belong to $\mathscr{B}^{(s)}$.

b. If $B, B' \in \mathscr{B}^{(s)}$ and $B \neq B'$, then B and B' are disjoint.

c. $\bigcup \mathscr{B}^{(s)} = \mathbf{Z}$.

d. $\mathscr{B}^{(s)}$ is a partition of $\mathbf{Z}$. (From (b) and (c).)

e. For any proposition H,

$$\mathscr{M}(H) = \sum_B [\mathscr{M}(B)\mathscr{C}(H \mid B)]. \qquad \text{(From } (d).)$$

f. For any propositions H, K ($K \neq \varnothing$),

$$\mathscr{C}(H \mid K) = \sum_B [\mathscr{C}(B \mid K)\mathscr{C}(H \mid B \cap K)]. \qquad \text{(From } (d).)$$

g. $\bigcup \mathscr{B}^{(s)}_A = A$.

h. $\mathscr{B}^{(s)}_A$ is a partition of A. (From (b) and (g).)

i. $\mathscr{M}(A) = \sum\limits_{B(A)} \mathscr{M}(B)$. (From (h).)

Theorem T4i shows that the following holds: If the values of $\mathcal{M}$ at the sample propositions for a sample are given, then the values of $\mathcal{M}$ at all propositions involving only individuals of this sample are uniquely determined.

The language $\mathcal{L}$ is a very simple language. But there is still a great variety of propositions on $\mathcal{L}$ to which the functions $\mathcal{M}$ and $\mathcal{C}$ may be applied. Even with respect to a qualitative family, we have quantitative propositions about the relative frequency (r.f.) of an attribute in a sample, or about the limit of its r.f. in the whole denumerable universe. In the case of a family based on a quantitative magnitude G, e.g., age, length, weight, or the like, we have propositions about the customary statistical parameters, e.g., the mean of G in a sample or in the universe, likewise the variance of G; and generally about any of the so-called random variables in statistics that we can define with the help of any mathematical concepts we like. [I use the term "random variable" only because it is generally used. A term like "random (or "stochastic" or "aleatory") function" would be more suitable.]

We shall now give definitions, first for the concept of random variable itself, and then for a few elementary examples of random variables whose use is often convenient, and for the important concept of the expectation **E** of a random variable. Then we shall state a few well-known theorems, here formulated in terms of our system. (For the definitions and theorems see Jeffrey [Art. **3**, §3], Kolmogorov [1956, chap. iii, §2], and Munroe [1953, chap. iii, §14].)

Random variables are defined as real-valued point functions of a special kind on any possibility space. Thus they are used in our system chiefly in the following two places: first, on **Z** for the whole universe, and second, for any given sample on the class of all possible sample propositions. For the sake of simplicity, we shall give the definitions for the initial s-sample.

The definition of the concept of random variable is designed to single out those functions f on a possibility space for which it is possible to apply probability functions (in our system, $\mathcal{M}$ and $\mathcal{C}$) to certain statements about these functions f and, in particular, to statements (propositions) of the form: "the value of f for a certain Z lies in the interval $(u, v]$", where u and v are arbitrary real numbers. Now this condition is certainly satisfied generally if it is satisfied for intervals of the special form $(-\infty, v]$ for any v. This is the reason for the following definition.

D3-7. Let f be a real-valued function on **Z**. f is a **random variable** $=_{\text{Df}}$ for every real number v, the class $\{Z: f(Z) \leq v\}$ belongs to $\mathcal{E}$.

D3-8. Let f be a random variable on **Z**. **The distribution function** $F^{(f)}$ of f is defined as follows:
for any real number u,

$$F^{(f)}(u) =_{Df} \mathscr{M}(\{Z : f(Z) \leq u\}).$$

Distribution functions are very useful for work with random variables on **Z** (but not for those on a countable space like $\mathscr{B}^{(s)}$).

Now let us consider the countable possibility space $\mathscr{B}^{(s)}$. Its points are the sample propositions of the s-sample Ind′ with index set D' with respect to the class $\mathfrak{F}'$, which may also include denumerable families. Here we have:

(3-8). A function f is a random variable on $\mathscr{B}^{(s)}$ if-if f is a real-valued function on $\mathscr{B}^{(s)}$.

We can easily see that in this case the requirement analogous to that in D7 is fulfilled automatically. $\mathscr{B}^{(s)}$ is itself countable, and hence likewise any subclass of it. Therefore, for any real number v, the class $\mathscr{B}_v$ of all those propositions in $\mathscr{B}^{(s)}$ for which f does not exceed v, is countable. Since $\mathscr{E}$ is closed with respect to countable union, $\bigcup \mathscr{B}_v \in \mathscr{E}$.

We shall now define a few random variables on $\mathscr{B}^{(s)}$. Such a function f is defined by a rule specifying its value f_p for every sample proposition B_p in $\mathscr{B}^{(s)}$. It is assumed that the propositions H, H_1, H_2, $A_1, \ldots, A_n$, which occur in the following definitions and theorems as arguments of random variables, involve only individuals of the s-sample Ind′. In contrast, the proposition E, which occurs as a second argument of **E**, may involve any individuals; but it is assumed to be nonempty.

D3-9. a. The (numerical, relative) **truth-value** $\text{TV}(H)$ of H in B_p:

$$\text{TV}_p(H) =_{Df} \begin{cases} 1 \text{ if-if } H \text{ holds (or is true) in} \\ B_p, \text{ i.e., } B_p \subset H; \\ 0 \text{ otherwise.} \end{cases}$$

b. Let $\mathscr{A} = \{A_1, A_2, \ldots, A_n\}$ be a class of n arbitrary propositions (it is not required that these propositions are inductively or deductively independent of each other). We define the *truth-frequency* $\text{TF}(\mathscr{A})$ in B_p, that is, the number of propositions in $\mathscr{A}$ that are true in B_p:

$$\text{TF}_p(\mathscr{A}) =_{Df} \sum_{r=1}^{n} \text{TV}_p(A_r).$$

Now we define the **expectation** of a random variable f in the space $\mathscr{B}^{(s)}$; first, the *absolute expectation* (D10a), then the *expectation with respect to given evidence E* (D10b). If all the families are finite, $\mathscr{B}^{(s)}$ is finite; let its cardinal number be m. If at least one of the families is denumerable, $\mathscr{B}^{(s)}$ is denumerable. In the first case, '$\sum\limits_{p}$' stands for '$\sum\limits_{p=1}^{m}$', in the second case for '$\sum\limits_{p=1}^{\infty}$'.

D3-10. a. $\mathbf{E}(f) =_{\mathrm{Df}} \sum\limits_{p} [f_p \mathscr{M}(B_p)]$.

b. For any proposition E ($\neq \varnothing$),

$$\mathbf{E}(f \mid E) =_{\mathrm{Df}} \sum_{p} [f_p \mathscr{C}(B_p \mid E)].$$

D3-11. The random variables f and g are *independent* of each other $=_{\mathrm{Df}}$ if p is any index in $\mathscr{B}^{(s)}$, v is any real number, and E_v is the proposition that $f_p \leqq v$, then E_v is initially irrelevant for the expectation of g, i.e., $\mathbf{E}(g \mid E_v) = \mathbf{E}(g)$.

T3-5. *Sum theorems.* $f + g$ is understood as the random variable whose value for B_p is the sum of the values of f and of g for B_p: $(f+g)_p = f_p + g_p$.

a. $\mathbf{E}(f+g) = \mathbf{E}(f) + \mathbf{E}(g)$.

b. For a finite sequence $f_1, \ldots, f_n$ of n random variables,

$$\mathbf{E}\left(\sum_{r=1}^{n} f_r\right) = \sum_{r=1}^{n} \mathbf{E}(f_r).$$

c. Let g be defined as a linear function of f: for any p, $g_p =_{\mathrm{Df}} af_p + b$, where a and b are fixed real numbers. Then

$$\mathbf{E}(g) = a\mathbf{E}(f) + b.$$

T3-6. *Product theorems.* Let the product fg of the random variables f and g be defined thus: for any p, $(fg)_p = f_p g_p$. Let f and g be independent of each other (D11).

a. $\mathbf{E}(fg) = \mathbf{E}(f)\mathbf{E}(g)$.

b. $\mathbf{E}(fg \mid E) = \mathbf{E}(f \mid E)\mathbf{E}(g \mid E)$.

Now a few special theorems about the random variables defined in D9.

T3-7. a. $\mathrm{TV}(H_1 \cap H_2) = \mathrm{TV}(H_1)\mathrm{TV}(H_2)$. (This is easily seen, since, in any B_p, $H_1 \cap H_2$ holds if-if both H_1 and H_2 hold).

b. $\mathbf{E}(\mathrm{TV}(H)) = \mathscr{M}(H)$.

Proof. By D10a,

$$\mathbf{E}(\mathrm{TV}(H)) = \sum_p [\mathrm{TV}_p(H) \mathscr{M}(B_p)],$$

$$= \sum_p \mathscr{M}(B_p) \text{ for all values } p \text{ such that } B_p \subset H, \quad (by \text{ D9a})$$

$$= \mathscr{M}(H). \qquad \text{(by T4i)} \ \blacksquare$$

c. $\mathbf{E}(\mathrm{TV}(H) \mid E) = \mathscr{C}(H \mid E)$. (Analogous to (b), with D10b.)
d. Let $\mathscr{A}$ be as in D9b. Then

$$\mathbf{E}(\mathrm{TF}(\mathscr{A}) \mid E) = \sum_{r=1}^{n} \mathscr{C}(A_r \mid E).$$

Proof. By D9b, the specified expectation equals $\mathbf{E}(\Sigma\, \mathrm{TV}(A_r) \mid E)$, and by T5d: $\sum \mathbf{E}(\mathrm{TV}(A_r) \mid E)$. Hence the assertion by (c). ■

4
Pure and Applied Inductive Logic

A. THE DISTINCTION BETWEEN PURE AND APPLIED LOGIC

It seems useful to distinguish two kinds of problems we have to deal with in *inductive logic* (abbreviated "IL" in this section). We will call them problems of "pure" and "applied" IL.

The relation between pure and applied IL is somewhat similar to that between pure (mathematical) and empirical (physical) *geometry*. With the help of this distinction, the controversies of the last century on the nature of geometry have been eliminated.[1] Since the distinction between mathematical and physical geometry is more completely clarified, this distinction may be used as a paradigmatic case, which helps us in understanding the distinction between pure and empirical theories in other fields of knowledge. In *mathematical geometry* we speak abstractly about certain numerical magnitudes of geometrical entities, for example, the lengths of the sides of a triangle and the measures of the three angles, but without specifying a procedure of measuring these magnitudes. General theorems are given, stating mathematical relations between these parameters. A variety of possible structures of three-dimensional space, the Euclidean and various non-Euclidean structures, are systematically studied. But the question which of these possible structures is the actual structure of the space of nature is not even raised. This question belongs to *physical geometry*. It is the task of the physicist to lay down rules for various procedures of measuring length, rules based partly on experience and partly on conventions. And with the help of these procedures, the physicist measures geometrical magnitudes together with other physical magnitudes like temperature and the like. Then he proposes hypotheses stating relations among these magnitudes and tests these hypotheses by experiments. This may include also hypotheses about the actual structure of the space of nature.

The situation in IL is analogous. In *applied IL*, we give an interpretation of the language. We say generally that the individuals are, for example, the inhabitants of a certain town or the throws of a certain die, or the states of the weather in Los Angeles at noon on the days of one year. We specify for each family the modality on which it is

---

[1] For a brief, very clear exposition of the distinction in geometry, see C. G. Hempel, "Geometry and empirical science", *Amer. Math. Monthly*, 52 (1945), reprinted in H. Feigl and W. Sellars (editors), *Readings in philosophical analysis* (New York, 1949).

based (e.g., color), the attribute space (color space), and the chosen partition of this space. We define a suitable metric for the attribute space, i.e., a distance function based on similarity relations. Sometimes a coordinate system is constructed, based upon the metric. Furthermore, we give as much information about the regions of the partition as seems relevant for IL. [In volume II I shall propose the conjecture (Part II, C 15-3) that the only relevant features of regions (at least of basic regions) are these two: the width w (volume) of each region, and the distance d between any two points and, derivatively, between regions.] Later in this section (in subsection C) we discuss some problems of applied IL in greater detail.

In contrast, in *pure* IL, we describe a language system in an abstract way, without giving an interpretation of the nonlogical constants (individual and predicate constants). Strictly speaking, we merely deal with unspecified individuals a_1, a_2, and so on, a family of, say, six unspecified attributes $P_1, P_2, \ldots, P_6$, with corresponding regions $X_1, X_2, \ldots, X_6$ in an abstract space $\mathbf{U}$, and with functions d and w. It is only for practical reasons of facilitating the understanding and helping our intuition that we mention unofficial interpretations, using the terms "width" and "distance" for "w" and "d", specifying six colors as the attributes designated by the six predicates, and the like.

Furthermore, we give in pure IL rules connecting values of $\mathscr{C}$ (and $\mathscr{M}$) with other such values (as by the axioms in §1B) or with values of d and w (and certain parameters to be introduced later (as the parameters γ and η in §16)). In pure IL, numerical values of $\mathscr{C}$ (different from 0 and 1) can be determined only conditionally, on the basis of suppositions about numerical values of w or d or other parameters.

B. REQUIREMENTS FOR PRIMITIVE ATTRIBUTES

It is one of the tasks of applied IL to lay down requirements that primitive attributes and relations must fulfill to be admissible as primitive concepts in an object language suitable for IL. (The discussion applies to an observational language; the situation in a theoretical language is, of course, entirely different.) At earlier occasions I have suggested that primitive concepts should be of a *purely qualitative* nature, in distinction to spatial or temporal *positional* concepts (as "in Africa" or "in 1950"). Today I would make the requirement more specific, as I will now explain.

The primitive attributes are to be introduced, not one by one, but grouped in families. For each family its modality must be specified. As I see the situation at present, the classification of attributes into different modalities is not unique but can be made in various ways. For example, with respect to colors (meant here as perceived qualities, without regard to physical processes), different methods seem to me admissible. For example, we may take all features of colors as belonging to one modality. Alternatively, it seems also possible to split these features up into three modalities. And this can be done in different ways. We may, following Wilhelm Ostwald, distinguish (a) hue, (b) white content, (c) black content; or we may, as is more customary in England and the U.S., distinguish (a) hue, (b) saturation, (c) intensity (brightness). Similarly, we may take all features of sound as belonging to one modality, or we may distinguish three modalities: (a) pitch, (b) intensity, (c) timbre.

I would furthermore think today that it is possible, and for our purposes here advisable, to distinguish several modalities for spatial features, and again several modalities for temporal features. And, in particular, we should distinguish in either case between features of location (or position) and other features. When I speak here of "locational" features, I mean this term in the sense of specification of *absolute*, not merely relative, *location*. This will become clearer by the distinction between absolute and relative coordinate systems, which will presently be explained. Both spatial and temporal *location* attributes may serve for the *identification* of an object or event. On the other hand, the various spatial and temporal nonlocational attributes serve for the *description of an identified* object. Therefore we will call them *descriptional* attributes. These attributes, although they are spatial or temporal, are in their function more similar to the qualitative attributes than to the locational, and therefore may be admitted as primitives.

Of temporal modalities there are mainly two: (a) temporal location, (b) duration. Thus we may ascribe attributes of duration, either in numerical or in nonnumerical terms, to thunderstorms, wars, or any other events. For space, since it has several dimensions, there is a greater variety of nonlocational modalities—for example, (a) distance or length, (b) area of a two-dimensional region, (c) volume of a three-dimensional region (e.g., a body), (d) shape of a two-dimensional region, (e) shape of a three-dimensional region. For each of these or other nonlocational modalities, we may construct an attribute space, and then choose a partition of it and thus obtain attributes which are admissible as primitives. An early indication of the importance of the distinction between locational and other spatiotemporal concepts was given by J. C. Maxwell, who said that physical laws never refer to absolute values of spatial or temporal coordinates, but only to differences of coordinates (cf. my *Philosophical foundations of physics* [1966], p. 211).

In this context it seems to me useful to distinguish two kinds of spatial or temporal coordinate systems, which I will call *absolute* and *relative coordinate systems*. Only the former systems are locational (in our strong sense of this term). Suppose a man shows us a map of a village, with scale and N-direction indicated. The map shows the (relative) location of the houses of the families about which he has reported. This map gives us information about the spatial relations among the houses, with respect to distance and direction. Even if the map shows a local coordinate system, with the origin at the village center, and the axes in N–S and E–W directions, this is for us only a *relative coordinate system*, since it shows only *relations* between the houses, but gives no answer to the question *where* this complex of houses is. In contrast, if the man specifies the location of the village in a coordinate system known to us, say, the customary geographical system of longitude and latitude, then he has answered the where-question and has given *locational* information. He can achieve the same by specifying the locational relation of the village to a place we know or can find on our map, e.g., by saying that the village lies a hundred miles south of Chicago. For us, the geographical coordinate system is absolute, but the system on the village map is only relative. But for the village people, the latter system is absolute. A coordinate system is absolute for a person if-if the specification of the coordinates of an object in the system tells him the spatial relation (so to speak, the path) between his own position and the object.

Thus the rule for choosing primitive attributes is as follows:

(4-1) For an intended investigation of a specified class of objects (the "domain of individuals") with respect to certain features, we proceed as follows:

(A) We divide the features to be studied into several *modalities* (such as color, pitch, size, and the like). We distinguish between three kinds of modalities:

- (1) spatial:
  - (1a) spatial-locational,
  - (1b) spatial-nonlocational.
- (2) temporal:
  - (2a) temporal-locational,
  - (2b) temporal-nonlocational.
- (3) qualitative (this kind is meant to include all modalities that are neither spatial nor temporal; they may be either quantitative or not).

For each modality, we choose a partition of its attribute space into some number k of parts ($k \geqq 2$). This partition specifies a family of k attributes.

(B) We call the concepts (modalities, families, attributes, coordinates, etc.) of the kinds (1a) and (2a) "*locational.*"
(C) The concepts of the nonlocational kinds (1b), (2b), and (3) we call "*descriptional.*"
(D) We admit as *primitive predicates* only those that designate descriptional attributes.

This is the strict rule. If we follow it, we are safe. But I think that an investigator may under certain conditions step beyond the borderline drawn by the rule and take even locational attributes as primitive, provided he keeps in mind the dangers involved. In particular, he must be careful not to use the same kinds of concepts within the same investigation for both purposes, first for the identification of individuals and second for description and classification, and then for determination of probabilities and estimates. Suppose a university admission office registers admitted students, assigns to each a registration number, notes the year and date of registration and some further facts about each student. Later somebody might make a statistical investigation of this material. He may count for certain features their frequency in the list, and calculate the correlation between certain features occurring at the same individual, identified by the registration number. On the basis of these data he may then calculate probabilities and estimates of frequencies and of correlations for future years. Now, among the features for which he makes such calculations, he might include also locational, spatial, or temporal characteristics, such as year of birth and place of birth. But here he must be cautious. Especially he must see to it that no logical or meaning relations (as distinguished from statistical relations) hold between the features used for identification and those for which inductive statistical statements are made. (For example, there are obvious relations between time of registration, birthday, and age (at the time of registration). If there are such relations between certain concepts used for inductive procedure but not for identification, then *B*-postulates must be laid down for them. This is explained in subsection C.)

As examples of concepts inadmissible as primitives we may take the predicates "grue" and "bleen", as defined by Nelson Goodman [1955, chap. iii, sec. 4]. The predicate "grue" applies to all things examined before [time] *t* just in case they are green but to other things just in case they are blue. The predicate "bleen" is defined similarly, but with the words "green" and "blue" interchanged. Goodman characterizes these concepts as examples of "nonprojectible" attributes. He calls an attribute "projectible" if one instance of it gives positive confirmation to other instances. Goodman was the first to call attention to the problem of finding a general criterion of projectibility. This is indeed an important problem. I think that the rule (4-1) serves easily in the case of Goodman's two concepts. Each of them, first, belongs not to a *pure* modality, but to a combination of two modalities. The second and more important defect lies in the fact that, though the one modality is that of colors and thus of a qualitative nature, the other is temporal, and, moreover, locational; it is the modality of the time coordinate.

But let us imagine a person who had lived from his birth in a community with a language similar to English but lacking the words "green" and "blue" and having instead the words "grue" and "bleen" with the specified meanings. Would he not regard them as quite normal? And if the words "blue" and "green" were proposed to him as defined on the basis of the other two adjectives, would he not regard them as rather strange and irregular? That might well be, at least in his childhood. But if he grew up and learned thinking about questions of language, logic, semantics, even if those two adjectives were never mentioned to him as examples of meaning analysis, I think he would soon discover for himself their irregular character. But I will not insist on this point; it is, after all, only a psychological question. The main questions are whether the given rule is sufficiently clear, and whether it is valid.

It would certainly be desirable to give further clarification for the concept of modality. I found that W. E. Johnson's concepts of a *determinable* and the *determinates* belonging to it are quite similar to my concepts of a modality and the attributes belonging to it. I think his detailed discussion in [1921] (especially in chap. xi) and his numerous examples will be helpful to the reader.

The proposed distinction between locational and descriptional concepts may perhaps become clearer when it is exemplified by a certain distinction made by physicists since classical times in the description of an instantaneous state of a physical system (e.g., the planetary system or a body of gas included in a vessel) or in the description of a process as a temporal series of such states. I am thinking of the distinction between the space coordinates of the parts of a system (in an absolute coordinate system) on the one hand, and, on the other, the state magnitudes (usually called "state variables") which characterize various aspects of the state of the system and of its parts. These aspects may include also certain temporal and spatial features, but only relative concepts, not locational features (in our absolute sense). Examples of spatiotemporal concepts admitted as state magnitudes are the velocity or the size of a part of the system, the distances between parts; and thus also spatial coordinates of parts with respect to a *relative* coordinate system—e.g., the spatial coordinates of the molecules of a gas body in a coordinate system defined by the walls of the vessel.

I wish to emphasize again that the rule (4-1) makes restrictions only for *primitive* attributes. There is no restriction for the introduction of new predicates by definition. If the definiens has molecular form, then we call the defined predicate and the attribute designated by it "*molecular*". A sentence consisting of a molecular predicate and an individual constant is logically equivalent to a molecular sentence in which all atomic components contain occurrences of the same individual constant. If the primitive attributes of a language satisfy the requirement (4-1), then the molecular attributes are likewise purely descriptional, free of locational components.

Let us briefly consider a richer language $\mathscr{L}'$ of such a kind that Goodman's abnormal predicates could be defined in it. (It may, for example, be a language with thing slices as individuals, as in language form IIA in my *Introduction to Symbolic Logic* (1958, §39). We assume that the primitive predicates of $\mathscr{L}'$ are descriptional, and that among them are the one-place qualitative predicates 'Blue' and 'Green', and the two-place predicate 'Earlier', which is temporal, but nonlocational. Let the individual constant 'b_{2000}' denote that slice of the standard calendar-clock which is characterized by the first appearance of the figure '2000' at the year-indicator of the clock. Let the rules for definitions of predicates in $\mathscr{L}'$ be of the customary kind for a first-order language. Then we can introduce a predicate essentially like Goodman's by the following definition:

(D) x is Grue $=_{\mathrm{Df}}$ (x is Earlier than $b_{2,000}$ and x is Green) or (x is not Earlier than $b_{2,000}$ and x is Blue).

Now it is clear that certain customary inductive procedures that are valid for 'Blue' and for 'Green' would lead to counterintuitive results if they were applied to the predicate 'Grue'. This predicate was introduced by Goodman in order to point out the difficulty we have to face here. This difficulty may be presented in the following way. Suppose that we are constructing a system of IL for the language $\mathscr{L}'$. We choose one of those procedures or principles which are valid for descriptional attributes like Blue and Green, but invalid for Grue and similar attributes. Suppose we wish to represent this principle by an axiom A of IL. [As an example we may think of the principle of instantial relevance. It says that for any attribute P of a certain kind the following holds: any two instances of P, e.g., the atomic propositions Pa_1 and Pa_5, are initially positively relevant to each other, so that $\mathscr{C}(Pa_5 \mid Pa_1) > \mathscr{M}(Pa_5)$. This principle is discussed later in §13. I believe that it is valid not only for the qualitative attributes designated by primitive or molecular predicates of our monadic predicate language $\mathscr{L}$, but also for all *descriptional* attributes, primitive or defined, in the richer language $\mathscr{L}'$ which we consider at present. I will not discuss here the question of its validity, however, but only the problem of its formulation, provided we regard it as valid for descriptional attributes.] The essential point in the problem of a correct formulation of the axiom A is the obvious necessity of including into A a suitable restricting condition, in order to prevent its application to attributes like Grue. And the exclusion of these attributes should be stated in *general* terms, not by a list of excluded attributes. Now we might think of expressing A in the following form:

(i) For any descriptional attribute P in $\mathscr{L}'$, primitive or defined, ...

This form would indeed have the desired restricting effect, but we cannot use it, because it contains the inadmissible term 'descriptional'. This term—like the terms 'temporal', 'locational', 'qualitative', which occur in its definition—concerns the *interpretation* of the object-language in question, here $\mathscr{L}'$. Therefore, it belongs to *applied* IL. But the axioms and axiomatic rules of a system of IL must contain only terms of *pure* IL. The following form satisfies this requirement:

(ii) For any attribute in $\mathscr{L}'$ which is either primitive, or defined by a definition free of individual constants, ...

While this axiom is formulated within pure IL, any argument intended to show its adequacy, and, in particular, to show that it excludes nondescriptional attributes like Grue, has to proceed within *applied* IL. Here it can easily be shown as follows. We have assumed that all primitive attributes and relations in $\mathscr{L}'$ are descriptional. Therefore any attribute or relation defined by a definition free of individual constants is likewise descriptional.

5

Basic Assumptions about Individuals, Attributes, and Relations

When a scientist makes a special investigation of some kinds of objects, he will usually adopt some general assumptions about these objects. He may be convinced of their truth, or he may just accept them hypothetically; at any rate, within this investigation he does not question them. Let us call them the *basic assumptions* of his investigation. We shall consider here some kinds of basic assumptions and the methods of dealing with them in IL. These methods belong to applied IL, because the assumptions presuppose an interpretation of the language $\mathscr{L}$ in question. Our discussion will be restricted to predicate languages; therefore we consider only assumptions about individuals, attributes, and relations, not those about quantitative concepts, like temperature.

We need not discuss here the more fundamental assumptions, namely, those of *deductive logic*. As mentioned earlier, we shall in this article always presuppose that for any language $\mathscr{L}$ used, a system of first-order logic with identity is presupposed, containing rules for the truth-functional connectives and for quantifiers with individual variables. This logic system may have any of the customary forms; the choice of the form is not essential for IL. In the method of IL used in this article, referring mostly not to sentences but to their truth sets called "propositions", deductive logic plays no great role. The most important concepts of deductive logic are the L-truth (logical truth) of sentences and the relation of L-implication among sentences. In our present method we refer, not to the infinitely many L-true sentences, but instead to the one proposition corresponding to them, namely the set **Z** of all models. And instead of L-implication between sentences, we have here the simple relation of subset among propositions.

It was said earlier that, in language $\mathscr{L}$, any two distinct individual constants, e.g., 'a_3' and 'a_4', denote distinct individuals. Now we make the following basic assumptions:

(5-1) **(a)** Any two distinct individuals are logically independent of each other.

The following says essentially the same:

(5-1) **(b)** The two subsets of the space-time continuum, corresponding to the one and the other of two distinct individuals, have no space-time-point in common.

From this we derive:

(5-2) Let a_i and a_j be two distinct individuals. Let $\mathscr{A}_i$ be a class of monadic atomic propositions involving a_i such that $A_i = \bigcap \mathscr{A}_i$ is not empty. Let A_j and $\mathscr{A}_j$ be similar with respect to a_j. Then $A_i \cap A_j$ is likewise not empty.

The *basic assumptions on attributes and relations* are of various kinds. Let us first consider those that I called originally "meaning postulates" (see [1952*b*]) and later "A-postulates" (i.e., analytic postulates). Postulates of this kind were first proposed by Kemeny in [1951] and used in his [1952] and [1953*a*]. I regard a sentence as analytic or A-true if its truth is based on the meanings of the terms occurring in it, and can therefore be established by considering merely these meanings, without regard to contingent facts. Examples are "all dogs are animals" and "no bachelor is married." The set $\mathscr{A}$ of A-postulates of an interpreted language $\mathscr{L}$ is chosen in such a way that (1) every sentence of $\mathscr{A}$ appears as analytic (in the informal sense just indicated) and (2) that all other analytic sentences of $\mathscr{L}$ (or as many of them as we care for) are L-implied by $\mathscr{A}$.

There is, furthermore, another important kind of basic assumption, which we will label as "phenomenological", because it plays an important role in the philosophical doctrine of phenomenology developed by Edmund Husserl and his followers; but our use of the term "phenomenological" is not to be understood as indicating acceptance of this doctrine. Here are a few examples of assumptions of this kind which we regard as valid for the attributes Blue and Green and the relation Warmer in a predicate language $\mathscr{L}$.

(5-3) **(a)** The colors Green and Blue are incompatible, i.e., they cannot occur simultaneously at the same place.

(b) For any x and y (at the same time), if x is warmer than y, y is not warmer than x. (Here 'warmer' is understood as based on directly perceived sensory qualities of warmth, not on measurements of temperature.)

(c) For any x, y, z, if x is warmer than y, and y is warmer than z, then x is warmer than z.

Now some assumptions concerning *similarity* of attributes.

(5-4) **(a)** Green is *similar* to Blue.

(b) Green is *more similar* to Blue than to Red.

(c) The *degree of similarity* between Green and Blue is *equal* to that between Green and Yellow.

(d) The *degree of similarity* between Green and Blue is *higher* than that between Green and Red.
(e) The *distance* (in the color space) between Green and Blue is *equal* to that between Green and Yellow.
(f) The *distance* between Green and Blue is *smaller* than that between Green and Red.

There are many controversies among philosophers about the logical nature of statements of these kinds, whether they are analytic or synthetic, and about their epistemological nature, whether they are known a priori, i.e., independently of factual experience, or a posteriori, on the basis of experience. At least the simpler ones (say, those under (3) and the first two under (4)) may be counted as phenomenological. Statements of this kind were regarded by Husserl as synthetic–a priori. In the Vienna Circle we regarded them likewise as a priori, but analytic. I have frequently offered such sentences as examples of A-postulates. For years now, however, my friends and I tend to a more cautious attitude with respect to the epistemological question. We think that so far no satisfactory explication has been given for the concepts of a priori versus empirical (a posteriori) knowledge. The phenomenological statements are boundary cases; whether they are to be counted as empirical or not depends upon the choice of a broader or a narrower meaning for the term "empirical".[1]

With respect to the assumptions on *similarity* of attributes under (f), we shall see in Volume II (§16) that it is of great importance for IL to have not only *comparative* statements like (b) but also statements on the *degree of similarity*, like (c) and (d); these can be expressed in terms of *distance* as in (e) and (f). For certain attribute spaces, for example, that of colors and that of the pitches of sounds, psychologists have succeeded in introducing a *metric* by defining a *distance function* which has a numerical value for each pair of attributes. Such a distance function is established experimentally on the basis of subjective judgements either on the equality of distances ("Of the three sounds just perceived, the second lies, with respect to pitch, in the middle between the first and the third") or judgments on just discernible differences. These are intuitive judgments based upon subjective impressions, like (b), not on physical measurements. Thus the resulting metric is based upon phenomenological judgments not essentially

---

[1] A thoroughgoing investigation of this whole complex of problems and a critical analysis of the two distinctions is given by Harald Delius in his book *Untersuchungen zur Problematik der sogenannten synthetischen Sätze apriori* (Göttingen, 1963).

different from those under (4). Therefore some might regard a quantitative statement based on the metric, e.g., "the distance between this shade of color and that is .36" as a priori. On the other hand, in view of the fact that the metric is established by a comprehensive experimental procedure, some others might say that quantitative statements, like the example just given, have a considerable empirical component. We shall see later that, with the help of the distance function, we can numerically determine the *width* (volume) of a region in the attribute space. We shall lay down a rule that says that, if the (normalized) width of the region of an attribute P is $w(P)$, then, for any atomic proposition A with P, we should take $\mathcal{M}(A) = w(P)$.

When we accept some basic assumptions generally for a language $\mathcal{L}$, and not merely for a special investigation, we will call them "basic principles" or "*B-principles*" for $\mathcal{L}$. Those sentences of $\mathcal{L}$ which are true by virtue of the B-principles (together with logical rules and A-postulates), without regard to contingent facts, we shall call "B-true" (the technical definition will be given later in D1a). In analogy to A-postulates, some of the B-true sentences are chosen as "*B-postulates*" in such a way that the other B-true sentences are A-implied by them. The situation here, however, is different from that of the A-postulates in this respect: some B-principles for $\mathcal{L}$ cannot be represented by sentences of $\mathcal{L}$, as we shall presently see.

The B-principles in (3) were stated for a language that contains predicates for the two colors and the relation involved. Let us take, as in the example (2-2), 'P_4^1' for Green and 'P_5^1' for Blue, and further the two-place predicate 'W' for the relation Warmer. Then the B-principles under (3) can be expressed by sentences of $\mathcal{L}$ itself, which we may take as *B-postulates:*

(5-5) **(a)** $(x)[\sim(P_5^1x \cdot P_4^1x)]$.
(b) $(x)(y)[W(x, y) \supset \sim W(y, x)]$.
(c) $(x)(y)(z)[W(x, y) \cdot W(y, z) \supset W(x, z)]$.

In contrast with the examples just formulated, the B-principles in (4) cannot be expressed in sentences in $\mathcal{L}$, but only in the language of IL. In the language $\mathcal{L}$ we can talk only about the entities of the conceptual system, namely, individuals, attributes, and relations. But in the language of IL we can talk not only about those entities, but also about models, propositions, and the functions $\mathcal{C}$ and $\mathcal{M}$. This language serves, in addition, as a metalanguage, in which we speak *about* the expressions and especially the sentences of $\mathcal{L}$. While the object language $\mathcal{L}$ is a constructed system with a fixed vocabulary and rules (or, at least, it is imagined to be so, while in actual practice we seldom state the rules explicitly), the language of IL is an open language. We are free to use any terms which seem to us sufficiently clear; in particular, all concepts of mathematics may be freely used. Thus we have used the term 'Red', which is the translation of the term 'P_1^1' of $\mathscr{L}$; but then we speak in (4) also about similarity among colors or other attributes, we use the comparative term "more similar than", and we even refer to the quantitative concept of degree of similarity and the related concept of distance in the attribute space.

Thus the basic assumptions are meant here in a broad sense. And the class of B-postulates, which express some of the basic assumptions, is understood as including the L- and the A-postulates, but possibly some others too. The description of a constructed language $\mathscr{L}$ must include lists of postulates of all three kinds, if sentences of these kinds are intended to occur.

With respect to any given B-principle, we need not decide the questions whether it is analytic or not, and whether it is a priori or not. As mentioned earlier, these distinctions are not of great consequence for IL.

For the languages chiefly studied in this article, the languages with families of monadic predicates, the following two B-principles are essential.

(5-6) *B-principles for a family of attributes.* Let F be a family of k attributes $P_1, \ldots, P_k$. Then the following holds for any individual a_i.

(a) For any two distinct attributes P_j and P_l, $P_j a_i \cap P_l a_i = \varnothing$.

(b) $P_1 a_i \cup P_2 a_i \cup \ldots \cup P_k a_i = \mathbf{Z}$.

These two B-principles say in effect that, for any family F, every individual has just one of the attributes of F. This is the same as the requirement that the regions of an attribute space $\mathbf{U}$, representing the attributes of a family, should form a partition of $\mathbf{U}$.

These B-principles can obviously be expressed by sentences of $\mathscr{L}$:

(5-7) The two *B-postulates for a family* F^m of k attributes:

(a) For any two distinct attribute indices j and l in F^m,

$$(x) \sim (P_j^m x \cdot P_h^m x);$$

(b) $(x)(P_1^m x \vee P_2^m x \vee \cdots \vee P_k^m x)$.

Each of these two formulas is a sentence schema, characterizing a whole class of sentences with various values of the parameters (free variables) 'm', 'j', 'l', and 'k'. (In (5)(a), we had a special case of (7)(a)).

It is easily seen that these two postulates are satisfied in each model of our class **Z**. According to D3-1 and 2, for any $Z \in \mathbf{Z}$, its model component $Z^{(m)}$ for the family F^m is a function that has, for any individual index i, just one value, and this value is an attribute index in F^m.

The question whether a certain B-principle is satisfied in a given model for a language $\mathscr{L}$ can only be raised for a B-postulate expressed in a sentence of $\mathscr{L}$. If a B-principle involves concepts that do not belong to the conceptual system of $\mathscr{L}$, e.g., the concept of similarity in (5), then it is not expressible by a sentence (or a class of sentences) in $\mathscr{L}$. A B-principle of this kind has no relation to the models. Therefore we refer in the following discussion only to B-postulates.

In my book [1950, §18B], I required that the atomic sentences of a language $\mathscr{L}$ should be independent of each other. This restriction is now abolished. Dependencies are allowed. But they must be represented by B-postulates.

Suppose an investigator has used a language form $\mathscr{L}$ in several statistical investigations, concerning various kinds of objects. (Strictly speaking, he used different, but similar, languages, say, one-family languages; the families had different interpretations and possibly different sizes, and the individual constants may have different interpretations.) Suppose he has used here a certain form of models M (not necessarily the form **Z** described in §3) of such a kind that all B-postulates were satisfied in all models. But now he begins a new investigation with a language form $\mathscr{L}'$, similar to, but somewhat different from, $\mathscr{L}$, with a set $\mathscr{B}'$ of B-postulates. The researcher uses first the class M' of models for $\mathscr{L}'$ constructed in a form analogous to M for $\mathscr{L}$, but adjusted to the families and attributes in $\mathscr{L}'$. Let $\mathscr{B}' = \{B_1, B_2, \ldots, B_n\}$ be the sequence of the n B-postulates. Each B_p ($p = 1, 2, \ldots, n$) is a postulate expressible by a sentence in $\mathscr{L}'$. More exactly speaking, we take B_p to be the truth-set of the sentence expressing the pth postulate. Thus B_p is, in our terminology, a proposition. Let $B' = \cap \mathscr{B}'$; hence it is the intersection of the n truth sets. This is the truth-set of the conjunction of the p sentences. Thus B' is a class of models: $B' \subset M'$.

Now the researcher determines whether the B-postulates are satisfied in all models. If this is the case, $B' = M'$. Then there is no problem about the postulates; he need not give any attention to them since they are automatically satisfied.

Suppose now that this is not the case. Then special measures must be taken to assure the fulfillment of the postulates. I shall indicate some methods that might be used for this purpose.

The first method is conservative. The researcher does not construct models of a new form. He retains the general form in M', but he restricts the models to be used to those of a proper subclass $M'' = B'$, that is, to the class of those models in which the postulates hold.

The second method (an alternative form of the first) leaves the class of models M' unchanged, but changes the function $\mathscr{C}$ into $\mathscr{C}'$, defined as follows:

(5-8) For any H and E such that $E \cap B' \neq \varnothing$,

$$\mathscr{C}'(H \mid E) =_{\text{Df}} \mathscr{C}(H \mid E \cap M').$$

In analogy to T1-5:

(5-9) For any $H, \mathscr{M}'(H) = \mathscr{C}'(H \mid M')$;

hence by (8): $= \mathscr{C}(H \mid M')$.

(This procedure was suggested for meaning-postulates, i.e., A-postulates, in [1952*b*] §4, (15) and (14).)

This method might be considered in cases where the situation does not seem to warrant a revolutionary changeover in the structure of the models.

Example for the second method. Let $\mathscr{L}'$ contain not only one-place predicates, but also three two-place primitive predicates for the dyadic relations R_1, R_2, R_3. Suppose that all B-postulates for the one-place predicates are satisfied in all models in M'. Then we have to take care only of the B-postulates for the relations. Suppose we have B-postulates similar to (5)(b) and (c), stating asymmetry and transitivity for R_1. Let B_1 be the proposition (truth set) corresponding to the conjunction of these two postulates. Similarly, let B_2 ascribe some structural properties to the relation R_2, and likewise B_3 to R_3. Let $B = B_1 \cap B_2 \cap B_3$. Let E be any proposition compatible with B, and H be any proposition. Then we define for $\mathscr{L}'$ the new $\mathscr{C}$-function $\mathscr{C}'$ as follows:

(5-10) $$\mathscr{C}'(H \mid E) =_{\text{Df}} \mathscr{C}(H \mid E \cap B).$$

A side remark on universal propositions. Some $\mathscr{C}$-functions, for example, those of the λ-system (in Part II in Volume II), are such that the corresponding $\mathscr{M}$-function has the value 0 for universal propositions involving an infinity of individuals. Therefore $\mathscr{M}(\mathscr{C} \cap B) = 0$ if B contains such universal propositions. This does not prevent the application of the method just explained. But the definition of $\mathscr{C}'$ is to be modified by the use of a limit procedure. Here only a brief indication will be given. The procedure will later be discussed in more exact and more general terms (in the section on limit axioms in Part II). Let S be a sentence containing quantifiers. For any n exceeding every individual index explicitly occurring in S, the sentence $S_{(n)}$, which involves only the first n individuals, is formed as follows. At each step, a subsentence of S of the form $(x)\varphi x$, where φx does not contain any quantifier, is replaced by the conjunction $\varphi a_1 \cdot \varphi a_2 \cdot \ldots \cdot \varphi a_n$ of the substitution instances of φ with the n first individual constants. Analogously, a subsentence $(\exists x)\varphi x$, where φx does not contain quantifiers, is replaced by the disjunction of the instances. This procedure is continued step for step until all quantifiers are eliminated. Then the result $S_{(n)}$ is a molecular sentence. In a similar way, if G is a proposition involving an infinite number of individuals, $G_{(n)}$ is intended to be a proposition analogous to G but not involving any individual index higher than n. (In an explicit formula for G, '$\bigcap^{\infty}$' is replaced by '$\bigcap^{n}$', and '$\bigcup^{\infty}$' by '$\bigcup^{n}$'.) Then $G_{(n)}$ is a molecular proposition. Hence, according to the axiom of regularity to be stated later (§7), $\mathscr{M}(G_{(n)}) > 0$. Now we use the following limit definition:

(5-11) $$\mathscr{C}'(H \mid E) =_{\mathrm{Df}} \lim_{n \to \infty} \mathscr{C}(H_{(n)} \mid E_{(n)} \cap B_{(n)}).$$

Suppose that $H \cap E$ is molecular. Then there is a highest individual index involved, say, p. In this case we can define in a simpler way:

(5-12) $$\mathscr{C}_{\mathrm{f}}(H \mid E) =_{\mathrm{Df}} \mathscr{C}(H \mid E \cap B_{(p)}).$$

The third method is more radical. Here a class M''' of models of a new form is constructed for language $\mathscr{L}'$ in such a way that all B-postulates for $\mathscr{L}'$ are automatically satisfied in any model of the new form M'''. Thus here no artificial restriction or change of $\mathscr{C}$ is necessary.

This method was used, for example, in the transition from the language dealt with in my [1950], which contained only independent primitive predicates, to the language used in this article. Since in the latter language the primitive predicates are grouped in families, we have here the B-postulates (7). Therefore the class **Z** of models was introduced with the new form of model functions, in contrast with the state descriptions in the old system [*ibid.*, §18A]. [Already at that time I indicated a new form of models ("state-descriptions") to be used for "families of related predicates" (see [*ibid*, §18C], the first paragraph in small print)]. We saw earlier (see the remarks following (7)) that the family postulates are satisfied in the models of the class **Z**.

Now we shall define some *semantical concepts*, applicable to sentences, not to propositions. We introduce them as counterparts to the L-concepts (e.g., L-truth or logical truth) and A-concepts (e.g., A-truth or analytic truth). These concepts will not be used frequently, since we refer mostly to propositions, not to sentences.

D5-1. Suppose that, for a language $\mathscr{L}$, we have defined a class M of models, and laid down a class $\mathscr{B}$ of B-postulates, which are sentences in $\mathscr{L}$. Let M_B be the subclass of M containing just those models in which the postulates $\mathscr{B}$ are satisfied. (We leave it open whether or not $M_B = M$.) Let S and S' be sentences of $\mathscr{L}$. Let A be the proposition corresponding to S (i.e., the truth set of S) and A' that of S'.

- **a.** S is *B-true* (in $\mathscr{L}$) $=_{\text{Df}}$ S is satisfied in all models of M_B (in other words, $M_B \subset A$).
- **b.** S is *B-false* (in $\mathscr{L}$) $=_{\text{Df}}$ the negation $\sim S$ is B-true.
- **c.** S is *B-determinate* in $\mathscr{L}$ $=_{\text{Df}}$ S is B-true or B-false in $\mathscr{L}$.
- **d.** S is *B-indeterminate* in $\mathscr{L}$ $=_{\text{Df}}$ S is neither B-true nor B-false in $\mathscr{L}$.
- **e.** S *B-implies* S' in $\mathscr{L}$ $=_{\text{Df}}$ $\sim S \vee S'$ is B-true (in other words, $(M_B \cap A) \subset (M_B \cap A')$).
- **f.** S is *B-equivalent* to S' in $\mathscr{L}$ $=_{\text{Df}}$ $S \equiv S'$ is B-true (in other words, $M_B \cap A = M_B \cap A'$) in $\mathscr{L}$.
- **g.** S and S' are *B-exclusive* (or B-incompatible) in $\mathscr{L}$ $=_{\text{Df}}$ $M_B \cap A \cap A' = \varnothing$.

T5-1. Let M, M_B, S, S', A, and A' be as in D1. Let $M_B = M$; in other words, the B-postulates are satisfied in all models in M. Then the following holds.

- **a.** S is B-true (in $\mathscr{L}$) if-if A is necessary (in other words, $A = M$).
- **b.** S is B-false if-if A is impossible ($A = \varnothing$).
- **c.** S is non-B-false if-if A is possible ($A \neq \varnothing$).
- **d.** S is B-determinate if-if A is noncontingent.
- **e.** S is B-indeterminate if-if A is contingent.
- **f.** S B-implies S' if-if $A \subset A'$.
- **g.** S is B-equivalent to S' if-if $A = A'$.
- **h.** S and S' are B-exclusive if-if A and A' are disjoint.

The definitions of the B-concepts in D1 are analogous to those of the corresponding L-concepts (in [1950] D20-1). [If we use both L-concepts and B-concepts with respect to a language $\mathscr{L}$, then every L-true sentence is also B-true. The converse, however, does not hold if we have a language with B-postulates that are not L-true. For example, on the basis of the B-postulate (7)(a) the sentence '$P_5^1 a_1 \supset \sim P_4^1 a_1$' is B-true but not L-true. For the languages dealt with in [1950], no basic relations hold between primitive predicates and therefore no

B-postulates occur; thus in those languages a sentence is B-true if-if it is L-true.]

For inductive logic, the B-concepts suffice and the L-concepts need not be considered. If a clause in a theorem of IL in [1950] or [1952*a*] contains an L-term, we shall now replace this term by the corresponding B-term (e.g., 'L-true' is replaced by 'B-true'). The result is still a theorem about sentences. According to our present method, referring mostly to propositions rather than to sentences, the clause is further transformed into a clause applying the corresponding concept (property or relation) of propositions (according to T1). [For example, [1950] T59-1b says: "If $\vdash e \supset h$ (i.e., if the sentence $e \supset h$ is L-true, in other words, if e L-implies h), then $c(h, e) = 1$". This is first transformed into: "If $e \supset h$ is B-true (in other words, if e B-implies h), then $c(h, e) = 1$". This theorem is somewhat more general than the original theorem, since it is applicable also to languages with B-postulates. To conform to our present method, the theorem is finally transformed into "If $E \subset H$, then $\mathscr{C}(H \mid E) = 1$" (which is T1-2b above).]

6
Sublanguages

When we speak of translation from one language into another, we usually do it in semantics, with respect to *sentences*. We say that a sentence S (or a set C of sentences; possibly infinite) in $\mathscr{L}$ is a *translation* of the sentence S' in $\mathscr{L}'$ if-if the relation of L-equivalence [or A- or B-equivalence] holds between them. This presupposes that the equivalence relation in question is defined not only among sentences and sets of sentences of *one* language, but also as a relation between items of two distinct languages (cf. [1956, §14]). And we say that $\mathscr{L}'$ is *translatable* into $\mathscr{L}$ if-if, for every sentence S' in $\mathscr{L}'$, there is a sentence or a set of sentences in $\mathscr{L}$ which is a translation of S'.

In our present system, we prefer to speak of *propositions* rather than of sentences. If the language $\mathscr{L}'$ is a sublanguage of the language $\mathscr{L}$ (which means, roughly speaking, that the conceptual system of $\mathscr{L}'$ is a part of that of $\mathscr{L}$) we shall define, instead of a translation of sentences, a transformation T that assigns to every proposition H' on $\mathscr{L}'$ the "corresponding proposition" $T(H')$ on $\mathscr{L}$. We intend to define T in such a way that, roughly speaking, $T(H')$ represents the same state of affairs as H' with respect to the individuals and the attributes.

We shall not try to define a general transformation T applicable to arbitrary kinds of sublanguages, but rather four transformations T_1, T_2, T_3, T_4 for four kinds of sublanguages. (I have studied also other kinds; whenever one occurs in a later article, the transformation for it will be specified.)

(6-1) *Convention on index numbers in a sublanguage*. Whenever we form a sublanguage $\mathscr{L}'$ of a given language $\mathscr{L}$, we shall assign to each item (individual, family, or attribute) of the conceptual system of $\mathscr{L}'$ the same index number that is assigned to this item in $\mathscr{L}$.

Example. Suppose that a certain object occurs among the individuals of $\mathscr{L}'$. Then it belongs also to those of $\mathscr{L}$. If now it is designated in $\mathscr{L}$ by 'a_8', then the convention (1) stipulates that we shall designate it in $\mathscr{L}'$ likewise by 'a_8' (without regard to the question whether 'a_1', . . . , 'a_7' do or do not occur in $\mathscr{L}'$).

(6-2) Let f be a function with domain A, and f' one with A'. We say that f' is a *subfunction* of f (in symbols: "$f' \subset f$") and, more specifically, that f' is the *restriction* of f to A', if-if (1) $A' \subset A$, and (2) for any $x \in A'$, $f'(x) = f(x)$.

The four definitions D1, D2, D3, D4, to be given later, apply each to one of the four kinds of sublanguages. Each definition Dn ($n = 1, 2, 3, 4$) for the nth kind of sublanguage $\mathscr{L}'_n$, consists of three parts (a), (b), and (c) as follows. Part (a) specifies the relation between the conceptual system of $\mathscr{L}'_n$ and that of $\mathscr{L}$ (in each case we shall refer here only to those parts of the conceptual systems which are different in $\mathscr{L}'_n$ and in $\mathscr{L}$; thus it is tacitly implied that the parts not mentioned are in $\mathscr{L}'_n$ the same as in $\mathscr{L}$). In (b) we shall define the class of models $\mathbf{Z}'_n$ for $\mathscr{L}'_n$. In (c) we shall give the first part of the definition of the transformation T_n; in this part we shall specify T_n for atomic propositions only. Other parts of the definition of T_n will be given in (4) in a general form, applying to sublanguages of any kind.

According to earlier definitions (see (2-6) and (2-5)), the main parts of the conceptual system for $\mathscr{L}$ and the index sets are as follows. Ind is the set of individuals, with index set D; $\mathscr{F}$ is the class of families, with index set $I_{\mathscr{F}}$ or simply I; F^m ($\in\mathscr{F}$) is the mth family containing the attributes $P_1^m, P_2^m, \ldots, P_{k_m}^m$; the index set of F^m is $\mathbf{N}_{k_m}$. In the sublanguage $\mathscr{L}'$ we have the sets Ind$'$, $\mathscr{F}'$, $F^{(m)'}$ as subsets (not necessarily proper subsets) of Ind, $\mathscr{F}$, and $F^{(m)}$, respectively, with the index sets D', I', and $\mathbf{N}_{k'_m}$, respectively, where k'_m (or simply k') is the number of attributes in $F^{(m)'}$.

Before stating the four definitions Dn, we shall give here some general definitions and theorems, which apply to sublanguages of general.

(6-3) We assume that the classes of the conceptual system of $\mathscr{L}$ (Ind, $\mathscr{F}$, $F^1, F^2, \ldots$) together with their index sets (D, $I_{\mathscr{F}}$ or briefly I, $\mathbf{N}_{k_m}$ for $m = 1, 2, \ldots$) are given, and likewise the classes and their index sets for $\mathscr{L}'$. For five further concepts with respect to $\mathscr{L}'$, we either give here the definition itself (only in (b)) or we refer to an earlier definition applying to languages in general.

a. The class $\mathbf{Z}'_n$ of the models for $\mathscr{L}'_n$ is defined in analogy to D3-2. Thus these models are the functions from $I' \times D'$ to $\mathbf{N}_{k'_m}$.

b. In accordance with D3-4a, we define any atomic proposition on $\mathscr{L}'_n$ with the indexes m, j, i belonging to the corresponding index sets for $\mathscr{L}'_n$, as follows:

$$P_j^m a_i =_{\mathrm{Df}} \{Z' \colon Z' \in \mathbf{Z}'_n, \text{ and } Z'(m, i) = j\}.$$

c. The class $\mathscr{E}_n^{at'}$ of the *atomic propositions* on $\mathscr{L}'_n$ is defined as in D3-4c, but with the index numbers in $\mathscr{L}'_n$.

d. The class $\mathscr{E}_n^{\mathrm{mol}'}$ of the *molecular propositions* on $\mathscr{L}'_n$ is defined as in D3-4d.

e. The class $\mathscr{E}'_n$ of the *propositions* on $\mathscr{L}'_n$ is defined as the σ-field generated by $\mathscr{E}^{\text{at}'}_n$ (D3-4e).

As mentioned before, we shall define in each of the definitions D_n the transformation T_n only for the atomic propositions n $\mathscr{L}'_n$. Here we shall specify how T_n is to be extended to further propositions which are generated by Boolean operations.

(6-4) Let H', G', H'_r $(r = 1, 2, \ldots)$ be any propositions on $\mathscr{L}'_n$.

a. $T_n(H' - G') =_{\text{Df}} T_n(H') - T_n(G')$.

b. $T_n(H' \cup G') =_{\text{Df}} T_n(H') \cup T_n(G')$.

c. $T_n\left(\bigcup_{r=1}^{\infty} H'_r\right) =_{\text{Df}} \bigcup_{r=1}^{\infty} T_n(H'_r)$.

On the basis of these definitions, the following theorems hold.

(6-5) **a.** $T_n(-G') = -T_n(G')$. (From (4)(a).)

b. $T_n(H' \cap G') = T_n(H') \cap T_n(G')$. (From (a) and (4)(c).)

c. $T_n\left(\bigcap_{r=1}^{\infty} H'_r\right) = \bigcap_{r=1}^{\infty} T_n(H'_r)$. (From (a) and (4)(c).)

d. Let $Z' \in \mathbf{Z}'$. Then $T_n(\{Z'\}) = \bigcap_{m\in I'} \bigcap_{i\in D'} \{T_n(\{P^m_j a_i\})$: $j = Z'(m, i)\}$, where every $P^m_j a_i$ is an atomic proposition on $\mathscr{L}'_n$.

Proof. From T3-1g: $\{Z'\} = A_{Z'} = \bigcap \mathscr{E}^{\text{at}'}_{(Z')} = \bigcap \{P^m_j a_i$: $m \in I'$, and $i \in D'$, and $j = Z'(m, i)\}$. Hence the assertion by (c). ■

e. In analogy to the empty proposition $\varnothing$ on $\mathscr{L}$, let $\varnothing'$ be the empty proposition on $\mathscr{L}'_n$. Then $T_n(\varnothing') = \varnothing$.

Proof. Let A' be an atomic proposition on $\mathscr{L}'_n$. Then $T_n(A')$ is determined by part (c) of *Dn* for $\mathscr{L}'_n$. Let $T_n(A')$ be the proposition A on $\mathscr{L}$. Then by (a): $T_n(-A') = -A$; and by (b): $T_n(A' \cap -A') = A \cap -A = \varnothing$. Hence the assertion, since $A' \cap -A' = \varnothing'$. ■

f. $T_n(\mathbf{Z}'_n) = \mathbf{Z}$. (The proof is analogous to that for (e), but with $A' \cup -A'$, which is $\mathbf{Z}'_n$, and $A \cup -A$, which is $\mathbf{Z}$.)

We define generally, for any n, the class $\mathscr{E}^*_n$ of those propositions on $\mathscr{L}$ which *correspond* to propositions on $\mathscr{L}'_n$, as the T_n-image of $\mathscr{E}'_n$ (cf. the definition (3-4)):

(6-6) $$\mathscr{E}^*_n =_{\text{Df}} T^*_n(\mathscr{E}'_n).$$

Now we state the four formal definitions, each with the parts (a), (b), and (c), which were characterized earlier.

D6-1. Sublanguage $\mathscr{L}'_1$ of the *first kind: Restriction of the set of individuals.*

a. Here we have Ind′ $\subset$ Ind, and $D' \subset D$.

b. $\mathbf{Z}'_1 =_{\mathrm{Df}} \{Z'$: for some $Z \in \mathbf{Z}$, Z' is the restriction of Z to $I \times D'\}$.

c. Let $P_j^m a_i$ be an atomic proposition on $\mathscr{L}'_1$; thus $i \in D'$. Then $T_1(P_j^m a_i)$ is the atomic proposition $P_j^m a_i$ on $\mathscr{L}$, with the same indexes m, j, and i.

(6-7) *Example* of a sublanguage of the *first kind.* Let $\mathscr{L}$ have a denumerable set of individuals, with index set $D = \mathbf{N}$.

a. Let the sublanguage $\mathscr{L}'_1$ of the first kind be characterized by the restricted set of individuals Ind′ containing the first hundred individuals, with index set $\mathbf{N}_{100}$. According to convention (1), a_8 in $\mathscr{L}$ is the same object as a_8 in $\mathscr{L}'$. The class $\mathscr{F}'$ of the families in $\mathscr{L}'_1$ is the same as $\mathscr{F}$ in $\mathscr{L}$.

b. For any model function $Z \in \mathbf{Z}$ for $\mathscr{L}$, we have for $\mathscr{L}'_1$ the subfunction $Z' \in \mathbf{Z}'_1$, which is the restriction of Z to $I \times \mathbf{N}_{100}$.

c. Let F^2 be the family of six color attributes described in (2-1). Then $P_1^2 a_8$ is an atomic proposition in $\mathscr{L}$; let us denote it by 'A'. Since $8 \in D'$ $(= \mathbf{N}_{100})$, there is in $\mathscr{L}'_1$ also an atomic proposition $P_1^2 a_8$; let us denote it by 'A'_1'. A says that the individual a_8 is red; A'_1 refers to the same individual and says likewise that it is red. Thus A and A'_1 have the same content, convey the same information, represent the same state of affairs. And, by D1c, $T_1(A'_1) = A$. Note, however, that $A_1 \neq A$. The models in A' belong to $\mathbf{Z}'_1$, those in A to $\mathbf{Z}$. The models in A'_1 are the restrictions of those in A to $I \times \mathbf{N}_{100}$ (cf. D1b).

d. A proposition H on $\mathscr{L}$ corresponds to a proposition on $\mathscr{L}'_1$ (see (6-6)) if-if H involves only individuals in Ind′ (here $a_1, \ldots, a_{100}$).

D6-2. Sublanguage $\mathscr{L}'_2$ of the *second kind: Restriction of the class of families.*

a. Here we have $\mathscr{F}' \subset \mathscr{F}$, and $I' \subset I$.

b. $\mathbf{Z}'_2 =_{\mathrm{Df}} \{Z'$: for some $Z \in \mathbf{Z}$, Z' is the restriction of Z to $I' \times D\}$.

c. Let $P_j^m a_i$ be an atomic proposition on $\mathscr{L}'_2$; thus $m \in I'$. Then $T_2(P_j^m a_i)$ is the atomic proposition $P_j^m a_i$ on $\mathscr{L}$, with the same indexes m, j, and i.

(6-8) *Example* of a sublanguage of the *second kind.*

a. Let $\mathscr{L}$ contain the families F^1, F^2, and F^3. For $\mathscr{L}'_2$ we take $\mathscr{F}'_2 = \{F^1, F^2\}$, with index set $I' = \{1, 2\}$. The set of individuals Ind remains the same.

b. The class of models $\mathbf{Z}'_2$ for $\mathscr{L}'_2$ contains, for any $Z \in \mathbf{Z}$, the restriction of Z to the set of those pairs (m, i) with $m = 1$ or 2. (In other words, we have for $\mathscr{L}'_2$ only the two model components $Z^{(1)}$ and $Z^{(2)}$, while $Z^{(3)}$ drops out.)

c. Let us take, as in (7)(c), the example of the atomic proposition $A = P^2_1a_8$ in $\mathscr{L}$. In analogy to A'_1, we consider here A'_2 in $\mathscr{L}'_2$, which is again $P^2_1a_8$. We have here $T_2(A'_2) = A$. The models in A'_2 are the restrictions of those in A to $I' \times D$.

d. A proposition H on $\mathscr{L}$ belongs to $\mathscr{E}^*$ and hence corresponds to a proposition on $\mathscr{L}'_2$ if-if H does not involve F^3.

D6-3. Sublanguage $\mathscr{L}'_3$ of the *third kind: Merger of two or more attributes* in a family.

a. $\mathscr{F}'$ for $\mathscr{L}'_3$ is formed from $\mathscr{F}$ by replacing a certain family F^p with k attributes by a family $F^{p'}$ (or simply F') with k' attributes ($0 < k' \leq k$, in the case of a *proper* sublanguage $1 < k' < k$). F' is formed from F^p as follows. $k' - 1$ attributes in F^p remain unchanged in F'; but the other $k + 1 - k'$ attributes in F^p are replaced in F' by one new attribute P' which is their disjunction; i.e., the region of P' in the attribute space of F^p is the union of the regions of the merged attributes. For the sake of simplicity we shall assume that *the first* $k' - 1$ attributes in F^p remain unchanged, while the attributes $P_{k'}, P_{k'+1}, \ldots, P_k$ are replaced in F' by $P'_{k'}$.

b. $\mathbf{Z}'_3 =_{\text{Df}} \{Z : Z \in \mathbf{Z};$ and, for any $i \in D$, $Z(p, i) \leqq k'\}$. (Hence $\mathbf{Z}'_3 \subset \mathbf{Z}$.)

c. Let $P^m_j a_i$ be an atomic proposition on $\mathscr{L}'_3$. We distinguish two cases.

(1) Let $m = p$ and $j = k'$; thus we have the atomic proposition $A' = P^p_{k'}a_i = P'a_i$, with the new attribute P'. Here $T_3(A') = A^\dagger = P^p_{k'}a_i \cup P^p_{k'+1}a_i \cup \ldots \cup P^p_k a_i$, which is the union of $k - k' + 1$ atomic propositions on $\mathscr{L}_3$, all with the same individual, but with the $k - k' + 1$ different attributes of the family F^p which were merged in F' into the one attribute $P''_{k'}$.

(2) In every other case (where either $m \neq p$, or $m = p$ but $j < k'$), $T_3(A') = A = P^m_j a_i$ in $\mathscr{L}_3$.

(6-9) *Example* of a sublanguage of the *third kind.*

6. Let $\mathscr{L}$ contain three families F^1, F^2, F^3. In $\mathscr{L}_3'$, F^1 and F^2 remain unchanged, F^3 is replaced by F' (hence $p = 3$). Let F^3 be again the family of six color attributes. Let $\mathscr{L}_3'$ contain, instead of F^3, the family F' of five attributes ($k = 6, k' = 5$), formed by merging P_5^3 (Blue) and P_6^3 (Violet) into one attribute P_5'. This is the property of being either blue or violet. Thus $\mathscr{L}$ is a richer language than $\mathscr{L}_3'$. For example, any sentence of $\mathscr{L}$ saying that a certain individual is blue (or that it is violet) is not translatable into $\mathscr{L}_3'$; but every sentence of $\mathscr{L}_3'$ is translatable into $\mathscr{L}$.

b. The model functions for $\mathscr{L}_3'$ are not obtained by an alteration of those for $\mathscr{L}$, but rather by a selection of some of them, namely, those whose values for $(3, i)$ with any i do not exceed k' (here 5). Attention should be given, however, to the following distinction. Let Z' be a certain model function for $\mathscr{L}_3'$ and Z the model function for $\mathscr{L}$ that has, for any arguments m and i, the same value as Z', so that Z' and Z are mathematically the same function. Then Z' and Z may nevertheless differ in their interpretations; they may represent different states of affairs. This holds if, for some individual index i, $Z(3, i) = k'$ (in our example: 5). Suppose that $Z(3, 8) = 5$, and also $Z'(3, 8) = 5$. Then the model Z says of the individual a_8 that it is blue, while Z' gives only the weaker information that it is blue or violet.

c. In $\mathscr{L}_3'$, we have in F' $(= F^{3'})$ the attribute $P_{k'}'$ $(= P_5')$. Let us consider the atomic proposition with this attribute for a_8: $P_5'a_8$. Let this be A'. According to D3c(1), we have $T_3(A') = P_5a_8 \cup P_6a_8$. Thus in this case T_3 maps an atomic proposition on $\mathscr{L}_3'$ into a nonatomic one on $\mathscr{L}_3$. But still, the two propositions represent the same state of affairs that the individual a_8 is blue or violet.

d. The class $\mathscr{E}_3^*$ of the propositions on $\mathscr{L}$ corresponding to those on $\mathscr{L}_3'$ is the σ-field generated by the following class $\mathscr{A}$. $\mathscr{A}$ is like $\mathscr{E}^{at}$ but with the following changes: we remove from $\mathscr{E}^{at}$ the atomic propositions with attribute P_5^3 or P_6^3 of F^3, and add instead the nonatomic propositions of the form $P_5^3a_i \cup P_6^3a_i$ with an individual. Thus $\mathscr{E}_3^*$ is the σ-field generated by $\mathscr{E}^{at} - \{P_j^3a_i\colon j$ is 5 or 6, and $i \in D\} \cup \{P_5^3a_i \cup P_6^3a_i\colon i \in D\}$.

D6-4. Sublanguage $\mathscr{L}_4'$ of the *fourth kind: Restriction of a family.*

a. $\mathscr{F}'$ for $\mathscr{L}_4'$ is formed out of $\mathscr{F}$ by replacing a certain family

F^p with k attributes by a subfamily $F^{p'}$ (or simply F') containing only k' of the k attributes of F^p ($1 < k' \leqq k$, in the case of a *proper* sublanguage: $1 < k' < k$). (For the sake of simplicity we shall assume that the attributes in F' are the *first* k' attributes in F^p.)

b. $\mathbf{Z}'_4 =_{\text{Df}} \{Z: Z \in \mathbf{Z}$; and, for any $i \in D$, $Z(p, i) \leqq k'\}$. (Hence, $\mathbf{Z}'_4 \subset \mathbf{Z}$.)

c. Let $A' = P^m_j a_i$ be an atomic proposition on $\mathscr{L}'_4$. Then $T_4(A')$ is the atomic proposition $P^m_j a_i$ on $\mathscr{L}$; let this be A.

(6-10) *Example* of a sublanguage of the *fourth kind.*

a. Let $\mathscr{L}$ and F^3 be as in (9)(a). But in $\mathscr{L}'_4$ we have, instead of F^3 ($p = 3$), the family $F^{3'}$ (or simply F') containing only the first four attributes of F^3 ($k' = 4$): P_1, P_2, P_3, P_4, which are the colors Red, Orange, Yellow, Green. This restriction may be motivated by the fact that the researcher, for an investigation of a special kind of object, say, the blossom leaves of the plants of a certain species, makes the basic assumption that any object of this kind has one of these four colors.

b. As in $\mathscr{L}'_3$, the class $\mathbf{Z}_4$ of the models for $\mathscr{L}'_4$ is a subclass of $\mathbf{Z}$. Any Z in $\mathbf{Z}$ belongs also to $\mathbf{Z}'_4$ if-if, for any i, $Z(3, i) \leqq 4$ ($= k'$). [In distinction to $\mathscr{L}'_3$, if Z' in $\mathbf{Z}'_4$ coincides with Z in $\mathbf{Z}$, then Z and Z' have also the same interpretation.]

c. Let us consider the atomic proposition $A' = P^3_1 a_8$ on $\mathscr{L}'_4$. We have $T_4(A') = P^3_1 a_8$ on $\mathscr{L}$; let this be A. A' and A seem to represent the same state of affairs, to convey the same information, namely, that the individual a_8 is red.

d. Let us pursue this relation of representing the same state of affairs still further, in connection with T_4; for brevity, let us use for this relation (in this section only) the term 'equivalence', both for propositions and for sentences. We are especially interested in the question whether a proposition G' on $\mathscr{L}'_4$ and the corresponding proposition $G = T_4(G')$ on $\mathscr{L}$ are always equivalent. Let S'_1 be the atomic sentence '$P^3_1 a_8$' in $\mathscr{L}'_4$, which designates the proposition A'_1 ($= P^3_1 a_8$) on $\mathscr{L}'_4$; and let S'_2, S'_3, and S'_4 be analogous with attribute indexes 2, 3, 4 instead of 1, designating the propositions A'_2, A'_3, and A'_4. Let the sentence S_1 in $\mathscr{L}$ consist of the same symbols as S'_1 in $\mathscr{L}'_4$: '$P^3_1 a_8$'; then S_1 designates the proposition A_1 ($= P^3_1 a_8$) on $\mathscr{L}$. For any $j = 1, 2, 3, 4$, S'_j in $\mathscr{L}'_4$ designates A'_j, and S_j in $\mathscr{L}$ designates A_j; $T_4(A'_j) = A_j$; and, according to (c), A'_j and A_j seem to be equivalent. Let S_c be the conjunction sentence of the negations of the four atomic sentences in $\mathscr{L}$ just mentioned: $S_c = \sim S_1 . \sim S_2 . \sim S_3 . \sim S_4$, and analogously S'_c in $\mathscr{L}'_4$. Then S_c designates the proposition $H = -A_1 \cap -A_2 \cap -A_3 \cap -A_4$ on $\mathscr{L}$, and S'_c the proposition $H' = -A'_1 \cap -A'_2 \cap -A'_3 \cap -A'_4$ on $\mathscr{L}'_4$. And we have $T_4(H') = H$, by (5)(a) and (b).

Now let us reconsider the results we seem to have found. At the beginning (in (d)) it seemed plausible to regard, for any $j = 1, 2, 3, 4$, corresponding atomic propositions A_j and A'_j as equivalent. Then we have also to take their complements $-A_j$ and $-A'_j$ as equivalent, and finally also H and H'. There is a great difference, however, between these two propositions. H' is the empty proposition $\varnothing'$ on $\mathscr{L}'_4$. Since the attribute space of family F' in $\mathscr{L}'_4$ is restricted to the first four colors, there is clearly no model for $\mathscr{L}'_4$ in which H' would hold and hence a_8 would have none of those four colors. On the other hand, H on $\mathscr{L}$ is certainly not empty; there are many models for $\mathscr{L}$, in which a_8 has in family F^3 either the attribute P^3_5 or P^3_6. While H' is the impossible event, H is quite possible. Hence H and H' cannot be equivalent.

Let us try to clarify this perplexing situation by determining the basis of the emptiness or impossibility of H'. In some cases the impossibility of a sentence is based upon the meanings of the descriptive terms occurring in it. This holds, for example, for the sentence "Jack is married and a bachelor". A corresponding sentence in a language system would not be L-false, but A-false, on the basis of an A-postulate to the effect that the two occurring predicates are mutually exclusive. In contrast, the conjunction sentence S'_c in $\mathscr{L}'_4$ is not A-false, but merely B-false (D5-1(b)), in virtue of the basic assumption that every individual, i.e., every object of the kind studied in the special investigation in question, has one of the first four colors. This assumption can be expressed by a B-postulate, a sentence in $\mathscr{L}'_4$:

(6-11) B-postulate of the restricted attribute space of family F' in $\mathscr{L}'_4$: $S_B =$ '$(x)[P^3_1x \vee P^3_2x \vee P^3_3x \vee P^3_4x]$'.

This B-postulate has neither the kind of necessity based on meaning relations, nor causal necessity based on accepted laws of nature (which may sometimes be taken as B-postulates). The present B-postulate S_B was accepted by the (imaginary) investigator only because he regarded the occurrence of exceptions, i.e., of blue or violet objects of the kind to be investigated, as highly improbable, and therefore decided, for the sake of simplicity, to proceed as if he knew that there were none. This is often the situation when a restriction of the attribute space is made, be it a restriction of a qualitative attribute space like that of the colors, or a restriction of the numerical value space for a measurable quantitative magnitude. As an example of the latter kind, with respect to age (see (2-2)), an investigator might take an age of 120 or even of 100 as maximum admitted value. Strictly speaking, the choice of age 200 as upper boundary of the value interval, as in (2-2) itself, is also an artificial restriction that must be regarded as a sublanguage of the fourth kind; but, of course, the probability of exceptions, although not 0, is here exceedingly small.

We started by regarding the corresponding atomic propositions A' in $\mathscr{L}'_4$ and A in $\mathscr{L}$ as equivalent, and consequently also H' and H. We then realized, however, that H' is empty while H is not, and we drew the conclusion that they are *not* equivalent. Must we then also deny that A' and A are equivalent? This would seem rather implausible in view of (c): both say that a_8 is red. I think we should distinguish here *two kinds of equivalence;* I suggest the following terms (only for this section).

(6-12) Let $\mathscr{L}'$ be a sublanguage (of some kind) of $\mathscr{L}$ with respect to the transformation T, and let $H' \in \mathscr{E}'$ on $\mathscr{L}'$, and $H \in \mathscr{E}$ on $\mathscr{L}$ be such that $T(H') = H$.

a. H' is *A-equivalent* (analytically equivalent) to $H =_{\text{Df}} H'$ is equivalent to H on the basis of the A-postulates, disregarding B-postulates.

b. H' is *B-equivalent* to $H =_{\text{Df}} H'$ is equivalent to H on the basis of all A- and B-postulates.

[If no B-postulates are stated, B-equivalence coincides with A-equivalence. If neither B- nor A-postulates are stated, B-equivalence and A-equivalence coincide with each other (and, for sentences, with L-equivalence).]

Now we can reconcile our previous, apparently conflicting results concerning the corresponding atomic propositions A' on $\mathscr{L}'_4$ and A on $\mathscr{L}$, and the propositions H' on $\mathscr{L}'_4$ and H on $\mathscr{L}$: A' and A are A-equivalent, and therefore likewise H' and H; and, on the other hand, H' and H are non–B-equivalent, and thus likewise A' and A.

D6-5. Let $\mathscr{L}'$ be a sublanguage of the language $\mathscr{L}$, with respect to the transformation T which maps $\mathscr{E}'$ for $\mathscr{L}'$ onto a subclass $\mathscr{E}^* \subset \mathscr{E}$ for $\mathscr{L}$. We call $\mathscr{L}'$ a *conservative sublange* of $\mathscr{L}$ with respect to T if-if, for any proposition H' in $\mathscr{L}'$, $T(H')$ is B-equivalent to H' in the sense of representing the same state of affairs (taking into consideration also B-postulates).

(6-13) According to our previous considerations, the following holds.

a. The sublanguage $\mathscr{L}'_1$, with respect to the transformation T_1, is a conservative sublanguage of $\mathscr{L}$.

b. Likewise $\mathscr{L}'_2$ with respect to T_2.

c. Likewise $\mathscr{L}'_3$ with respect to T_3.

d. $\mathscr{L}'_4$, with respect to T_4, is *not* a conservative sublanguage of $\mathscr{L}$.

e. If $\mathscr{L}'$ is a conservative sublanguage of $\mathscr{L}$ with respect to T'_1 and likewise $\mathscr{L}''$ of $\mathscr{L}'$ with respect to T'', then $\mathscr{L}''$ is a conservative sublanguage of $\mathscr{L}$ with respect to the relative product of T' and T''. (If $H = T'(H')$ and $H' = T''(H'')$, then $H = T'(T''(H''))$.)

f. The relation of conservative sublanguage is transitive. (From (e), by mathematical induction.)

Suppose an investigator has so far used the language $\mathscr{L}$ and has adopted for $\mathscr{L}$ a $\mathscr{C}$-function $\mathscr{C}$ that satisfies all axioms and seems to him satisfactory. Now he intends to use for a new investigation a language $\mathscr{L}'$ which is a conservative sublanguage of $\mathscr{L}$ with respect to the transformation T. Then it would appear reasonable to use for $\mathscr{L}'$ that function $\mathscr{C}'$ whose value for two propositions on $\mathscr{L}'$ is always the same as the value of $\mathscr{C}$ for the corresponding propositions on $\mathscr{L}$. Therefore we lay down the following rule.

R6-1. *Rule of the $\mathscr{C}$-function for a conservative sublanguage.* Suppose that for language $\mathscr{L}$ the function $\mathscr{C}$ has been accepted and that it satisfies all axioms. Let $\mathscr{L}'$ be any conservative sublanguage of $\mathscr{L}$ with respect to the transformation T. Then for $\mathscr{L}'$ that function $\mathscr{C}'$ should be used which is defined as follows:

For any propositions H', E', on $\mathscr{L}'$ (E' nonempty),

$$\mathscr{C}'(H' \mid E') =_{\mathrm{Df}} \mathscr{C}(T(H') \mid T'(E')).$$

We call $\mathscr{C}'$ "the $\mathscr{C}$-function for $\mathscr{L}'$ *corresponding* to $\mathscr{C}$ for $\mathscr{L}$".

As mentioned earlier (at the beginning of §2A), we take as basic language for IL always a language $\mathscr{L}^\infty$ with a denumerable domain of individuals. Especially in the discussion of general methods for defining $\mathscr{C}$- or $\mathscr{M}$-functions fulfilling certain requirements, we shall always assume a language with a denumerable domain. But sometimes we consider a language $\mathscr{L}^N$ with a finite domain Ind_N of N individuals, with index set $\mathbf{N}_N$. Such a language $\mathscr{L}^N$ is always to be understood as a sublanguage of $\mathscr{L}^\infty$. And a function $\mathscr{C}$ for $\mathscr{L}^N$ will be required to be extensible to $\mathscr{L}^\infty$. This concept will now be defined in D6, and then the requirement will be laid down in R2.

D6-6. Let AS be a set of axioms for $\mathscr{C}$-functions (not necessarily axioms in our system). Let $\mathscr{L}'$ and $\mathscr{L}$ be two languages such that $\mathscr{L}'$ is a sublanguage of the first kind of $\mathscr{L}$. Let $\mathscr{C}'$ be a $\mathscr{C}$-function for $\mathscr{L}'$ satisfying the axioms AS.

a. $\mathscr{C}'$ is *extensible* to $\mathscr{L}$ (with respect to AS) $=_{\text{Df}}$ there is a $\mathscr{C}$-function $\mathscr{C}$ for $\mathscr{L}$ such that (1) $\mathscr{C}$ satisfies AS, and (2) $\mathscr{C}'$ is the $\mathscr{C}$-function for $\mathscr{L}'$ corresponding to $\mathscr{C}$ (R1).

b. Let $\mathscr{M}'$ be an $\mathscr{M}$-function for $\mathscr{L}'$. Let $\mathscr{C}'$ be the function related to $\mathscr{M}'$. $\mathscr{M}'$ is *extensible* to $\mathscr{L}$ (with respect to AS) $=_{\text{Df}}$ $\mathscr{C}'$ is extensible to $\mathscr{L}$ (with respect to AS).

R6-2. *Rule of extensibility* for a $\mathscr{C}$-function for a *finite language* $\mathscr{L}^N$. Let AS be the system of axioms accepted at some time. Suppose that, at this time, a $\mathscr{C}$-function $\mathscr{C}$ for $\mathscr{L}^N$ which satisfies AS is considered. Let $\mathscr{L}^\infty$ be a deumerable language such that $\mathscr{L}^N$ is a sublanguage of the first kind of $\mathscr{L}^\infty$. Then $\mathscr{C}$ is admissible only if $\mathscr{C}$ is extensible to $\mathscr{L}^\infty$.

R1 applies only to conservative sublanguages. How should we proceed in the case of a nonconservative sublanguage like $\mathscr{L}'_4$? The restriction in $\mathscr{L}'_4$ is based entirely on B-assumption. The following discussion will consider only cases of this kind.

Let us first consider B-principles for cases like $\mathscr{L}'_4$, where the investigator assumes that some attributes of the family F^p do not occur in his universe of individuals. Instead of abolishing these attributes and thus use the restricted family F' in the sublanguage $\mathscr{L}'_4$, we may stay with the unrestricted family F^p in the original language $\mathscr{L}$ but lay down some B-principles to the effect that no individual has one of those attributes.

(6-14) **a.** The B-principle B^p_j which says that the attribute P^p_j of family F^p is empty, is defined:

$$B^p_j =_{\text{Df}} \bigcap_{i=1}^{\infty} (-P^p_j a_i).$$

b. We take as B-principle for F^p the intersection of the various propositions B^p_j with the indexes j of those attributes that are assumed to be empty. Thus, in the example (10)(a),

$$B^3 = B^3_5 \cap B^3_6.$$

c. If this procedure is to be applied to several families, B is defined as the intersection of B^p-propositions with the indexes of the families concerned. If, as in the above example, only one family F^p is concerned, $B = B^p$; thus, in the example: $B = B^3$.

d. The proposition B can be expressed by a sentence S_B in $\mathscr{L}$; see the example given in (11). In other words, B is the truth set of S_B. Thus S_B may serve as a B-postulate in $\mathscr{L}$. B is identical with the subclass $\mathbf{Z}'_4$ of $\mathbf{Z}$ (see D4b and (10)(b)).

Once B is defined, we have to look for a suitable way of defining the new function $\mathscr{C}'$ with respect to B. The following method, described in §5 as the "second method", seems to me most suitable (see (5-10)):

(6-15) **a.** Definition of a $\mathscr{C}$-function $\mathscr{C}'$ to take the place of $\mathscr{C}$, based on a B-principle B:

For any propositions E and H such that $E \cap B \neq \varnothing$,

$$\mathscr{C}'(H \mid E) =_{\mathrm{Df}} \mathscr{C}(H \mid E \cap B).$$

b. Suppose that, for some proposition E, $E \cap B = \varnothing$. Then E is incompatible with the accepted B-principle B, and hence E does not come into consideration as (conceivable) evidence. If, however, E represents *actual* observation results, which clash with B, then the investigator must, of course, abandon or weaken the assumptions B.

c. Suppose that B involves an infinite number of individuals (as in the example (14)(a)). If now $E \cap H$ involves only a finite number of individuals, with p being the highest individual index involved, then we replace in the definition in (a) 'B' by '$B_{(p)}$', as in (5-12). If, on the other hand, $E \cap H$ involves also an infinite number of individuals, the limit definition (5-11) can be applied.

d. If $\mathscr{M}$ is related to $\mathscr{C}$, and $\mathscr{M}'$ to $\mathscr{C}'$, then we have: $\mathscr{M}'(H) = \mathscr{C}(H \mid B)$.

Proof. By T1-5:

$$\mathscr{M}'(H) = \mathscr{C}'(H \mid \mathbf{Z});$$

by (a):

$$= \mathscr{C}(H \mid \mathbf{Z} \cap B)$$

$$= \mathscr{C}(H \mid B). \quad \blacksquare$$

(6-16) *Example* for (15). As H in example (10) we take the atomic proposition $P^3_1 a_1$; however, now we do not go over to the sublanguage $\mathscr{L}'_4$ but stay with $\mathscr{L}$. By (14)(a) we have, with respect to the family F^3:

$$B^3 = B^3_5 \cap B^3_6,$$

$$= \bigcap_{i=1}^{\infty} (-P^3_5 a_i \cap -P^3_6 a_i),$$

Let us take $A_{ji} = P^3_j a_i$;

$$\text{then } B^3 = \bigcap_{i=1}^{\infty} (-A_{5i} \cap -A_{6i}). \qquad \text{(i)}$$

We assume that B^3 is the only B-principle that does not hold in every model in **Z**. (The family principles (5-6) hold in every model, because we constructed the models with this aim.) In virtue of the family principles, with $k = 6$:

$$\bigcup_{j=i}^{6} A_{j1} = \mathbf{Z};$$

$$\text{and hence: } \sum_{j=1}^{6} \mathcal{M}(A_{j1}) = 1. \qquad \text{(ii)}$$

We assume that in $\mathscr{L}$, before the introduction of the new principle B^3, $\mathcal{M}$ had equal values for A_{j1} with $j = 1, 2, \ldots, 6$; let this value be u. (The conditions under which this assumption of "γ-equality" may or must be made will he discussed in Volume II §16A.) Therefore, from (ii):

$$6u = 1; \qquad u = \tfrac{1}{6}.$$

$$\mathcal{M}(A_{11}) = u = \tfrac{1}{6}. \qquad \text{(iii)}$$

We wish to determine $\mathcal{M}'(A_{11})$ on the basis of the new principle B^3. By (15)(d):

$$\mathcal{M}'(A_{11}) = \mathscr{C}(A_{11} \mid B^3). \qquad \text{(iv)}$$

Now the only individual index involved in A_{11} is 1; hence $i^* = 1$. Thus by (15)(c) we may take in (iv) $B^3_{(1)}$ instead of B^3:

$$\mathcal{M}'(A_{11}) = \mathscr{C}(A_{11} \mid B^3_{(1)}) \qquad \text{(v)}$$

From (i):

$$B^3_{(1)} = -A_{51} \cap -A_{61};$$

hence by the family principle:

$$B^3_{(1)} = A_{11} \cup A_{21} \cup A_{31} \cup A_{41}\,. \qquad \text{(vi)}$$

Hence:

$$\mathcal{M}(B^3_{(1)}) = 4u. \qquad \text{(vii)}$$

From (vi):

$$A_{11} \cap B^3_{(1)} = A_{11}\,, \qquad \text{(viii)}$$

since, for $j = 2, 3, 4$, $A_{11} \cap A_{j1} = \varnothing$. From (v):

$$\mathcal{M}'(A_{11}) = \frac{\mathcal{M}((A_{11}) \cap B^3_{(1)})}{(B^3_{(1)})};$$

hence by (viii):

$$= \frac{\mathcal{M}(A_{11})}{\mathcal{M}(B^3{}_{(1)})};$$

with (iii) and (vii): $= u/(4u) = \tfrac{1}{4}$.

The discrepancy between $\mathscr{M}(A_{11}) = \frac{1}{6}$ (iii) and $\mathscr{M}'(A_{11}) = \frac{1}{4}$ is due to the fact that the latter value is based upon the B-principle B^3 introduced for the new investigation.

The following two theorems refer to one language only; but their proofs make use of sublanguages and are based on the rule R1.

T6-1. Let $\mathscr{L}$ be a language with the class $\mathscr{F}$ of families and the set Ind of individuals. Let H and E be any propositions on $\mathscr{L}$, E nonempty.

a. $\mathscr{C}(H \mid E)$ is independent of the existence and the number of those individuals in Ind which are not involved by E or H.

Proof. Let Ind′ be the set of individuals involved by E or H. Let $\mathscr{L}'_1$ be the sublanguage (of the first kind) of $\mathscr{L}$ restricted to Ind′. Let T_1 be the transformation for $\mathscr{L}'_1$, defined according to D1c and (4)(a), (b), (c). We assume that Ind′ is a *proper* subset of Ind (otherwise the assertion (a) is trivial). Hence Ind″ = Ind − Ind′ is not empty. There are propositions H' and E' on $\mathscr{L}'_1$ to which H and E correspond (see (7)(d)): $T_1(E') = E$ and $T_1(H') = H$. Let $\mathscr{C}'$ be the function for $\mathscr{L}'_1$ corresponding to $\mathscr{C}$. Then, in virtue of rule R1, $\mathscr{C}'(H' \mid E') = \mathscr{C}(H \mid E)$. Now the individuals in Ind″ do not occur in $\mathscr{L}'_1$; therefore $\mathscr{C}'(H' \mid E')$ cannot possibly be dependent on their existence or their number. Then the same must hold for $\mathscr{C}(H \mid E)$. ∎

b. $\mathscr{C}(H \mid E)$ is independent of the existence and the number of those families in $\mathscr{F}$ which are not involved by E or H, and hence also independent of the specific characteristics of these families as, for example, the number k of attributes. (The proof is analogous to that of (a), but with a sublanguage $\mathscr{L}'_2$ of the second kind.)

[T1(a) and (b) correspond to my earlier axioms A10 and A11, respectively, in [1964*b*], and to the axioms NA10 and NA11 in [1959, p. 247]. As I indicated in those two places, the earlier requirement of the completeness of the language with respect to families, attributes, and individuals is abandoned. I had stated this requirement in [1950 §18B]; but it led to awkward consequences.]

7
Regular $\mathscr{C}$-Functions

We shall now define the important property of the regularity of $\mathscr{C}$- and $\mathscr{M}$-functions, and then state an axiom ascribing this property to $\mathscr{C}$.

D7-1. It is assumed in (a) and (b) that E and H are any propositions on $\mathscr{L}$ satisfying the following three conditions:

(1) $E \cap H \neq \varnothing$.

(2) E and H are *molecular* propositions.

(3) Every family involved in E or in H is finite.

a. $\mathscr{C}$ is a REGULAR $\mathscr{C}$-function $=_{\mathrm{Df}} \mathscr{C}(H \mid E) > 0$.

b. $\mathscr{M}$ is a REGULAR $\mathscr{M}$-function $=_{\mathrm{Df}} \mathscr{M}(H) > 0$.

The restricting conditons for E and H in D1 are made for the following reasons. The restriction (2) to molecular propositions is made because some $\mathscr{C}$-functions which we accept have the value 0 for universal hypotheses on a denumerable population on the basis of any finite evidence (e.g., my earlier function c^* in [1950, §110F, (12)] and the $\lambda - \mathscr{C}$-functions to be explained in a later section). The restriction (3) to finite families is made because in the case of an infinite family F it might sometimes appear natural to take $\mathscr{C}(H \mid E) = 0$; for example, if E is a finite sample proposition for F in which the attribute P_5 of F does not occur, and H is an atomic proposition with P_5 and an individual not occurring in E.

A5. *Axiom of regularity.* $\mathscr{C}$ is regular.

This axiom can be justified in the context of decision theory: if $\mathscr{C}$ is not regular, it is not strictly coherent; this means that it will lead to the acceptance of certain unreasonable betting systems. This is explained later (in §8 on coherent $\mathscr{C}$-functions). Before I learned about this justification in terms of bets, I had stated the requirement of regularity (with this term) in [1945, §3] and [1950, C53-3 and D55-4], because it seemed to me intuitively compelling.

T7-1. Let E and H satisfy the conditions (1), (2), and (3) in D1. Let $\mathscr{C}$ be regular, and $\mathscr{M}$ be related to $\mathscr{C}$. Then the following holds.

a. $\mathscr{M}$ is regular.

b. $\mathscr{C}(H \mid E) < 1$.

Proof. By D1a, $\mathscr{C}(-H \mid E) > 0$. Hence

$$\mathscr{C}(H \mid E) = 1 - \mathscr{C}(-H \mid E) < 1. \quad \blacksquare$$

c. $\mathscr{M}(H) > 0$.

Proof. By T1-5, $\mathcal{M}(H) = \mathcal{C}(H \mid \mathbf{Z})$; hence the assertion by D1a. ■

d. $\mathcal{M}(H) < 1$. (By proof for (c), and (b).)

T7-2. Let $\mathcal{M}$ be an $\mathcal{M}$-function for $\mathcal{L}$ on $\mathcal{E}'$ such that $\mathcal{E}^{\text{mol}} \subset \mathcal{E}' \subset \mathcal{E}$. Each of the following conditions (a) to (c) is a sufficient and necessary condition for $\mathcal{M}$ being a *regular $\mathcal{M}$-function.*

a. If $\mathcal{A}$ is any finite subclass of $\mathcal{E}^{\text{at}}$ and $\bigcap \mathcal{A} \neq \varnothing$, then $\mathcal{M}(\bigcap \mathcal{A}) > 0$.

b. For any $s > 0$, and any finite class $\mathcal{F}'$ of finite families, if E is any sample state for the initial s-sample with respect to $\mathcal{F}'$, then $\mathcal{M}(E) > 0$.

Proof. 1. Let $\mathcal{M}$ be regular; then by (a) $\mathcal{M}(E) > 0$.—2. Let the condition (b) be fulfilled. We have to show that $\mathcal{M}$ is regular. Let $H \in \mathcal{E}^{\text{mol}}$, $H \neq \varnothing$. Let $\mathcal{F}'$ be the class of families involved in H, and let each of these families be finite. We have to show that $\mathcal{M}(H) \neq 0$. Let the highest individual index involved in H be s. Let $\mathcal{B}^{(s)}$ be, as in D3-6d, the class of the sample propositions for the initial s-sample with respect to $\mathcal{F}'$. By (b), for any $A \in \mathcal{B}^{(s)}$, $\mathcal{M}(A) > 0$. Then (by D3-6e and T3-4i) there is a nonempty subclass $\mathcal{B}_H^{(s)} \subset \mathcal{B}^{(s)}$ such that $\mathcal{M}(H) = \sum \mathcal{M}(A)$ $(A \in \mathcal{A}_H^{(s)})$. Therefore $\mathcal{M}(H) > 0$. ■

c. $\mathcal{M}$ is related to a regular $\mathcal{C}$-function on $\mathcal{E}'$. (From T1-4.)

T7-3. Let $\mathcal{C}$ be a $\mathcal{C}$-function for $\mathcal{L}$ on $\mathcal{E}'$ such that $\mathcal{E}^{\text{mol}} \subset \mathcal{E}' \subset \mathcal{E}$. Each of the following conditions (a) and (b) is a sufficient and necessary condition for $\mathcal{C}$ being a *regular $\mathcal{C}$-function.* (Any propositions H and E here occurring are assumed to satisfy the conditions (1), (2), and (3), in D1a.)

a. $\mathcal{C}$ is related to a regular $\mathcal{M}$-function on $\mathcal{E}'$.

Proof. 1. Let $\mathcal{C}$ be related to $\mathcal{M}$, where $\mathcal{M}$ is a regular $\mathcal{M}$-function on $\mathcal{E}'$. Then, for any H' and E' satisfying the conditions (1), (2), and (3) in D1, $\mathcal{M}(E') > 0$ and $\mathcal{M}(E' \cap H') > 0$. By T1-4: $\mathcal{C}(H' \mid E') = \mathcal{M}(E \cap H')/\mathcal{M}(E') > 0$. Hence $\mathcal{C}$ is regular (D1a).—2. Let $\mathcal{C}$ be regular. Let $\mathcal{M}$ be defined as follows: for any $A \in \mathcal{E}'$, $\mathcal{M}(A) =_{\text{Df}} \mathcal{C}(A \mid \mathbf{Z})$. Then $\mathcal{M}$ is an $\mathcal{M}$-function, is related to $\mathcal{C}$ (T1-4), and is regular (T2c). ■

b. If $H \in \mathcal{E}^{\text{at}}$ and $E = \bigcap \mathcal{A}$, where $\mathcal{A}$ is any finite subclass of $\mathcal{E}^{\text{at}}$ such that $E \cap H \neq \varnothing$, then $\mathcal{C}(H \mid E) > 0$.

Proof. 1. Let $\mathscr{C}$ be regular. Then by D1a, $\mathscr{C}(H \mid E) > 0$.—2. Let the condition (b) be fulfilled. We have to show that $\mathscr{C}$ is regular. Let $\mathscr{M}$ be defined as follows: for any $A \in \mathscr{E}'$, $\mathscr{M}(A) =_{\text{Df}} \mathscr{C}(A \mid \mathbf{Z})$. Then $\mathscr{M}$ is an $\mathscr{M}$-function (T1-3) and is related to $\mathscr{C}$ (T1-4). If $\mathscr{A}$, E, and H are as specified in (b), then $\mathscr{M}(E \cap H) > 0$ and $\mathscr{M}(E) > 0$. Hence, by T2a, $\mathscr{M}$ is regular. Thus, by (a), $\mathscr{C}$ is regular too. ■

T7-4. Let $\mathscr{M}$ be a regular $\mathscr{M}$-function on $\mathscr{E}^{\text{mol}}$ for $\mathscr{L}$.

a. There is one and only one $\mathscr{C}$-function on $\mathscr{E}^{\text{mol}}$ which is related to $\mathscr{M}$, namely, the function $\mathscr{C}'$ defined by:

$$\mathscr{C}'(H \mid E) =_{\text{Df}} \frac{\mathscr{M}(E \cap H)}{\mathscr{M}(E)}. \quad \text{(From T1-4.)}$$

b. $\mathscr{C}'$ is likewise regular. (From T3a.)

In contrast with this result, consider a nonregular $\mathscr{M}$ on $\mathscr{E}^{\text{mol}}$ for $\mathscr{L}$. By D1b, there is at least one nonempty, molecular E such that $\mathscr{M}(E) = 0$. Hence for any $H \in \mathscr{E}^{\text{mol}}$, $\mathscr{M}(E \cap H) = 0$. Therefore the equation in D1-11 is fulfilled, no matter what the value of $\mathscr{C}(H \mid E)$ is. Thus there are generally many $\mathscr{C}$-functions related to the given $\mathscr{M}$-function. (Concerning the possibilities for choosing these $\mathscr{C}$-functions, see Kemeny [1955] §6.)

T4 (together with T1-4) leads to the following theorem.

T7-5. There is a one-to-one correspondence between the *regular* $\mathscr{M}$-functions and the *regular* $\mathscr{C}$-functions, both on $\mathscr{E}^{\text{mol}}$ for $\mathscr{L}$. This correspondence can be formulated by each of the following conditions (a), (b), (c), which are equivalent to each other.

a. $\mathscr{M}$ and $\mathscr{C}$ are related.

b. For any $E = \phi$ and any H, $\mathscr{C}(H \mid E) = \dfrac{\mathscr{M}(E \cap H)}{\mathscr{M}(E)}$.

c. For any H, $\mathscr{M}(H) = \mathscr{C}(H \mid \mathbf{Z})$.

From now on we shall always assume that, with respect to a language like $\mathscr{L}$, $\mathscr{C}$ is a regular $\mathscr{C}$-function and $\mathscr{M}$ is a regular $\mathscr{M}$-function, unless the contrary is stated. Therefore we shall make use of the theorems on regular functions given in [1950, chaps. v and vi] (for a predicate language similar to $\mathscr{L}$). [The previous definitions in [*ibid.*] for "regular $\mathscr{M}$-function" (D55-1, D55-2) and for "regular $\mathscr{C}$-function" (D55-4) differ from those given here (D7-1b and a) but are equivalent to them. The previous definition for "regular $\mathscr{M}$-function" is similar to T2b here, and that for "regular $\mathscr{C}$-function" is similar to T3a here.]

We shall usually assume in our discussions that $\mathscr{C}$- and $\mathscr{M}$-functions for $\mathscr{L}$ are defined on $\mathscr{E}$. This is justified by the following reasons:

(1) We shall usually assume that $\mathscr{C}$ or $\mathscr{M}$ is primarily defined either on the class $\mathscr{E}^{\text{mol}}$ or on a subclass of $\mathscr{E}^{\text{mol}}$.

(2) If $\mathscr{C}$ is defined only on a proper subclass $\mathscr{E}'$ of $\mathscr{E}^{\text{mol}}$ (e.g., by specifying values for some selected elements of $\mathscr{E}^{\text{mol}}$), and $\mathscr{C}$ satisfies the axioms Al through A4, then $\mathscr{C}$ can be extended to a function $\mathscr{C}'$ on $\mathscr{E}^{\text{mol}}$ which likewise fulfills those axioms. (This follows from an interesting theorem proved by R. Sherman Lehman [1955, Theorem 4, p. 257].) This implies the analogous result for $\mathscr{M}$.

(3) If $\mathscr{C}$ or $\mathscr{M}$ is defined on $\mathscr{E}^{\text{mol}}$, there is a unique extension to $\mathscr{E}$ by a limit procedure (based on the axiom of σ-additivity, which will be explained in a later section).

Some authors use probability functions that, though nonregular, are still similar to regular functions, since they deviate from regularity only in some special cases. Therefore I shall now define a weaker regularity concept that includes those functions, in addition to all regular functions in the sense of D1. [This concept does not occur in my earlier publications; it will be used in later sections: in §12 on representative functions and in Part II (in Volume II) in the section on $\lambda - \mathscr{C}$-functions.]

D7-2. **a.** $\mathscr{C}$ is a *semiregular* $\mathscr{C}$-function $=_{\text{Df}}$ if F is any finite family of k attributes, and E is any finite sample proposition for F, and **s** is the k-tuple for E (see (3-7)(b)), and the number s_j in **s** for the attribute P_j is positive, and A is an atomic proposition $P_j a_i$ such that a_i is not involved in E, then $\mathscr{C}(A \mid E) > 0$.

b. $\mathscr{M}$ is semiregular $=_{\text{Df}} \mathscr{M}$ is related to a semiregular $\mathscr{C}$-function.

(7-1) If $\mathscr{C}$ is regular, then it is also semiregular.

A function $\mathscr{C}$ that is not regular but at least semiregular, appears less unreasonable than a function $\mathscr{C}'$ that is not even semiregular. For $\mathscr{C}'$ there is a situation of the kind described in D2a where $\mathscr{C}'(A \mid E) = 0$ although, according to E, at least one individual with the attribute P_j has been observed; in contrast, $\mathscr{C}(A \mid E) > 0$.

The most important, because widely accepted, example of a non-regular semiregular probability function is that $\mathscr{C}$-function ${}^0\mathscr{C}$ for which, in the case described in D2a, we have ${}^0\mathscr{C}(A \mid E) = s_j/s$. (This function, which I call "the straight rule" [1952*a*, §14], will be critically discussed in the later section on $\lambda - \mathscr{C}$-functions in Volume II; it is the function characterized by the value 0 of the parameter λ.)

8
Coherent $\mathscr{C}$-Functions

It is the task of *pure* inductive logic to state axioms for $\mathscr{C}$-functions and derive theorems from these axioms. In applied IL, the theorems are used for practical purposes, e.g., for the determination of the credibility of a hypothesis under consideration in a given knowledge situation, or for the choice of a rational decision. Justifying an inductive method and, more specifically, offering reasons for the acceptance of a proposed axiom, is a kind of reasoning that lies outside pure IL and takes into consideration the *application* of $\mathscr{C}$-functions. What is relevant in this context is not merely the consideration of *actual* situations, but rather that of *all possible* situations.

Suppose that the person X has chosen the $\mathscr{C}$-function $\mathscr{C}$ as a tool for determining his decisions. X intends to use $\mathscr{C}$ in any given situation where there are several alternatives for his action and where he does not know with certainty the outcome of each possible action. For the present discussion, it will be sufficient to explain the application of $\mathscr{C}$ on the basis of a highly simplified schema involving only a finite number of possible cases. Let the total observational knowledge of X at the time T in question be K_T. Let $\mathscr{A} = \{A_1, A_2, \ldots\}$ be the class of the *possible acts* that X takes into consideration at T. X chooses one of these acts in view of certain consequences or outcomes to which his act may lead and which are of interest to him. Let the class of these *possible outcomes* be $\mathscr{O}$. Which outcome will happen depends in general not only on the act chosen by X, but also on the *state of nature*, or of a relevant part of nature, aside from his act. Let $\mathscr{W} = \{W_1, W_2, \ldots\}$ be the class of those states of nature which X regards as possible and as relevant for the outcome of his action. X may not know which of these possible states actually holds; and, at the time T, he has not yet made up his mind which of the acts he is going to perform. We make the following assumptions:

(8-1) **a.** $\mathscr{W}$, $\mathscr{A}$, and $\mathscr{O}$ are subclasses of $\mathscr{E}' \subset \mathscr{E}$, where $\mathscr{E}'$ is the class on which $\mathscr{C}$ is defined.

b. For any m and n, X knows that, if he performs the act A_m and the state W_n holds, then the outcome $O_{m,n} \in \mathscr{O}$ will result, where $O_{m,n}$ is uniquely determined by A_m and W_n.

c. X knows his preferences with respect to the possible outcomes; more specifically, he knows his quantitative utility function U on $\mathscr{O}$. Since the function U is real-valued, it is for X a random variable on the product space $\mathscr{A} \times \mathscr{W}$.

d. Thus X can calculate, for any index numbers m and n, the following value of his function $\mathscr{C}$: $\mathscr{C}(W_n \mid K_T \cap A_m)$, that is, the probability of the state W_n, given his actual knowledge K_T and the (not actual, but merely contemplated) act A_m.

e. X can calculate, for every act A_m, the expectation of the utility of the outcome if he carried out the act A_m:

$$\underset{n}{\mathbf{E}}(U(O_{m,n})/K_T \cap A_m) = \sum_n [U(O_{m,n})\mathscr{C}(W_n \mid K_T \cap A_m)],$$

where $\underset{n}{\mathbf{E}}$ and $\sum_n$ cover all n such that $W_n \in \mathscr{W}$.

We accept the following well-known principle of decision making:

(8-2) *Bayes' principle.* It is rational to choose one of those acts for which the expectation of the resulting utility has the maximum value.

In the case of an offered wager, this general principle leads to the following *rule for betting:*

(8-3) It is rational for X to make a bet on a prediction H only if the betting quotient is not higher than $C(H \mid K_T)$.

(As is well known, this is merely an approximative rule that is applicable only if X's stake that he might possibly lose is so small in relation to his present total fortune that the utility of the outcome may be regarded as a linear function of the amount of money in question.)

Arguments in favor of a particular $\mathscr{C}$-function have to show that the decisions to which its application would lead in possible situations would be rational. However, arguments supporting the acceptance of any particular $\mathscr{C}$-function are not easy to find. It seems more promising to look for *arguments in favor of axioms* of inductive logic. Suppose that we are able to show with respect to an axiom A, that the restriction of the choice of $\mathscr{C}$-functions to those that satisfy A does not appear as implausible. Then this may be regarded as an argument in favor of the axiom, though not as a strong one. A strong reason for the acceptance of A would be given by showing that every $\mathscr{C}$-function that violates the axiom would lead in certain possible situations to irrational decisions. In this case, rationality requires the acceptance of the axiom. Strong arguments of this kind can be given for the axioms A1 through A5. Such arguments based on considerations of bets were first given by F. P. Ramsey and Bruno de Finetti (see below, the remark preceding T1).

For X to make a *bet* with Y for the proposition H, with the *betting quotient* q $(0 \leqq q \leqq 1)$ and the *total stake* s (at present assumed to be positive) is a contract to the following effect: if H turns out to be true, Y shall pay to X the amount of $(1 - q)s$; if H is false, X shall pay to Y

the amount qs. In other words, the *net gains* from the bet (losses counted as negative gains) are as follows:

(8-4) Suppose that X bets with Y *for* H with betting quotient q and stake s.

	Net gain of X	Net gain of Y
a. If H is true:	$(1 - q)s$	$-(1 - q)s$
b. If H is false:	$-qs$	qs

We say in this case that X bets *for* H, and Y bets *against* H. It might be that X would instead decide to bet *against* H, in other words, to exchange roles with Y. In this case, the net gain of X in each of the two cases would be those specified in (4) for Y. The same results would be obtained by substituting '$-s$' for 's' in the amounts given above for X. This shows that we can regard a bet of X *against* H with stake s as a bet of X *for* H with stake $-s$. Therefore we shall admit $s \gtreqless 0$. We assume that, if X regards q (determined by his function $\mathscr{C}$) as a fair betting quotient for H, then he is willing to make a bet with the betting quotient q for H on either side, that is, either for H or against H.

Suppose that, in examining the function $\mathscr{C}$ used by X, we were to find the following result. We can specify a nonempty proposition K^*, n propositions $H_1, H_2, \ldots, H_n$, and a series of n conceivable bets as follows. For any i $(= 1, \ldots, n)$, the ith bet is on H_i with a specified stake s_i; but we take in each case the betting quotient $q_i = \mathscr{C}(H_i \mid K^*)$. This means that in an imaginary but possible situation such that X's total observational knowledge were K^* instead of K_T, all these bets would appear to X as rationally acceptable. But suppose further, that we can show by purely logical considerations that in every possible outcome of the bets, X would suffer a net loss from all the bets together. Then obviously the willingness of X to make these bets is unreasonable, and so is his use of $\mathscr{C}$. If, on the other hand, $\mathscr{C}$ is such that there cannot be any betting system of this kind, we shall say that $\mathscr{C}$ is "*coherent*". (We take this term from de Finetti. He applies it, not to $\mathscr{C}$, but to the system of the beliefs of X at a certain time, i.e., a set of propositions with numbers assigned to them by X as their "subjective probabilities", indicating betting quotients acceptable to X.)

On the basis of the informal explanations just given, we shall now state exact definitions for "bet", "betting system", "gain", "coherent", and a stronger concept "strictly coherent". Then we shall state theorems about these concepts, proved by the authors mentioned above and others. These theorems will give a justification for the axioms A1 through A5. In what follows, $\mathscr{L}$ is a language and $\mathscr{E}$ is the class of propositions on $\mathscr{L}$. Note that we refer to the person X only in the informal explanations given above but not in the subsequent definitions and theorems.

We shall define the concept of bet in a wide sense so as to include *conditional bets*. A bet on H conditional on E is canceled (i.e., no payments are made) if E turns out to be false. (This is formally stated in D2c. The only case of such a cancellation in the subsequent analysis of axioms occurs in the proof of T1, in connection with A4.)

D8-1. B is a *bet* in $\mathscr{L}$ on H, conditional on E, with *betting quotient* q and *stake* $s =_{\text{Df}} B$ is the ordered quintuple $\langle \mathscr{L}, H, E, q, s \rangle$ where $H, E \in \mathscr{E}$, and q and s are real numbers, $0 \leqq q \leqq 1$.

This definition includes also a nonconditional bet on H, since this is a bet on H conditional on the necessary proposition **Z**.

We shall now define $g(B, W)$, i.e., the *net gain* (positive, negative, or zero) of a person who has made the bet B on H conditional on E, in the case W, where W is a proposition determining the outcome of the bet:

D8-2. Let B be the bet $\langle \mathscr{L}, H, E, q, s \rangle$. Let W be a nonempty proposition on $\mathscr{L}$ contained in at least one (and therefore in exactly one) of the following three propositions: $E \cap H$, $E \cap -H$, $-E$. Then the value of the **net gain** is determined as follows:

a. If $W \subset E \cap H$, then $g(B, W) = (1 - q)s$.
b. If $W \subset E \cap -H$, then $g(B, W) = -qs$.
c. If $W \subset -E$, then $g(B, W) = 0$.

We shall now define the concept of a betting system based upon an *assumption* K^*. It is essential that, in order to test the rationality of X's function $\mathscr{C}$, we consider not only bets based upon X's actual knowledge K_T with his actual betting quotient $q = \mathscr{C}(H \mid K_T)$, but also bets in any arbitrary imaginary situation in which X's knowledge would be K^* instead of K_T. The assumed proposition K^* is merely required to be possible; it need not be true; it may even be known by X to be false (i.e., $K^* \cap K_T = \varnothing$). X's betting quotient for the bet on H based on K^* is then taken to be $\mathscr{C}(H \mid K^*)$ or, in a bet conditional on E, $\mathscr{C}(H \mid K^* \cap E)$. For a system of such bets based upon an arbitrary assumption K^*, we cannot, of course, speak about the actual state of nature and about X's actual gain. But we can investigate the totality of the states that are possible in the assumed situation (i.e., compatible with K^*) and X's gain in each of these possible cases. And this is all that is needed in order to test the coherence of $\mathscr{C}$. We shall arrange a system of bets always so that the ith bet B_i is a bet on H_i conditional on E_i, and that we take $K^* = \bigcup_i E_i$. (Thus, for every E_i, $E_i \subset K^*$ and hence $K^* \cap E_i = E_i$.)

D8-3. BS is the *betting system* with the class $\mathscr{B}'$ of bets in $\mathscr{L}$, in accordance with funtion $\mathscr{C}$ $=_{\text{Df}}$ BS is the ordered triple $\langle \mathscr{B}', \mathscr{L}, \mathscr{C} \rangle$, where $\mathscr{B}' \subset \mathscr{B}$ is a nonempty class of bets, and for every $B_i \in \mathscr{B}'$, B_i is the bet $\langle \mathscr{L}, H_i, E_i, q_i, s_i \rangle$, $E_i \neq \varnothing$, $\mathscr{C}$ is a real-valued function with the domain $\mathscr{E}' \times (\mathscr{E}' - \{\varnothing\})$, where $\mathscr{E}' \subset \mathscr{E}$, and $q_i = \mathscr{C}(H_i \mid E_i)$.

Note that D3 does not require that $\mathscr{C}$ is a $\mathscr{C}$-function, i.e., that it satisfies the basic axioms. The class $\mathscr{B}'$ of bets in D3 may be finite or denumerable. The following discussion is restricted to finite betting systems. (A remark on denumerable betting systems is made at the end of this section.)

We define the class $\mathscr{W}_{\text{BS}}$ of the *possible states of nature* relevant for the betting system BS:

D8-4. Let BS be a betting system $\langle \mathscr{B}', \mathscr{L}, \mathscr{C} \rangle$. Let $\mathscr{B}'$ be a class of m bets $\{B_1, \ldots, B_m\}$. (In the following, '$\bigcup_i$' is meant for $i = 1, \ldots, m$; analogously '$\bigcap_i$' and '$\sum_i$'.) Let $K^* = \bigcup_i E_i$. For any $i \leqq m$, let $W_1^i = E_i \cap H_i$, $W_2^i = E_i - H_i$, $W_3^i = K^* - E_i$. Then: $\mathscr{W}_{\text{BS}} =_{\text{Df}} \{W$: for some sequence $n_1, \ldots, n_m$, with each $n_i \in \{1, 2, 3\}$, $W = \bigcap_i W_{n_i}^i$, and $W \neq \varnothing\}$.

It is easily seen that, for any $i \leqq m$ and any $n_i \in \{1, 2, 3\}$, $W_{n_i}^i \subset K^*$; and therefore, for any $W \in \mathscr{W}_{\text{BS}}$, $W \in K^*$.

We shall now define $G(BS, W)$, the *net total gain* (positive, zero, or negative) from the betting system BS in the case of the state W:

D8-5. Let BS be a betting system $\{\mathscr{B}', \mathscr{L}, \mathscr{C}\}$. Let $W \in \mathscr{W}_{\text{BS}}$. Then $G(\text{BS}, W) =_{\text{Df}} \sum_i g(B_i, W)$.

We define a few convenient phrases concerning loss or positive gain for a betting system BS:

D8.6. Let BS be a betting system.

- **a.** For BS, *loss is necessary* $=_{\text{Df}}$ for every $W \in \mathscr{W}_{\text{BS}}$, $G(\text{BS}, W) < 0$.
- **b.** For BS, *loss is possible* $=_{\text{Df}}$ for some $W \in \mathscr{W}_{\text{BS}}$, $G(\text{BS}, W) < 0$.
- **c.** For BS, *positive gain is impossible* $=_{\text{Df}}$ for every $W \in \mathscr{W}_{\text{BS}}$, $G(\text{BS}, W) \leqq 0$.
- **d.** For BS, *positive gain is possible* $=_{\text{Df}}$ for some $W \in \mathscr{W}_{\text{BS}}$, $G(BS, W) > 0$.
- **e.** BS is *vacuous* $=_{\text{Df}}$ for every $W \in \mathscr{W}_{BS}$, $G(\text{BS}, W) = 0$.

Now the concept of *coherence* is defined:

D8-7. Let $\mathscr{C}$ be a function for language $\mathscr{L}$ (as in D3). $\mathscr{C}$ is **coherent** $=_{\text{Df}}$ for no betting system in accordance with $\mathscr{C}$, loss is necessary (in other words, for any nonvacuous betting system BS, there is a possible state W in which the outcome is not a loss).

The following important result was found independently of each other by Frank P. Ramsey [1931*a*, pp. 182 f.] and by Bruno de Finetti [1931, p. 313] and [1937, pp. 7 f., 14 f.] (English [1964, pp. 103 f., 109 f.]).

T8-1. *If $\mathscr{C}$ is coherent, then $\mathscr{C}$ satisfies the basic axioms A1 through A4.* In other words, if $\mathscr{C}$ violates at least one of these axioms, then there is a betting system BS (and, moreover, a finite system) in accordance with $\mathscr{C}$, such that for BS loss is necessary.

Proof. For each of the four axioms we shall proceed as follows. We assume that a language $\mathscr{L}$ is given, which we do not specify. We suppose that the function $\mathscr{C}_j$ for $\mathscr{L}$ violates the jth axiom ($j = 1, 2, 3, 4$). Then we construct a betting system $\text{BS}_j = \{\mathscr{B}_j, \mathscr{L}, \mathscr{C}_j\}$ for which loss is necessary. Each $\mathscr{B}_j$ contains one, two, or three bets $B_{j,i}$ ($i = 1, \ldots$). In table (8-5) we specify $B_{j,i} = \langle \mathscr{L}, H_{j,i}, E_{j,i}, q_{j,i}, s_{j,i} \rangle$ by specifying $E_{j,i}$, $H_{j,i}$, $s_{j,i}$ (which may be positive or negative), and $q_{.ij}$ (which is $\mathscr{C}_j(H_{j,i} \mid E_{j,i})$); (for simplicity, we shall omit the subscript corresponding to 'j'). In each of these systems BS_j, the basic assumption $K_j^* = \bigcup_i E_{j,i}$ happens to be the same as $E_{j,1}$. Then we determine, for each of the possible cases $W \in \mathscr{W}_{BS_j}$ first the net gain $g(B_{j,i}, W)$ (by D2), and finally the net gain for the whole betting system, $G(BS_j, W)$ (by D5). We find for each of the four axioms that, for every W, $G < 0$.

1. Suppose that $\mathscr{C}_1$ *violates axiom A1*. This means that, for some $H_{1,1}$ and $E_{1,1}$, $\mathscr{C}_1(H_{1,1} \mid E_{1,1}) < 0$. Let c_1 be this negative value of $\mathscr{C}_1$. BS_1 consists of only one bet $B_{1,1}$, as given in the table (8-5).

2. Suppose that $\mathscr{C}_2$ *violates A2*. Then, for some $E_{2,1}$, $c_{2,1} = \mathscr{C}_2(E_{2,1} \mid E_{2,1}) \neq 1$. BS_2 consists of only one bet. Note that the chosen $s_{2,1}$, namely, $c_{2,1} - 1$, is positive if $c_{2,1} > 1$, but negative if $c_{2,1} < 1$; in the latter case the bet with the specified s is such that X must, on the basis of $E_{2,1}$, bet *against* $E_{2,1}$.

3. Suppose that $\mathscr{C}_3$ *violates A3*. Then, for some $H_{3,1}$ and $E_{3,1}$, $\mathscr{C}_3(H_{3,1} \mid E_{3,1}) + \mathscr{C}_3(-H_{3,1} \mid E_{3,1}) \neq 1$. Let $c_{3,1}$ be the first of the two $\mathscr{C}_3$-values, and $c_{3,2}$ the second. Let $d = c_{3,1} + c_{3,2} - 1$; then either $d > 0$ or $d < 0$; in the latter case, $s < 0$. BS_3 consists of two bets.

4. Let $\mathscr{C}_4$ *violate A4*, the general multiplication principle. Then, for some $E_{4,1}$, $H_{4,1}$, and $H_{4,2}$, $\mathscr{C}_4(H_{4,1} \mid E_{4,1})\mathscr{C}_4(H_{4,2} \mid E_{4,1} \cap H_{4,1}) \neq \mathscr{C}_4(H_{4,1} \cap H_{4,2} \mid E_{4,1})$. Let $c_{4,1}$ be the first of these three $\mathscr{C}_4$-values, $c_{4,2}$ the second, and $c_{4,3}$ the third. Let $d = c_{4,1}c_{4,2} - c_{4,3}$; hence $d \neq 0$. [Among all the bets considered in the present proof for T1 and the

later proof for T3, $B_{4,2}$ is the only bet in which $E_{j,i}$ is not simply K_j^*. $E_{4,2}$ is rather $E_{4,1} \cap H_{4,1} = K_4^* \cap H_{4,1}$. Thus, even on the assumption K_4^*, $E_{4,2}$ may be false, namely, if $H_{4,1}$ is false. Therefore $B_{4,2}$ is the only bet in the table in which a value $g = 0$ occurs, in accordance with D2c. This is the only place in the proofs of T1 and T3, where it is essential to use a conditional bet.] ∎

Following Abner Shimony [1955], we shall introduce also a concept of coherence in a stronger sense. I propose for it the term "strictly coherent" (more precisely: "strictly coherent in the finite", but I shall mostly omit the phrase "in the finite"). This concept, like that of regularity, with which it is closely connected, will be defined only for the predicate language $\mathscr{L}$ (§4).

D8-8. Let $\mathscr{C}$ be a function for pairs of propositions in $\mathscr{L}$. (This $\mathscr{C}$, like that in D3,is not necessarily a $\mathscr{C}$-function.) $\mathscr{C}$ is **strictly coherent** (in the finite) $=_{\mathrm{Df}}$ $\mathscr{C}$ is coherent; and there is no betting system $BS = \langle \mathscr{B}', \mathscr{L}, \mathscr{C} \rangle$ such that (a) $\mathscr{B}'$ is finite, (b) for every $B_i \in \mathscr{B}'$, the propositions E_i and H_i in B_i are molecular, (c) for BS loss is possible and positive gain is impossible; in other words, for every nonvacuous betting system satisfying (a) and (b), positive gain is possible.

We shall now study the relation between coherence and regularity. The following theorem T2 is essentially due to Shimony.

T8-2. Let $\mathscr{C}$ be a function for language $\mathscr{L}$.

a. If $\mathscr{C}$ *violates the axiom A5 of regularity*, then $\mathscr{C}$ is not strictly coherent.

Proof. Suppose that $\mathscr{C}$ violates A5. Then, for some molecular propositions E and H in $\mathscr{L}$, $E \cap H \neq \varnothing$, but $\mathscr{C}(H \mid E) = 0$. We take the betting system BS_5 in the earlier table (5) under $j = 5$. The possible values of G are -1 and, if $E - H \neq \varnothing$, 0. Hence $\mathscr{C}$ is not strictly coherent. ∎

b. Suppose that $E, H \in \mathscr{E}^{\mathrm{mol}}$, not $E \subset H$, hence $E - H \neq \varnothing$, but $\mathscr{C}(H \mid E) = 1$. Then $\mathscr{C}$ is not strictly coherent.

Proof is similar to that for (a), but with betting system BS_6 in the table. The possible values of G are -1 and, if $E \cap H \neq \varnothing$, 0. ∎

c. Suppose that $\mathscr{C}$ is strictly coherent, $E, H \in \mathscr{E}^{\mathrm{mol}}$, $E \neq \varnothing$. Then $\mathscr{C}(H \mid E) = 0$ only if $E \cap H = \varnothing$; and $\mathscr{C}(H \mid E) = 1$ only if $E \subset H$. (From (a) and (b).)

(8-5) *Betting systems for the proofs of T1 and T2.*

j	i	B_i					$g(B_i, W)$			Result for G
		E_i	H_i	s_i	q_i		W_1	W_2	W_3	
1						W:	$E \cap H$	$E - H$		
(for A1)	1	E	H	-1	$c\ (<0)$		$(1 - c)(-1)$	$-c(-1)$		
						$G=$	$c - 1$	c		$G < 0$
2						W:	E			
(for A2)	1	E	E	$\frac{1}{c - 1}$	$c\ (\neq 1)$		$\frac{1 - c}{c - 1}$			
						$G=$	-1			$G < 0$
3						W:	$E \cap H$	$E - H$		
(for A3)	1	E	H	$\frac{1}{d}$	c_1		$\frac{1 - c_1}{d}$	$-\frac{c_1}{d}$		
	2	E	$-H$	$\frac{1}{d}$	c_2		$\frac{-c_2}{d}$	$\frac{1 - c_2}{d}$		
						$G=$	-1	-1		$G < 0$

4						W:	$E \cap H_1 \cap H_2$	$E \cap H_1 - H_2$	$E - H_1 \cap H_2$ $E - H_1 - H_2$	
(for A4)	1	E	H_1	$\frac{c_2}{d}$	c_1		$\frac{(1-c_1)c_2}{d}$	$\frac{(1-c_1)c_2}{d}$	$-\frac{c_1c_2}{d}$	
	2	$E \cap H_1$	H_2	$\frac{1}{d}$	c_2		$\frac{1-c_2}{d}$	$-\frac{c_2}{d}$	0	
	3	E	$H_1 \cap H_2$	$-\frac{1}{d}$	c_3		$-\frac{1-c_3}{d}$	$\frac{c_3}{d}$	$\frac{c_3}{d}$	
						$G =$	-1	-1	-1	$G < 0$
5						W:	$E \cap H$	$E - H$		
(for A5, T2a)	1	E	H	-1	0		-1	0		
						$G =$	-1	0		$G \leqq 0$
6						W:	$E \cap H$	$E - H$		
(for T2b)	1	E	H	1	1		0	-1		
						$G =$	0	-1		$G \leqq 0$

d. If $\mathscr{C}$ is strictly coherent, then $\mathscr{C}$ satisfies the axioms A1 through A5. (From (a) and T1.)

It seems to me that not only the requirement of coherence but also that of *strict coherence is indispensable*. It is clearly unreasonable to enter a contract involving the risk of a loss which is not balanced by the possibility of a gain. Therefore T2a gives a justification in the strong sense for the axiom A5 of regularity, just as T1 does for the basic axioms A1 through A4. Only few earlier authors required regularity or strict coherence (cf. [1950, §62]), among them Keynes [1921, Def. II] and Koopman [1940*a*, axiom I] (see my [1950, T83-32], which implies regularity). The great majority, up to the present time, do not. I required regularity, which is equivalent to strict coherence (T6 below) in [1950, p. 287, remark on C53-3] and in [1952*a*, pp. 42 ff.]. Some of my arguments pointed out that certain bets, similar to the one mentioned above in the proof of T2b, were unreasonable ([1950, p. 227], [1952*a*, p. 43]). Strict coherence has recently been required by Shimony [1955, pp. 9 ff.], Kemeny [1955, p. 264], and Ernest Adams [1959, p. 9].

Terminological remarks. For the two concepts of coherence, the original concept I (Ramsey, de Finetti) and the stronger concept II (Shimony), the following terms have been used; a dash indicates that the author named does not consider the concept in question. [Shimony considers the first concept but does not use a special term for it. Lehman's Definition 5 for "rational" refers clearly to concept I. Adams [1959, p. 9 n. 1] believes, however, that Lehman was actually thinking of concept II. I do not see clear evidence for this assumption.]

	I	II
Ramsey [1931*a*, p. 182]:	"consistent"	—
de Finetti [1937, p. 7]:	"coherent"	—
Shimony [1955, p. 9]:	—	"coherent"
Kemeny [1955, p. 264]:	"fair"	"strictly fair"
R. S. Lehman [1955, p. 253]:	"rational"	—
Adams [1959, p. 9]:	"weakly rational"	"rational"
Carnap [1955, p. 7]:	"coherent"	"strictly coherent"

Shimony adopts de Finetti's term "coherent"; but he remarks himself that he gives to this term a stronger sense than de Finetti did. It seems to me prefereable to use for concept II another term, all the more so since both concepts seem to be of interest. The terms "fair" and "rational" do not appear to me appropriate. It is indeed true that coherence, in either of the two senses I and II is a *necessary* condition for $\mathscr{C}$ being rational (in the customary sense of reasonableness). But even strict coherence is far from being a *sufficient* condition of rationality. Suppose that the function $\mathscr{C}$ chosen by X for his betting decisions satisfies the axioms A1 through A5, but violates one of the other requirements that we regard as necessary conditions of rationality and shall therefore adopt as additional axioms, e.g., symmetry with respect to individuals (for certain languages). We could easily specify a bet that is obviously unreasonable but which X would accept because it is in accordance with his $\mathscr{C}$-function. Then the use of this function $\mathscr{C}$, although it satisfies the axioms A1 through A5 and hence possesses both coherence properties I and II, would be irrational. Therefore it seems to me misleading to apply to this function $\mathscr{C}$ the terms "fair" and even "strictly fair" or "rational".

As we have seen, the analysis of finite betting systems has yielded a justification for certain axioms. Would it be possible to justify other axioms with the help of the same method? This question is answered in the negative by the following theorems T3 and T4. T3 was asserted without proof by Ramsey, and proved by de Finetti [1931, p. 313]. It was independently found later by John G. Kemeny [1955, p. 269, Th. 3] and also by R. Sherman Lehman [1955, p. 256, Th. 3]. T4 was proved simultaneously and independently of each other by Kemeny and by Lehman. The proofs for T3 and T4, which are rather lengthy, will not be given here.

T8-3. If a function $\mathscr{C}$ satisfies the axioms A1 through A4, then $\mathscr{C}$ is *coherent*.

T8-4. If a function $\mathscr{C}$ (for the predicate language $\mathscr{L}$) satisfies the axioms A1 through A5, then $\mathscr{C}$ is *strictly coherent*.

Combining T1 and T3, we obtain the following:

T8-5. A function $\mathscr{C}$ is *coherent* if-if $\mathscr{C}$ satisfies the axioms A1 through A4, in other words, if-if $\mathscr{C}$ is a conditional probability function ($\mathscr{C}$-function, D1-5).

Similarly, we obtain from T2 and T4 the following:

T8-6. Let $\mathscr{C}$ be a function for language $\mathscr{L}$. $\mathscr{C}$ is *strictly coherent* if-if $\mathscr{C}$ satisfies the axioms A1 through A5; in other words, *if-if* $\mathscr{C}$ is a *regular* $\mathscr{C}$*-function*.

The definition of strict coherence (D8) refers only to finite betting systems with only molecular propositions of language $\mathscr{L}$. Here the question arises as to whether and how analogous requirements should be stated with a wider scope, first for nonmolecular propositions in $\mathscr{L}$, and second for propositions in a much richer language containing quantitative magnitudes. Even the first extension leads to complicated problems. Shimony (pp. 18–20) has pointed out the serious difficulties in dealing with infinite classes of propositions and infinite betting systems. Adams (§4) has begun the first systematic studies on infinite betting systems for language $\mathscr{L}$. Further investigations in this direction would be desirable.

9
Symmetric $\mathscr{C}$-Functions

The system of axioms stated in the preceding sections is very weak. It does not determine the value of $\mathscr{C}(H \mid E)$ for given propositions H and E, with exception of the values 0 and 1 in special cases. Moreover the following holds: for any given molecular propositions E and H such that neither $E \subset H$ nor $E \subset -H$, and for any given real number r such that $0 < r < 1$, there is a $\mathscr{C}$-function $\mathscr{C}$ which satisfies the axioms stated and which has the value $\mathscr{C}(H \mid E) = r$ (see [1950, T59-5f]). Thus the axioms admit $\mathscr{C}$-functions that would obviously be unreasonable if taken as personal probabilities (more specifically, as credibility functions, see Art. **1**, §4). Therefore it seems to me that for the purpose of inductive logic we must adopt additional axioms. In particular we shall state axioms or rules of invariance which say that $\mathscr{C}(H \mid E)$ is invariant under certain transformations of H and E. The most important one among the axioms of invariance, and the one most frequently used, is the axiom of symmetry to be stated in this section. Other axioms or rules of invariance will follow in later sections.

In this section we direct our attention mainly on the *individuals*. Let us summarize the main points about them.

(9-1) *Basic assumptions about the individuals* in language $\mathscr{L}$.

- **a.** The set Ind of the individuals is countable.
- **b.** Every individual in Ind is designated by an individual constant.
- **c.** Two individual constants with distinct indexes designate distinct individuals.

Now we define some concepts related to permutations. They will be applied mainly to individual indices.

D9-1. Let J be a nonempty set of nonnegative integers. Let π be a *permutation* of J, i.e., a one-to-one mapping (function) of J onto J.

- **a.** Let $n \in J$. The *displacement* of n by $\pi =_{\mathrm{Df}} |\pi(n) - n|$.
- **b.** π is a *finite permutation* $=_{\mathrm{Df}}$ the number of elements of J with positive displacement by π is finite.
- **c.** m is the *maximum displacement* by permutation $\pi =_{\mathrm{Df}}$ for any $n \in J$, the displacement of n by π is $\leq m$, and for some $n \in J$, the displacement of n by π is m.
- **d.** π is a *bounded permutation* $=_{\mathrm{Df}}$ some finite m is the maximum replacement by π.

D9-2. Let π be a permutation of the index set D of Ind in $\mathscr{L}$.

a. π' is *the mapping of* $\mathbf{Z}$ *onto* $\mathbf{Z}$, *induced by* π $=_{\text{Df}}$ for any $Z \in \mathbf{Z}$, $\pi'(Z)$ is the model $Z' \in \mathbf{Z}$ defined as follows: for any $i \in D$ and any $m \in I_{\mathscr{F}}$, $Z'(m, i) = Z(m, \pi^{-1}(i))$.

b. Let $Z, Z' \in \mathbf{Z}$. Z' is isomorphic to Z $=_{\text{Df}}$ for some permutation π, $Z' = \pi'(Z)$.

c. Let π' be induced by π (in the sense of (a)). π'' is *the mapping of* $\mathscr{E}$ *onto* $\mathscr{E}$ *induced by* π $=_{\text{Df}}$ for any $A \in \mathscr{E}$, $\pi''(A) = \{Z'$: for some $Z \in A, Z' = \pi'(Z)\}$.

d. Let $A, B \in \mathscr{E}$. A is *isomorphic* to B $=_{\text{Df}}$ for some permutation π of D, if π'' is induced by π (in the sense of (c)), $A = \pi''(B)$.

D9-3. **a.** Let $\mathscr{C}$ be a $\mathscr{C}$-function (not necessarily regular). $\mathscr{C}$ is **symmetric** (with respect to individuals) $=_{\text{Df}}$ $\mathscr{C}$ is invariant under any finite permutation π (for D); i.e., for any $E, H \in \mathscr{E}, E \neq \varnothing$, $\mathscr{C}(H \mid E) = \mathscr{C}(\pi''(H) \mid \pi''(E))$.

b. Let $\mathscr{M}$ be an $\mathscr{M}$-function. $\mathscr{M}$ is **symmetric** $=_{\text{Df}}$ $\mathscr{M}$ is invariant under any finite permutation π (for D); i.e., for any $E \in \mathscr{E}$, $\mathscr{M}(E) = \mathscr{M}(\pi''(E))$.

T9-1. Let $\mathscr{C}$ be a $\mathscr{C}$-function for $\mathscr{L}$, and $\mathscr{M}$ be related to $\mathscr{C}$.

a. If $\mathscr{C}$ is symmetric, $\mathscr{M}$ is symmetric. (From T1-5.)

b. If $\mathscr{M}$ is symmetric, $\mathscr{C}$ is symmetric. (From T1-4.)

A6. *Axiom of symmetry:* $\mathscr{C}$ is symmetric (with respect to individuals).

It seems to me that symmetry with respect to individuals must be required in inductive logic. I have explained my reasons for this view at other places ([1950, §§90 and 91] and Art. **1**, §4, R4). The most important reason is the following. Suppose that the proposition E says something about the individuals $a, b, \ldots$, and E' is isomorphic to E. Then E' says exactly the same about some (possibly other) individuals $a', b', \ldots$. In this case it would appear as whimsical and therefore unjustified to assign to E' an $\mathscr{M}$-value different from that assigned to E; and a similar argument holds for $\mathscr{C}$.

As I explained in Art. **1**, §4, symmetry must be required of a $\mathscr{C}$-function only because it is meant to represent credibility, not credence. A nonsymmetric credence function may still be rational. It may be perfectly reasonable for X to have a higher credence value, that is to say, a higher degree of belief in the proposition that Mr. Smith is more than thirty years old, than in the analogous proposition about Mr. Brown. Therefore those authors who interpret the term "probability" (often "subjective probability" or "personal probability") in the sense of credence (as, for example, de Finetti, Savage, and R. Jeffrey in [1965*b*]) are quite right in restricting symmetry to special cases.

The requirement of symmetry may gain additional plausibility by a comparison with the situation in *deductive logic*. Here the invariance under any permutation of individuals is usually taken for granted so much that it is seldom mentioned explicitly. But this invariance has the important, well-known consequence that the logical axioms (in the customary language forms) can be stated in a purely general form, i.e., without the use of individual constants. A study of the question of a similar generalized form for the axioms of inductive logic would be of great interest. This would require a language form in which the argument expressions attached to the function signs for absolute or relative probability would be neither names of sentences (as in [1950]) nor names of sets (as in the present system), but sentences or open sentential formulas. This would have to be an intensional language with signs of logical modalities (see [1950, pp. 280 ff.]).

It is to be noted that symmetry with respect to individuals should be required only for those languages in which all individual constants have the same logical nature. The situation is different for a *coordinate language*, i.e., one in which the standard individual expressions indicate the positions of the individuals; for example, the expressions '0', '0′', '0″' may denote the first three positions of a spatial or temporal series (cf. [1956, p. 75]), or in a language of physics the individuals may be space-time points, each denoted by a quadruple of real-number expressions. In a language of this kind, the distance between two individuals may be logically determined. Therefore a permutation of individuals might change the logical situation and thus influence the values of $\mathscr{C}$ and $\mathscr{M}$. Some later articles will deal with coordinate languages and, in particular, with time series; for those languages the axiom of symmetry will not be adopted. (Some remarks on coordinate languages will be made in Part II, §17C in Volume II; it will be indicated that an IL for such a language has to take into account the nearness of one individual to another, the "proximity influence".)

(9-2) **a.** π is a *cyclic permutation* $(i_1, i_2, \ldots, i_p) =_{\mathrm{Df}} \pi$ maps every i_r $(r = 1, 2, \ldots, p-1)$ into i_{r+1}, and i_p into i_1.
b. A cyclic permutation (i, i') is called a *transposition*.

T9-2. **a.** Suppose that, for every $i \in D$, $\mathscr{M}$ is invariant under the transposition of i and $i+1$. Then $\mathscr{M}$ is symmetric.
b. Suppose that, for any $i \in D$, for some $n > 0$, $\mathscr{M}$ is invariant under the transposition $(i, i+n)$. Then $\mathscr{M}$ is symmetric. (From (a).)

c. Suppose that, for every $s > 0$, $\mathscr{M}$ has the same value for any two isomorphic sample propositions (D3-6b) for the initial s-sample. Then $\mathscr{M}$ is symmetric. (From (b).)

In some series of events, the temporal order has no influence. For example, we find that, in a long series of throws of any die, even if it is loaded, the relative frequency of an ace among those throws that follow immediately on an ace (or a deuce), is not essentially different from the relative frequency of an ace in the whole series. Thus experience shows here statistical independence; and therefore we treat the members of such a series as inductively independent. In contrast, we find a strong dependence in a series of meterological observations made at a fixed place at noon of every day; and still higher dependence if made at intervals of one hour. The relative frequency of rain immediately following on rain is much higher than in the whole. If now in elementary inductive logic, we decide to accept the principle of symmetry for a certain investigation, this decision may either be based on the assumption that statistical independence actually holds; or else on the assumption that there is some dependence, but so small that we may neglect it for the sake of simplicity; or finally on the assumption that there may be noticeable dependencies in the actual temporal order represented in *another* (unknown) language $\mathscr{L}'$, and that the order of indexes in our language $\mathscr{L}$ was produced by an (unknown) permutation π of the indexes in $\mathscr{L}'$, where π is an infinite permutation with bounded displacement. [The purpose of the assumption of bounded displacement is as follows. Let R_j^m be the limit of the relative frequency of the attribute P_j^m in the family F^m. This is an important random variable on **Z** for a temporal coordinate language $\mathscr{L}'$, because here it means the limit of relative frequency with respect to the temporal order. On the other hand, in another language, where the individual indexes do not represent the temporal order, the limit has in general no significance. But for our language $\mathscr{L}$, the situation is different. Here the assumption that π has bounded displacement entrails the result that π produces only *local* disturbances of the temporal order but leaves the limit R_j^m unchanged. Although the indexical order in $\mathscr{L}$ differs from the temporal order, nevertheless the limit in $\mathscr{L}$ is equal to the limit with respect to the temporal order.]

From now on we shall assume that $\mathscr{M}$ and $\mathscr{C}$ are symmetric, unless the contrary is stated. Therefore we shall apply the theorems on symmetric $\mathscr{M}$- and $\mathscr{C}$-functions given in [1950, chap. viii], among them the theorems on the direct inductive inference (§94), i.e., theorems on $\mathscr{C}(H \mid E)$ where E concerns a population and H a sample, and in particular the binomial law (§95) and Bernoulli's limit theorem (§96).

10
One Family of Attributes

From here on we shall work mainly with a language $\mathscr{L}_1$ with the following properties. $\mathscr{L}_1$ is a monadic predicate language of the form $\mathscr{L}$ described in §3; but it has *only one family* F^1 (or simply F) of attributes and a denumerable set Ind of individuals. We assume that the family F contains only a finite number k of predicates ($k \geqq 2$): 'P_1', 'P_2', . . . , 'P_k', which designate the attributes $P_1, \ldots, P_k$, respectively. According to the rule R6-1 for sublanguages, the values of $\mathscr{M}(E)$ and $\mathscr{C}(H \mid E)$ in $\mathscr{L}$ are the same as those for the corresponding propositions in another language $\mathscr{L}$ containing $\mathscr{L}_1$ as a sublanguage of the second kind. Therefore the results obtained in this section and in the rest of this article can be applied also to propositions, say, E and H, in languages containing several families, provided that these propositions involve only one finite family.

[In later volumes in this series, the results about $\mathscr{L}_1$ will be applied in a still wider field. We shall admit also the case that the k predicates of F, though taken as primitive in $\mathscr{L}_1$, are interpreted as synonymous with k predicates defined in a language of the general form $\mathscr{L}$ on the basis of primitive predicates taken from any number of families, provided that these k predicates form a partition (D1-1d). In this case the set F does not satisfy the requirements for a genuine family explained in §4B. Nevertheless F may be formally treated in certain respects like a genuine family. We shall later call a set of predicates treated in this way a "*quasi-family*". For our present purposes it does not matter whether F is a genuine family or a quasi-family, since this difference is irrelevant for the problems discussed here. This is, however, not the case for some of the problems to be studied later.]

Since here only $m = 1$ occurs, we may simplify the notations of D3-1 and D3-2 thus: a model Z has only the one component $Z^{(1)}$; therefore we write simply '$Z(i)$' instead of '$Z(1, i)$' or '$Z^{(1)}(i)$'. Similarly we shall omit the subscript '1' for 'm' in the notations introduced by D3-4a, b and D3-5a, b. Since we have here only the k-family F, '$\sum_j$' stands always for '$\sum_{j=1}^{k}$'; similarly with '$\prod_j$', '$\bigcup_j$', and the like.

The following definitions are analogous to those in D3-6.

D10-1. Let Ind$'$ be a subset of Ind, and D' be the index set of Ind$'$.

a. The class of the atomic propositions with the individual index i: $\mathscr{E}_i^{\text{at}} =_{\text{Df}} \{P_j a_i : j \leqq k\}$.

b. The class of the atomic propositions for Ind′:

$$\mathscr{E}_{D'}^{\text{at}} =_{\text{Df}} \bigcup_{i \in D'} \mathscr{E}_i^{\text{at}}.$$

c. E is a *sample proposition* (s.p.) for the sample Ind′ $=_{\text{Df}}$ there is a class $\mathscr{A} \subset \mathscr{E}_{D'}^{\text{at}}$ such that, for every $i \in D'$, $\mathscr{A}$ contains exactly one atomic proposition in $\mathscr{E}_i^{\text{at}}$ and nothing else, and $E = \bigcap \mathscr{A}$.

The remaining concepts defined in D3-6 can now likewise be applied here.

Let Ind_s be an s-sample with the index set D_s. (In this context, '$\sum_i$', '$\prod_i$', '$\bigcup_i$', and '$\bigcap_i$' are understood for $i \in D_s$.)

D10-2. Let E_s be a sample proposition for Ind_s with index set D_s. Let Z'_s be a submodel for Ind_s.

a. E_s is *the s.p. corresponding to* $Z'_s =_{\text{Df}} E_s = \{Z\colon Z \in \mathbf{Z};$ and $Z'_s \subset Z\}$.

b. For a given E_s, Z'_s is *the submodel corresponding to* $E_s =_{\text{Df}} Z'_s$ is the restriction to D_s of any $Z \in E_s$.

Thus E_s and Z'_s determine each other uniquely. There is a one-to-one correspondence between the s.p.'s for any sample and the submodels for the sample.

Earlier (in D3-9) we defined some *random variables* on the class $\mathscr{B}^{(s)}$ of the s.p.'s for Ind_s. Now we shall define some more:

D10-3. **a.** For any attribute index j, $(s_j)_p =_{\text{Df}} \sum_i \text{TV}_p(P_j a_i)$.

b. $\mathbf{s}_p =_{\text{Df}} \langle (s_1)_p, (s_2)_p, \ldots, (s_k)_p \rangle$. This is the k-tuple of the s.p. B_p.

c. $(r_j)_p =_{\text{Df}} (s_j)_p/s$. This is the relative frequency of the attribute P_j in B_p.

Then we have:

(10-1) (a) $\sum_j s_j = s$.

(b) $\sum_j r_j = 1$.

(c) Corresponding E_s and Z'_s have the same k-tuple $\langle s_1, \ldots, s_k \rangle$.

(d) E_s is an intersection of s atomic propositions: $E_s = \bigcap_i P_j a_i$, where $j = Z'_s(i)$.

(e) Two s.p.'s for the same sample have the same k-tuple if-if they are isomorphic (D9-2d).

Usually we have $s > 0$; but sometimes we apply the same notations also to the case $s = 0$; then we have:

(10-2) Ind_0 is the empty set of individuals; E_0 has the k-tuple $\mathbf{s}_0$ (3-7c); and $E_0 = \mathbf{Z}$.

(10-3) In connection with E_s, for an arbitrarily chosen individual index i not contained in D_s, we shall understand the k propositions H_j ($j = 1, \ldots, k$) to be the atomic propositions $P_j a_i$.

D10-4. **a.** S is *the structure corresponding to the sample proposition* E_s (with the index set D_s) $=_{\text{Df}} S = \bigcup \mathscr{B}$, where $\mathscr{B} = \{B\colon B$ is an s.p. on D_s; and B is isomorphic to $E_s\}$. (For "isomorphic", see D9-2d.)

b. S is *a structure* (for Ind_s or for D_s) $=_{\text{Df}}$ for some s.p. E on Ind_s, S is the structure corresponding to E.

Instead of the term "structure", the more explicit term "structure proposition" might be used, or "statistical proposition". We ascribe the common k-tuple of the s.p.'s in $\mathscr{B}$ also to S. In the special case that one of the k numbers of E_s is s and thus all others are 0, we have $\mathscr{B} = \{E_s\}$ and hence $S = E_s$. In all other cases, E_s is a proper subclass of S; here S says less about Ind_s than E_s does; S gives merely statistical information, namely, for each attribute P_j only the number s_j, without saying *which* individuals have this attribute. The class of all structures for a given sample is disjoint, and is a partition of $\mathbf{Z}$. [Comparing the concepts here used with those in [1950], the concept of sample proposition corresponds to the earlier concept of individual distribution including state descriptions ([1950] D26-6a and D18-1a); the concept of structure corresponds to the earlier concept of statistical distribution including structure descriptions (D26-6b, c and D27-1).]

T10-1. Let $\mathscr{B}$ and S be defined on the basis of E_s as above.

a. The number of s.p.'s in $\mathscr{B}$ is

$$\xi' = \frac{s!}{s_1!s_2!\ldots s_k!}. \qquad ([1950, \text{T40-32b}].)$$

b. The s.p.'s in $\mathscr{B}$ have equal $\mathscr{M}$-values. (From A6, symmetry.)

c. $\mathscr{M}(S) = \dfrac{s!}{s_1!\ldots s_k!}\mathscr{M}(E_s)$. (From (a) and (b); comp. [1950, T92-1j].)

The following theorem holds for partitions (D1-1d) in any language.

T10-2. Let $\mathscr{A} = \{A_1, A_2, \ldots\}$ be *a countable partition of* $\mathbf{Z}$ with index set D. Let $\mathscr{M}$ be an arbitrary $\mathscr{M}$-function; $\mathscr{M}$ need not be regular or symmetric, but if $\mathscr{A}$ is denumerable, $\mathscr{M}$ must be σ-additive. Let $\mathscr{C}$ be a $\mathscr{C}$-function related to $\mathscr{M}$. Then the following holds for any proposition B. ('$\bigcup$' and '$\sum$' cover all $m \in D$.)

a. $\bigcup A_m = \mathbf{Z}$.
b. $\sum \mathscr{M}(A_m) = 1.$ (From (*a*).)
c. $\mathscr{M}(B) = \sum \mathscr{M}(B \cap A_m)$.

Proof. $\bigcup (B \cap A_m) = B \cap \bigcup A_m = B \cap \mathbf{Z} = B.$ ■

d. $\sum \mathscr{C}(A_m \mid B) = 1.$ (From (c).)
e. If, for every $m \in D$, $\mathscr{M}(A_m) > 0$, then

$$\mathscr{M}(B) = \sum [\mathscr{M}(A_m)\mathscr{C}(B \mid A_m)].$$

(From (c).)

Now we go back to the language $\mathscr{L}_1$, with E_s and H_j ($j = 1, \ldots, k$) as earlier specified.

T10-3. Let $\mathscr{M}$ be an arbitrary $\mathscr{M}$-function (not necessarily regular or symmetric); let $\mathscr{C}$ be a $\mathscr{C}$-function related to $\mathscr{M}$.

a. If $j \neq j'$, H_j and $H_{j'}$ are disjoint. (From T3-2a.)
b. $\bigcup_j H_j = \mathbf{Z}$. (From T3-2b.)
c. $\{H_1, \ldots, H_k\}$ is a finite partition of $\mathbf{Z}$. (From T3-2c.)
d. $\sum_j \mathscr{M}(H_j) = 1.$ (From (c) and T2b.)
e. $\sum_j \mathscr{C}(H_j \mid E_s) = 1.$ (From T2d.)
f. *Sum theorem for* $\mathscr{M}$. $\mathscr{M}(E_s) = \sum_j \mathscr{M}(E_s \cap H_j)$. (From T2c.)

We shall now consider a *finite sublanguage* $\mathscr{L}'$ of the language $\mathscr{L}_1$ specified earlier. $\mathscr{L}'$ is restricted to the set Ind_N of the first N individuals ($N \in \mathbf{N}$); hence the index set of Ind_N is $\mathbf{N}_N$. Thus $\mathscr{L}'$ is a sublanguage of the first kind (D6-1), with transformation T_1. We may think of Ind_N as a *population* (of persons or grains of wheat or lamp bulbs or whatever else) which is under investigation. Samples from this population may have been observed, and the results are represented in the form of s.p.'s like E_s. Let $\mathbf{Z}'$ be the class of the models for $\mathscr{L}'$, $\mathscr{E}'$ be the class of the propositions for $\mathscr{L}'$, and $\mathscr{S}'$ be the class of the structures for $\mathscr{L}'$. Let $\mathscr{M}'$ and $\mathscr{C}'$ for $\mathscr{L}'$ be related to each other and satisfy the rule R6-1 for sublanguages. Hence for any propositions E ($\neq \varnothing$) and H in $\mathscr{L}'$, $\mathscr{C}'(H \mid E) = \mathscr{C}(T_1(H) \mid T_1(E))$; and $\mathscr{M}'(H) = \mathscr{M}(T_1(H))$.

T10-4. Here it is not assumed that $\mathscr{M}$ and $\mathscr{C}$ are symmetric, but only that they are regular.

a. The cardinal number ζ of $\mathbf{Z}'$ for $\mathscr{L}'$, which is equal to the number of the s.p.'s for the sample Ind_N in $\mathscr{L}_1$ (see the remark following D2): $\zeta = k^N$. (From [1950, T40-31a].)

b. The cardinal number ρ of $\mathscr{E}'$ is equal to the number of all subsets of $\mathbf{Z}'$, and equal to the number of those propositions on $\mathscr{L}_1$ which involve only individuals of Ind_N (these are the propositions of $\mathscr{L}_1$ corresponding to propositions of $\mathscr{L}'$): $\rho = 2^\zeta$. ([1950, T40-31h].)

c. The cardinal number τ of $\mathscr{S}'$ is equal to the number of the structures (statistical propositions) for the population Ind_N in $\mathscr{L}_1$: $\tau = \binom{N+k-1}{N}$. ([1950, T40-33a].)

d. Let $\mathscr{S}' = \{S_1, \ldots, S_\tau\}$ be the class of the *population structures* in $\mathscr{L}'$. Then $\sum_{m=1}^{\tau} \mathscr{M}(S_m) = 1$. (From T2b, since $\mathscr{S}'$ is a partition of **Z**.)

e. For any proposition B in $\mathscr{L}'$, $\mathscr{M}(B) = \sum_{m=1}^{\tau} [\mathscr{M}(S_m)\mathscr{C}(B \mid S_m)]$. (From T2e; since $\mathscr{M}$ is regular, the condition that $\mathscr{M}(A_m) > 0$ is satisfied.)

In the following definitions and theorems on some mathematical functions, z is a real number, and m and n are nonnegative integers. We define first the function $(z)_n$. For $n > 0$, $(z)_n$ is a product of n factors, beginning with z and ascending by 1, thus ending with $z + n - 1$ (see T5b below).

D10-5. Recursive definition of $(z)_n$:

a. $(z)_0 =_{\text{Df}} 1$.

b. $(z)_{n+1} =_{\text{Df}} (z)_n(z + n)$.

[*Remarks on the notation.* Let u be the last factor in the product, thus $u = z + n - 1$. In my earlier publications [1950, D40-a] and [1952*a*, (10-8)], I used the notation '$\begin{bmatrix} u \\ n \end{bmatrix}$' (in [1950] only in the special form $\begin{bmatrix} m \\ n \end{bmatrix}$ with an integer $m > n$). I chose this symbol because of its similarity with the customary symbol '$\binom{m}{n}$' for the binomial coefficient (see [Prob.], the last paragraph in §92). These two functions are closely related and occur often in pairs of corresponding theorems on s.p.'s and structures (e.g., [1950, T94-1a(2) and b(2)]). I think now, however, that the symbol '$(z)_n$' is preferable because more easily printed. It has been used by H. Bateman (A. Erdelyi, ed.), F. Lösch (F. Schoblik), and in the *Handbook of mathematical functions* (National Bureau of Standards, Washington, D.C. 1964, p. 256), where it is called "Pochhammer symbol". Other notations taking the smallest factor of the product (here z) as argument: Christian Kramp (Strasbourg 1808): '$z^{n/1}$'; W. Gröbner and N. Hofreiter: '$(z; 1; n)$'. Other notations with the largest factor (here $u = z + n - 1$) have been used by Kramp: '$u^{n/-1}$'; M. G. Kendall: '$u^{[n]}$'; L. Hogben: '$u^{(n)}$'; likewise W. E. Milne, who says that this function is called "factorial polynomial" (*Numerical calculus*, 1949, p. 145); W. Feller: '$(u)_n$', likewise E. Parzen.]

T10-5. On the basis of D5, the following theorems hold for any real number z, and any m and $n \in {}^0\mathbf{N}$.

a. $(z)_1 = z$.

b. If $n > 0$, $(z)_n = z(z + 1) \ldots (z + n - 1)$.

c. If $m < n$, $(-m)_n = 0$.

d. $(1)_n = n!$

e. $(z)_n = \dfrac{\Gamma(z + n)}{\Gamma(z)}$. (From (b) and the recursion formula: $\Gamma(x + 1) = x\Gamma(x)$. The equation (e) could also be taken as an explicit definition for $(z)_n$.)

f. if $m > 0$, $(m)_n = \dfrac{(m + n - 1)!}{(m - 1)!}$. (From (e).)

It is sometimes useful to have the binomial coefficient $\binom{m}{n}$ not only defined in the elementary form (a), but also in the generalized form (b) with any real number z:

D10-6. **a.** For $m > n$, $\binom{m}{n} =_{\text{Df}} \dfrac{m!}{n!(m - n)!}$.

b. $\binom{z}{n} =_{\text{Df}} \dfrac{(z - n + 1)_n}{n!}$.

If we substitute 'z' for 'm' in D6a and use the gamma-function for the two factorials containing 'z', we find by T5e, that the quotient of these two terms equals $(z - n + 1)_n$. This shows that D6b is indeed a generalization of D6a.

T10-6. **a.** $\binom{z}{0} = 1$. (From D5a.)

b. $\binom{z}{1} = z.$ (From T5a.)

c. If $m < n$, $\binom{m}{n} = 0.$ (From T5c.)

d. $\binom{n}{n} = 1.$ (From T5d.)

e. $\binom{n+m}{n} = \frac{(n+m)!}{n!m!} = \binom{n+m}{m}.$

f. $\binom{z+1}{n+1} = \binom{z}{n} + \binom{z}{n+1}.$

We return to the finite sublanguage $\mathscr{L}'$, with the population (set of individuals) Ind_N. Now we assume again that $\mathscr{M}$ and $\mathscr{C}$ satisfy all axioms, including those of symmetry. $\mathbf{Z}'$, $\mathscr{E}'$, and $\mathscr{S}'$ are as specified earlier for $\mathscr{L}'$. Let the population structures in $\mathscr{S}'$ be $S_1^N, \ldots, S_\tau^N$. Let E_s be, as earlier, a s.p. for the sample $\text{Ind}_s \subset \text{Ind}_N$. Let S^s be the sample structure for Ind_s corresponding to the sample proposition E_s. Let the mth population structure S_m^N ($m = 1, \ldots, \tau$) have the k-tuple $\langle N_{m,1}, N_{m,2}, \ldots, N_{m,k}\rangle$. For any j ($j = 1, \ldots, k$), let $R_{m,j} = N_{m,j}/N$. (Thus $R_{m,j}$ is the *relative frequency* of the attribute P_j in the structure S_m^N.) (In the following, it would be sufficient for the product $\prod_j$ to range over those j for which $N_{m,j} > 0$; if $N_{m,j} = 0$, then $s_j = 0$, and thus by D5a $(N_{m,j} - s_j + 1)_{s_j} = 1$, and by T6a $\binom{N_{m,j}}{s_j} = 1$.)

T10-7. Here we determine the probability of a sample proposition E_s or a sample structure S^s, given a population structure S_m^N.

a. $$\mathscr{C}(E_s \mid S_m^N) = \frac{\prod_j (N_{m,j} - s_j + 1)s_j}{(N - s + 1)_s}.$$

(From [1950, T94-1a].)

b. For $N \gg s$, we have the approximation:

$$\mathscr{C}(E_s \mid S_m^N) \simeq \prod_j R_{m,j}^{s_j}. \qquad \text{([1950, T95-1a].)}$$

c. $$\mathscr{C}(S^s \mid S_m^N) = \frac{s!}{s_1! \ldots s_k!}\mathscr{C}(E_s \mid S_m^N). \qquad \text{(From T1a, b.)}$$

d. $$\mathscr{C}(S^s \mid S_m^N) = \frac{\prod_j \binom{N_{m,j}}{s_j}}{\binom{N}{s}}. \qquad \text{(From (c) and (a).)}$$

e. Approximation for $N \gg s$:

$$\mathscr{C}(S^s \mid S_m^N) = \frac{s!}{s_1! \ldots s_k!} \prod_j R_{m,j}^{s_j}. \qquad \text{(From (c) and (b).)}$$

f. $$\mathscr{M}(E_s) = \sum_{m=1}^{\tau} \mathscr{M}(S_m^N) \frac{\prod_j (N_{m,j} - s_j + 1)_{s_j}}{(N - s + 1)_s}.$$

(From (a) and T4d.)

g. Approximation for $N \gg s$:

$$\mathscr{M}(E_s) \cong \sum_{m=1}^{\tau} \left[\mathscr{M}(S_m^N) \prod_j R_{m,j}^{s_j} \right]. \qquad \text{(From (b) and T4e.)}$$

T10-8. Let $\mathscr{M}$ be an $\mathscr{M}$-function for $\mathscr{L}'$ (not necessarily regular or symmetric). Let $\mathscr{C}$ be related to $\mathscr{M}$. Suppose that we know the values of $\mathscr{M}$ for the *population propositions* in $\mathscr{L}'$, i.e., the sample propositions for the initial N-sample in $\mathscr{L}_1$, which is the whole population in $\mathscr{L}'$. In analogy to $\mathscr{B}^{(s)}$ in D3-6d and e, let $\mathscr{B}^{(N)}$ be the class of the population propositions in $\mathscr{L}'$; and for an arbitrary nonempty proposition A in $\mathscr{L}'$, let $\mathscr{B}_A^{(N)}$ be the class of those B in $\mathscr{B}^{(N)}$ for which $B \subset A$. (In the following, '$\sum$' is to be understood for all B in $\mathscr{B}^{(N)}$, and '$\sum_{B(A)}$' for all B in $\mathscr{B}_A^{(N)}$.)

a. For any A ($\neq \varnothing$) in $\mathscr{L}'$, $\mathscr{M}(A) = \sum_{B(A)} \mathscr{M}(B)$. (From T3-4i.)

b. For any propositions H, K in $\mathscr{L}'$, ($K \neq \varnothing$), $\mathscr{C}(H \mid K) = \sum [\mathscr{C}(B \mid K)\mathscr{C}(H \mid B)]$. (From T3-4f.)

c. Since $A \neq \varnothing$, $\mathscr{B}_A^{(N)}$ is a nonempty subclass of $\mathscr{B}^{(N)}$. (From T3-4g.)

d. If the values of $\mathscr{M}$ for every B in $\mathscr{B}^{(N)}$ are given, then by (a) $\mathscr{M}(A)$ is uniquely determined. Since $A \neq \varnothing$, $\mathscr{B}_A^{(N)}$ is nonempty; and if, for at least one B in $\mathscr{B}_A^{(N)}$, $\mathscr{M}(B) > 0$, then $\mathscr{M}(A) > 0$.

e. Let $\mathscr{M}$ be *regular*. Then for any B in $\mathscr{B}^{(N)}$ and for any (nonempty) A, $\mathscr{M} > 0$. In this case, if $K \neq \varnothing$, $\mathscr{M}(K) > 0$, and hence $\mathscr{C}(H \mid K) = \mathscr{M}(K \cap H)/\mathscr{M}(K)$.

f. Suppose that $\mathscr{M}$ is not yet defined. If now we choose arbitrary positive real numbers whose sum is 1, as $\mathscr{M}$-values for all propositions B in $\mathscr{B}^{(N)}$, then all values of $\mathscr{M}$ and of the $\mathscr{C}$ related to $\mathscr{M}$, for any propositions in $\mathscr{L}'$ are uniquely determined.

T10-9. Let $\mathscr{M}$ be *regular and symmetric*. Let $\mathscr{C}$ be related to $\mathscr{M}$. Suppose that the values of $\mathscr{M}$ for the *population structures* $\mathscr{S}'$ in $\mathscr{L}'$ are given. We shall show that hereby all values of $\mathscr{M}$ and of $\mathscr{C}$ for propositions in $\mathscr{L}'$ are uniquely determined.

a. Let $B \in \mathscr{B}^{(N)}$ be a population proposition in $\mathscr{L}'$. Let S be the structure corresponding to B. According to our assumption, $\mathscr{M}(S)$ is given. Then $\mathscr{M}(B)$ is determined by T1c. The same holds for all other population propositions in $\mathscr{L}'$.

b. If we choose arbitrary positive values whose sum is 1 as $\mathscr{M}$-values for the population structures $\mathscr{S}'$ in $\mathscr{L}'$, then all values of $\mathscr{M}$ and $\mathscr{C}$ for propositions in $\mathscr{L}'$ are thereby uniquely determined. (From (a) and T8f.)

Let us use the results just stated for measuring the effect which the addition of the symmetry axiom A6 to the previous axioms has on the freedom in choosing an $\mathscr{M}$-function for the language $\mathscr{L}'$ with N individuals. Let us take (as in T4a and c) ζ as the number of models (or s.p.'s) $= k^N$ (T4a), and τ as the number of structures $= \binom{N+k-1}{N}$ (T4c). Then the axiom A6 reduces the degrees of freedom from $\zeta - 1$ (1 is deducted because of the sum condition) to $\tau - 1$. As the following table of a few example values of N shows, there is a considerable reduction even for rather small numbers N and k.

(10-4) The *number of sample propositions* ζ and the *number of structures* τ for $k = 4$ and various N:

N	ζ	τ
1	4	4
3	64	20
6	4,096	84
10	1,048,576	286
20	$\cong 10^{12}$	1,771

11
Representative Functions for $\mathscr{M}$

A. MI-FUNCTIONS

While the $\mathscr{M}$-functions are set-functions, it is convenient to use corresponding *numerical functions*, i.e., those with numbers as arguments. We shall introduce in this section numerical representative functions for the symmetric $\mathscr{M}$-functions. If $\mathscr{M}$ is symmetric, then the corresponding function is representative of $\mathscr{M}$ in the sense that $\mathscr{M}$ is uniquely determined by this function. We shall introduce two kinds of functions for $\mathscr{M}$; first MI, which we shall apply most frequently in this and future articles, and then MS. (These symbols have been chosen because MI represents the $\mathscr{M}$-values of *individual* sample propositions (s.p.'s), and MS those of *structures*.)

We use again the language $\mathscr{L}_1$ with one family of attributes, as in the preceding section.

If $\mathscr{M}$ is symmetric, then, for any given k-tuple $\mathbf{s} = \langle s_1, \ldots, s_k \rangle$, $\mathscr{M}$ has the same value for all s.p.'s with this k-tuple, since these s.p.'s are isomorphic to one another (10-1c). We shall assign this value of $\mathscr{M}$ to $\mathrm{MI}(s_1, \ldots, s_k)$ (or to $\mathrm{MI}(\mathbf{s})$, as we shall write for convenience). Although we shall use MI-functions practically only for symmetric $\mathscr{M}$-functions, in the following definition D1 we do not presuppose that $\mathscr{M}$ is symmetric. To assure the uniqueness of MI for any given $\mathscr{M}$, we must in the definition specify, for any given k-tuple $\mathbf{s}$, one particular s.p. $E^*_{s,\mathbf{s}}$ which has this k-tuple. The choice of the specification is inessential; all that matters is the uniqueness of $E^*_{s,\mathbf{s}}$ for the given $\mathbf{s}$. (One can easily see that $E^*_{s,\mathbf{s}}$, as specified in D1, is an s.p. for the initial s-sample, and that it ascribes the attribute P_1 to the first s_1 individuals, then P_2 to the next s_2 individuals, etc., and finally P_k to the last s_k individuals of the sample. But no consequence will be drawn from this particular pattern chosen for $E^*_{s,\mathbf{s}}$.)

D11-1. Let $\mathscr{M}$ be any real-valued function on $\mathscr{E}^{\mathrm{mol}}$ for $\mathscr{L}_1$. *The representative function* MI of $\mathscr{M}$ is defined as follows. For any k-tuple $\mathbf{s} = \langle s_1, \ldots, s_k \rangle$ in ${}^0\mathbf{N}^{k,s}$,

$$\mathrm{MI}(\mathbf{s}) =_{\mathrm{Df}} \mathscr{M}(E^*_{s,\mathbf{s}}),$$

where $E^*_{s,\mathbf{s}}$ is defined as follows. For the given k-tuple $\mathbf{s}$, let $m_j = \sum_{l=1}^{i} s_l$, and $m_0 = 0$; and let $Z'_\mathbf{s}$ be the submodel restricted to $\mathbf{N}_s$ such that, for

$j = 1, \ldots, k$, $Z'_s(i) = j$ if-if $m_{j-1} < i \leqq m_j$. $E^*_{s,\mathbf{s}}$ is defined as the proposition corresponding to Z'_s (D10-2a).

As in the preceding section, E_s is an arbitrary s.p. for an s-sample with the k-tuple $\mathbf{s} = \langle s_1, \ldots, s_k \rangle$. Let S be the structure corresponding to E_s.

T11-1. Let $\mathcal{M}$ be a *symmetric* (but not necessarily regular) $\mathcal{M}$-function on $\mathcal{E}^{\text{mol}}$ for $\mathcal{L}_1$. Let MI be the representative function for $\mathcal{M}$. (For '$\mathbf{s}_0$' and '$\mathbf{s}^j$' see (3-7)(c), (b).)

a. $\mathcal{M}(E_s) = \text{MI}(\mathbf{s})$.

Proof. Let $E^*_{s,\mathbf{s}}$ be as in D1, with the same $\mathbf{s}$ as E_s. By D1, $\mathcal{M}(E^*_{s,\mathbf{s}}) = \text{MI}(\mathbf{s})$. Since E_s and $E^*_{s,\mathbf{s}}$ are isomorphic, $\mathcal{M}(E_s) = \mathcal{M}(E^*_{s,\mathbf{s}})$. ■

b. $\text{MI}(\mathbf{s}_0) = 1$. (From (10-2).)

c. *Sum theorem for* MI. For any $s_1, \ldots, s_k$, $\text{MI}(\mathbf{s}) = \sum_j \text{MI}(\mathbf{s}^j)$. (For '$\mathbf{s}^j$', see (3-7)(b).)

Proof. For any j, $E_s \cap H_j$ (see (10-3)) is an s.p. for an $(s + 1)$-sample with k-tuple $\mathbf{s}^j$. Therefore, by (a), $\mathcal{M}(E_s \cap H_j) = \text{MI}(\mathbf{s}^j)$. Hence the assertion by T10-3f. ■

d. If $\mathcal{M}$ is *regular*, then $\text{MI}(\mathbf{s}) > 0$. (From T7-2b.)

e. If S is the structure corresponding to E_s,

$$\mathcal{M}(S) = \frac{s!}{s_1! \ldots s_k!}\,\text{MI}(\mathbf{s}). \qquad \text{(From (a) and T10-1c.)}$$

D11-2. Let MI be an arbitrary real-valued function defined on ${}^0\mathbf{N}^{k,s}$. We say that the function $\mathcal{M}'$ is **generated by** MI if-if $\mathcal{M}'$ is defined on $\mathcal{E}^{\text{mol}}$ for $\mathcal{L}_1$ by the following rules (a) through (d):

a. $\mathcal{M}'(\varnothing) =_{\text{Df}} 0$.

b. $\mathcal{M}'(\mathbf{Z}) =_{\text{Df}} \text{MI}(\mathbf{s}_0)$.

c. For any $s > 0$, for any k-tuple $\mathbf{s}$ in ${}^0\mathbf{N}^{k,s}$, let $E'_{s,\mathbf{s}}$ be any s.p. for the *initial* s-sample with $\mathbf{s}$ (not necessarily $E^*_{s,\mathbf{s}}$). Then

$$\mathcal{M}'(E'_{s,\mathbf{s}}) =_{\text{Df}} \text{MI}(\mathbf{s}).$$

d. Let A be any *molecular proposition* in $\mathcal{L}_1$, having a form different from the three mentioned in (a), (b), and (c). The number of the individuals involved in A is positive and finite; let s be the highest individual index involved in A $(0 < s < \infty)$. Let $\mathcal{B}_A^{(s)}$ be defined on the basis of s and A as in D3-6a. $\mathcal{B}_A^{(s)}$ is a finite class of s.p.'s for the initial

s-sample; thus for any $B \in \mathscr{B}_A^{(s)}$, $\mathscr{M}'(B)$ is determined by (c). Then $\mathscr{M}'(A) =_{\text{Df}} \sum \mathscr{M}'(B)$ (the sum ranges over all $B \in \mathscr{B}_A^{(s)}$).

T11-2. **a.** For any MI, there is one and only one function $\mathscr{M}'$ generated by MI.

b. For any $H \in \mathscr{E}^{\text{mol}}$ in $\mathscr{L}_1$, $\mathscr{M}'(H)$ is uniquely determined. $\mathscr{M}'$ is not necessarily an $\mathscr{M}$-function; we shall later state conditions for MI (in D3) which will assure that $\mathscr{M}'$ is an $\mathscr{M}$-function.

The definition D1 specifies a transformation or mapping r that assigns to any function $\mathscr{M}$ its unique representative function MI:

(11-1) $$r(\mathscr{M}) = \text{MI}.$$

Similarly, D2 specifies a mapping g that assigns to any function MI the unique function $\mathscr{M}'$ generated by MI:

(11-2) $$g(\text{MI}) = \mathscr{M}'.$$

The subsequent theorem T3 says in effect that:

(11-3) for any function MI, $r(g(\text{MI})) = \text{MI}$; in other words,

(11-4) $$\text{if } g(\text{MI}) = \mathscr{M}, \text{ then } r(\mathscr{M}) = \text{MI}.$$

We see from D2c that, if MI and MI′ are distinct functions (i.e., for some $\mathbf{s}$, $\text{MI}(\mathbf{s}) \neq \text{MI}'(\mathbf{s})$), then the functions $\mathscr{M}$ and $\mathscr{M}'$ generated by MI and MI′ respectively are likewise distinct. We shall see later that the analogue for r does not hold generally, but only for symmetric $\mathscr{M}$-functions.

T11-3. Let MI be as in D2. Let $\mathscr{M}'$ be generated by MI (D2). Let MI′ be defined as the representative function of $\mathscr{M}'$ (D1). Then the functions MI and MI′ are identical, i.e., for any $\mathbf{s}$, $\text{MI}(\mathbf{s}) = \text{MI}'(\mathbf{s})$.

Proof. Let $\mathbf{s}$ be an arbitrary k-tuple in ${}^0\mathbf{N}^{k,s}$; let its sum be s. For this $\mathbf{s}$, let the s.p. $E^*_{s,\mathbf{s}}$ be defined as in D1. Then by D1, $\mathscr{M}'(E^*_{s,\mathbf{s}}) = \text{MI}'(\mathbf{s})$. Since $\mathscr{M}'$ is generated by MI, $\mathscr{M}'(E^*_{s,\mathbf{s}}) = \text{MI}(\mathbf{s})$ (D2c). Hence $\text{MI}(\mathbf{s}) = \text{MI}'(\mathbf{s})$. ■

Now let us examine the question whether for any function $\mathscr{M}$, $g(r(\mathscr{M})) = \mathscr{M}$. This is not generally the case. But the following theorem T4 shows that it holds for symmetric $\mathscr{M}$.

T11-4. Let $\mathscr{M}$ be a *symmetric* $\mathscr{M}$-function on $\mathscr{E}^{mol}$ for $\mathscr{L}_1$. Let MI be the representative function of $\mathscr{M}$. Let $\mathscr{M}'$ be generated by MI. Then the functions $\mathscr{M}'$ and $\mathscr{M}$ are identical.

Proof. 1. $\mathscr{M}'(\varnothing) = \mathscr{M}(\varnothing) = 0$ (by D2a and D1-7).—2. $\mathscr{M}'(\mathbf{Z}) = \mathscr{M}(\mathbf{Z}) = 1$ (by D2b and (10-2)).—3. For any $E'_{s,\mathbf{s}}$ of the form specified in D2c, $\mathscr{M}'(E'_{s,\mathbf{s}}) = \mathscr{M}(E'_{s,\mathbf{s}}) = \text{MI}(\mathbf{s})$ (by D2c and T1a); here it is essential that $\mathscr{M}$ is symmetric.—4. For A as in D2d, $\mathscr{M}'(A) = \sum \mathscr{M}'(B)$ ($\sum$ ranges over all B in $\mathscr{B}_A^{(s)}$) $= \sum \mathscr{M}(B)$ (by (3), since every B has the form $E'_{s,\mathbf{s}}$) $= \mathscr{M}(A)$ (by T3-4f).—5. The assertion follows from (1), (2), (3), (4). ■

T4 says in effect:

(11-5) If $\mathscr{M}$ is symmetric, $g(r(\mathscr{M})) = \mathscr{M}$. In other words, if $\mathscr{M}$ is symmetric and $r(\mathscr{M}) = \text{MI}$, then $g(\text{MI}) = \mathscr{M}$.

Thus, with (11-4):

(11-6) If $\mathscr{M}$ is symmetric, then, for any MI, $r(\mathscr{M}) = \text{MI}$ if-if $g(\text{MI}) = \mathscr{M}$.

Hence:

(11-7) For symmetric $\mathscr{M}$, r is a *one-to-one* correspondence, and g *is the inverse of* r and thus is likewise one-to-one.

We shall use MI-functions only for symmetric $\mathscr{M}$-functions. Only in this case is MI representative for $\mathscr{M}$ in the strict sense that MI allows us to determine uniquely all values of $\mathscr{M}$ for molecular propositions. If $\mathscr{M}$ is σ-additive (we shall later, in Part II in Volume II, state an axiom to this effect, which is equivalent to Kolmogorov's axiom of continuity), then also the values of $\mathscr{M}$ for all other propositions are determined by MI.

That the restriction of T4 to symmetric $\mathscr{M}$-functions is necessary can be seen as follows. As we see from D1, for any function $\mathscr{M}$, only certain special values are *directly* represented by its representative function $r(\mathscr{M}) = \text{MI}$, namely, the values for propositions of the special form $E^*_{s,\mathbf{s}}$ described in D1. Suppose that $\mathscr{M}$ and $\mathscr{M}'$ agree in these values but differ for other propositions. Then $\mathscr{M}$ and $\mathscr{M}'$, though non-identical, have the same function MI; thus MI would not be genuinely representative. According to T4, this can occur only if either $\mathscr{M}$ or $\mathscr{M}'$ or both are nonsymmetric.

So far we have considered only those functions MI that we formed as representative functions of given $\mathscr{M}$-functions. Now we shall characterize the class of *symmetric MI-functions* and that of *regular* symmetric MI-functions by purely mathematical conditions without reference to $\mathcal{M}$-functions.

D11-3. Let MI be a real-valued function on ${}^{0}\mathbf{N}^{k,s}$.

a. MI is a **symmetric MI-function** $=_{\mathrm{Df}}$ MI satisfies the following three conditions:

(1) $\mathrm{MI}(\mathbf{s}_0) = 1$.

(2) *Sum condition.* For any $\mathbf{s} = \langle s_1, \ldots, s_k \rangle$ in ${}^{0}\mathbf{N}^{k,s}$, $\mathrm{MI}(\mathbf{s}) = \sum_j \mathrm{MI}(\mathbf{s}^j)$.

(3) For any $\mathbf{s}$, $\mathrm{MI}(\mathbf{s}) \geqq 0$.

b. MI is a **regular, symmetric MI-function** $=_{\mathrm{Df}}$ MI satisfies the above conditions (1) and (2), and, instead of (3), the following stronger condition: (3′) For any $\mathbf{s}$ in ${}^{0}\mathbf{N}^{k,s}$, $\mathrm{MI}(\mathbf{s}) > 0$.

The reasons for the choice of the terms introduced will soon become clear when we show that the function $\mathcal{M}$ generated by MI will be in the case (a) a symmetric $\mathcal{M}$-function (T6j), and in the case (b) a regular, symmetric $\mathcal{M}$-function (T6k).

T11-5. Let $\mathcal{M}$ be an $\mathcal{M}$-function on $\mathcal{E}^{\mathrm{mol}}$ for $\mathcal{L}_1$. Let MI be the representative function of $\mathcal{M}$.

a. If $\mathcal{M}$ is symmetric, MI is symmetric. (From T1b, c, D1.)

b. If $\mathcal{M}$ is symmetric and regular, MI is likewise. (From (a) and T1d.)

These results are easily obtained. Now we have the more complicated task of proving the inverse results. This is of great importance for the use of the representative MI-functions; it shows the adequacy of their definition in D3. The main result will be that an $\mathcal{M}$ generated by a symmetric (or a regular symmetric) MI-function is a symmetric (or regular symmetric, respectively) $\mathcal{M}$-function (T6j and k).

T11-6. Let MI be a *symmetric MI-function.* Let $\mathcal{M}$ be generated by MI (D2). The main results are (j) and (k); the items (a) through (i) are lemmas for (j).

a. $\mathcal{M}(\varnothing) = 0$. (From D2a.)

b. $\mathcal{M}(\mathbf{Z}) = 1$. (From D2b.)

c. For any $H \in \mathcal{E}^{\mathrm{mol}}$, $\mathcal{M}(H) \geqq 0$. (From D2a, b, c, d and D3a(3).)

d. For any $s > 0$, and any k-tuple $\mathbf{s}$ in ${}^{0}\mathbf{N}^{k,s}$, let $E^*_{s,\mathbf{s}}$ be as in D1, and $E'_{s,\mathbf{s}}$ as in D2c, both with the same $\mathbf{s}$. Then

$$\mathcal{M}(E^*_{s,\mathbf{s}}) = \mathcal{M}(E'_{s,\mathbf{s}}) = \mathrm{MI}(\mathbf{s}). \quad \text{(From D2c.)}$$

Thus, for any s, any two isomorphic s.p.'s for the initial s-sample have the same $\mathscr{M}$-value.

e. Let $E'_{s,\mathbf{s}}$ be as in D2c. Then

$$(E'_{s,\mathbf{s}}) = \sum_j \mathscr{M}(E'_{s,\mathbf{s}} \cap H_j). \quad \text{(From D3a(2).)}$$

$E'_{s,\mathbf{s}} \cap H_j$ is an s.p. for the initial $(s+1)$-sample with k-tuple $\mathbf{s}^j$.)

f. Let H_n be the union of n s.p.'s of the form $E'_{s,\mathbf{s}}$ as in D2c, all n s.p.'s with the same s (but possibly different $\mathbf{s}$); for $n = 1$, H_1 is an s.p. of the specified form. For any $m \geqq 0$, let $\mathscr{B}_{H_n}^{(s+m)}$ be defined on the basis of $s + m$ and H_n as specified in D3-6e. Then

$$\binom{*}{m} \mathscr{M}(H_n) = \sum \mathscr{M}(B) \quad (\text{for all } B \in \mathscr{B}_{H_n}^{(s+m)}).$$

(The *proofs* of T6f, g, h, i, j, and k are given below.)

g. Let H and H' be two disjoint molecular propositions. Then

$$\mathscr{M}(H \cup H') = \mathscr{M}(H) + \mathscr{M}(H').$$

Thus $\mathscr{M}$ is *additive*, and hence a measure function (D1-6, by (c)), a probability function (D1-7, by (b)), and an $\mathscr{M}$-function on $\mathscr{E}^{\text{mol}}$ (D1-10).

h. For any $s > 0$, let E_s be an s.p. for any s-sample with any k-tuple $\mathbf{s}$ in ${}^0\mathbf{N}^{k,s}$. Then $\mathscr{M}(E_s) = \text{MI}(\mathbf{s})$.

i. *Symmetry*. Let H be any molecular proposition, and π be any finite permutation of the individual index set. Then $\mathscr{M}(H) = \mathscr{M}(\pi''(H))$.

j. $\mathscr{M}$ is a *symmetric $\mathscr{M}$-function*. (From (c) and (i).)

k. *Regularity*. If MI is, moreover, regular (D3b), then $\mathscr{M}$ is *regular*, i.e., for any nonempty molecular proposition H, $\mathscr{M}(H) > 0$.

Proofs *for T6f, g, h, i, k.*

Proof for T6f. (Note that we cannot simply derive T6f from T3-4i, because at this state we have not yet ascertained that $\mathscr{M}$ is an $\mathscr{M}$-function. This result will be obtained in (g).)

1. Let $\binom{*}{0}$ be the instance of the assertion $\binom{*}{m}$ for $m = 0$:

$$\binom{*}{0} \mathscr{M}(H_n) = \sum \mathscr{M}(B) \quad (\text{for all } B \in \mathscr{B}_{H_n}^{(s)}).$$

Since these B are those s.p.'s of the form $E'_{s,s}$ whose union is H_n, $\binom{*}{0}$ follows from D2d.

2. Suppose that $\binom{*}{m}$ holds for a given m. We shall show that, under this assumption, likewise $\binom{*}{m+1}$ holds; i.e., that the following statement holds:

(*) $\sum \mathscr{M}(B)$ (for all $B \in \mathscr{B}$) $= \sum \mathscr{M}(B')$ (for all $B' \in \mathscr{B}'$)
where $\mathscr{B} = \mathscr{B}_{H_n}^{(s+m)}$, and $\mathscr{B}' = \mathscr{B}_{H_n}^{(s+m+1)}$.

For any $B \in \mathscr{B}$ and for any j ($j = 1, \ldots, k$), let $B_j = B \cap P_j a_{s+m+1}$ (for this atomic proposition see D3-4a). Thus for each s.p. B in $\mathscr{B}$ there are k corresponding disjoint s.p.'s B_j ($j = 1, \ldots, k$) in $\mathscr{B}'$, and for each s.p. in $\mathscr{B}'$, there is just one corresponding s.p. in $\mathscr{B}$. The s.p.'s in $\mathscr{B}$ are disjoint (T3-4b); likewise those in $\mathscr{B}'$. For any s.p. B in $\mathscr{B}$ and the k corresponding s.p.'s B_j in $\mathscr{B}'$, we have, by (e): $\mathscr{M}(B) = \sum_j \mathscr{M}(B_j)$. Therefore (*) holds.

3. The assertion follows from $\binom{*}{0}$ and (*) by mathematical induction with respect to m. ■

Proof for T6g. The assertion is obvious if $H' = \varnothing$, and hence $\mathscr{M}(H') = 0$, by (a). Likewise if $H = \mathbf{Z}$ and hence $H' = \varnothing$.—We assume now that H and H' are neither $\varnothing$ nor $\mathbf{Z}$. Let n and n' be the highest individual indexes involved in H and in H', respectively. Let $m = \max(n, n')$. Let $\mathscr{B} = \mathscr{B}_H^{(m)}$ be defined on the basis of H and m as in D3-6e; likewise $\mathscr{B}' = \mathscr{B}_{H'}^{(m)}$, and $\mathscr{B}'' = \mathscr{B}_{H \cup H'}^{(m)}$. Then we have from D3-6e the following three statements:

$$\mathscr{B} = \{B\colon B \in \mathscr{B}^{(m)} \text{ and } B \in H\}, \tag{1a}$$

$$\mathscr{B}' = \{B'\colon B' \in \mathscr{B}^{(m)} \text{ and } B' \subset H'\}, \tag{1b}$$

$$\mathscr{B}'' = \{B''\colon B'' \in \mathscr{B}^{(m)} \text{ and } B'' \subset H \cup H'\}, \tag{1c}$$

and from T3-4g:

$H = \bigcup \mathscr{B}$ (2a); $H' = \bigcup \mathscr{B}'$ (2b); $H \cup H' = \bigcup \mathscr{B}''$. (2c).

Consequently H, H', and $H \cup H'$ have the form of H_n in (f); therefore:

$$\mathscr{M}(H) = \sum \mathscr{M}(B) \quad (\text{for all } B \in \mathscr{B}). \tag{3a}$$

$$\mathscr{M}(H') = \sum \mathscr{M}(B') \quad (\text{for all } B' \in \mathscr{B}'). \tag{3b}$$

$$\mathscr{M}(H \cup H') = \sum \mathscr{M}(B'') \quad (\text{for all } B'' \in \mathscr{B}''). \tag{3c}$$

If $B \in \mathscr{B}$, $B' \in \mathscr{B}'$, and $B'' \in \mathscr{B}''$, then by (1a), (1b), (1c) the following holds:

$$B \in \mathscr{B}^{(m)} \quad (4a); \qquad B' \in \mathscr{B}^{(m)} \quad (4b); \qquad B'' \in \mathscr{B}^{(m)} \quad (4c);$$

and

$$B \subset H \quad (5a); \qquad B' \subset H' \quad (5b); \qquad B'' \subset H \cup H'. \quad (5c).$$

We assumed:

$$H \text{ and } H' \text{ are disjoint.} \tag{6}$$

Hence, with (5a) and (5b), $B \neq B'$; therefore:

$$\mathscr{B} \text{ and } \mathscr{B}' \text{ are disjoint.} \tag{7}$$

By T3-4g, either $B'' \subset H$ or $B'' \subset -H$; and either $B'' \subset H'$ or $B'' \subset -H'$. Hence with (6): Either $B'' \subset H$ and $B'' \subset -H'$, or $B'' \subset H'$ and $B'' \subset -H$. Hence, with (4c), (1a), (1b), either $B'' \in \mathscr{B}$ or $B'' \in \mathscr{B}'$. Thus $B'' \in \mathscr{B} \cup \mathscr{B}'$, and:

$$\mathscr{B}'' \subset \mathscr{B} \cup \mathscr{B}'. \tag{8}$$

From (5a), $B \subset H \cup H'$. Hence, with (4a) and (1c), $B \in \mathscr{B}''$; thus $\mathscr{B} \subset \mathscr{B}''$. Similarly, with (5b), (4b), and (1c), $\mathscr{B}' \subset \mathscr{B}''$. Thus $\mathscr{B} \cup \mathscr{B}' \subset \mathscr{B}''$. Hence, with (8), $\mathscr{B}'' = \mathscr{B} \cup \mathscr{B}'$. Then the assertion follows from (7), (3a), (3b), (3c). ■

Proof for T6h. 1. If the s-sample of E_s is the initial s-sample, see (d).—2. Let the s-sample of E_s be a noninitial s-sample with index set D'_s. The highest index in D'_s is higher than s; let it be $s + m$ $(m > 0)$. Let $D_{s+m} = \mathbf{N}_{s+m}$, and $D_s = \mathbf{N}_s$. Let π be a permutation of D_{s+m}, that is, a mapping of D_{s+m} onto itself such that π maps D'_s onto D_s in an arbitrary way, and π maps the complement $D_{s+m} - D'_s$ in an arbitrary way onto $D_{s+m} - D_s$. Let $E''_s = \pi''(E_s)$. Then E''_s is an s.p. for the initial s-sample, with the same k-tuple $\mathbf{s}$ as E_s. Hence by D2c:

$$\mathscr{M}(E''_s) = \mathrm{MI}(\mathbf{s}). \tag{i}$$

To E_s, D2c is not applicable, but D2d is. This yields, by taking $\mathscr{B} = \mathscr{B}^{(s+m)}_{E_s}$:

$$\mathscr{M}(E_s) = \sum \mathscr{M}(B) \quad (\text{for all } B \in \mathscr{B}). \tag{ii}$$

These B's are those s.p.'s for D_{s+m} for which $B \subset E_s$; these are those that within D'_s agree with E_s and for the rest are arbitrary. Thus their number p is k^m (T10-4e); let them be $B_1, \ldots, B_p$. Thus from (ii):

$$\mathscr{M}(E_s) = \sum_{l=1}^{p} \mathscr{M}(B_l). \tag{iii}$$

For every l ($l = 1, \ldots, p$), let $B'_l = \pi''(B_l)$. Thus, for any l, B'_l is an s.p. for D_{s+m}, and is isomorphic to B_l. Hence by (d), for any l, $\mathscr{M}(B_l) = \mathscr{M}(B'_l)$. Therefore from (iii):

$$\mathscr{M}(E_s) = \sum_{l=1}^{p} \mathscr{M}(B'_l). \qquad \text{(iv)}$$

We have by (f), taking $\mathscr{B}'' = \mathscr{B}^{(s+m)}_{E''_s}$:

$$\mathscr{M}(E''_s) = \sum \mathscr{M}(B') \quad (\text{for all } B' \in \mathscr{B}''). \qquad \text{(v)}$$

In analogy to the above remark on (ii), the B' in $\mathscr{B}''$ are those s.p.'s for D_{s+m} which are subsets of E''_s; they are those that within D_s agree with E''_s and for the rest, which is an m-sample, represent all possible cases; thus their number is $p = k^m$. And indeed, these are the p s.p.'s B'_l ($l = 1, \ldots, p$) defined earlier. Thus we have from (v):

$$\mathscr{M}(E''_s) = \sum_{l=1}^{p} \mathscr{M}(B'_l),$$

$$= \mathscr{M}(E_s) \quad (\text{by (iv)}).$$

Hence with (i):

$$\mathscr{M}(E_s) = \text{MI}(\mathbf{s}). \quad \blacksquare$$

Proof for T6i. Let $H' = \pi''(H)$. The assertion is obvious if $H = \varnothing$, and hence $H' = \varnothing$; likewise if $H = \mathbf{Z}$, and hence $H' = \mathbf{Z}$. We assume now that H is a contingent proposition; then H' is likewise. Let $n, n', m, \mathscr{B}, \mathscr{B}'$ be defined as in the proof of T6g. Then the following items stated there hold here too: (1a), (1b), (2a), (2b), (3a), (3b); and, for any $B \in \mathscr{B}$ and $B' \in \mathscr{B}'$, we have (4a), (4b), (5a), (5b). Let φ be a permutation of $\mathbf{N}_m$ such that, for any i involved in H, $\varphi(i) = \pi(i)$, while for any other $i \leqq m$, $\varphi(i)$ is arbitrary. For any $B \in \mathscr{B}$, B is an s.p. for the initial m-sample. Therefore by (d), since $\varphi''(B)$ is isomorphic to B,

$$\mathscr{M}(\varphi''(B)) = \mathscr{M}(B).$$

Then we have:

$$H' = \pi''(H) = \varphi''(H) = \varphi''(\bigcup \mathscr{B}) = \bigcup \{\varphi''(B) : B \in \mathscr{B}\}.$$

Therefore

$$\mathscr{M}(H') = \sum \mathscr{M}(\varphi''(B)) \quad (\text{for all } B \in \mathscr{B}),$$

$$= \sum \mathscr{M}(B) \quad (\text{for all } B \in \mathscr{B}),$$

$$= \mathscr{M}(H). \quad \blacksquare$$

Proof for T6k. The assertion is obvious if $H = \mathbf{Z}$ and hence $\mathscr{M}(H) = 1$, by (b). We assume now that H is contingent. Let s be the highest individual index involved in H, and let $\mathscr{B}^{(s)}$ and $\mathscr{B} = \mathscr{B}^{(s)}_H$ be defined as in D3-6d and e. Then $\mathscr{M}(H) = \sum \mathscr{M}(B)$ (for all $B \in \mathscr{B}$) by T3-4i. $\mathscr{B}$ is nonempty. For any $B \in \mathscr{B}$, B has the form of $E'_{s,s}$ in (d), with $s > 0$. Hence by (d) and D3b, $\mathscr{M}(B) > 0$. Therefore $\mathscr{M}(E) > 0$. ■

This is the end of the proofs for T6.

B. MI-SEQUENCES

We have seen earlier that, if $\mathscr{M}$ is a symmetric $\mathscr{M}$-function, then its representative function MI is a symmetric MI-function (T5a) and the $\mathscr{M}$-function generated by this MI is $\mathscr{M}$ itself (T4). Thus there is a one-to-one correspondence between the class of all symmetric $\mathscr{M}$-functions and a subclass of the class of symmetric MI-functions. This subclass is the class of the representatives of symmetric $\mathscr{M}$-functions; it is the same as the class of those MI-functions that generate symmetric $\mathscr{M}$-functions. Now we see from T6j that this subclass is actually the class of *all* symmetric MI-functions. This is important because, if we wish to construct a symmetric $\mathscr{M}$-function for certain purposes, all we have to do is construct a suitable MI-function satisfying the mathematical conditions of D3a; we know then that it represents a symmetric $\mathscr{M}$-function.

Thus we have a one-to-one correspondence between all symmetric $\mathscr{M}$-functions and all symmetric MI-functions. Here the functions r and g are inverses of each other.

According to T6k, analogous results hold for the regular, symmetric $\mathscr{M}$-functions and the regular, symmetric MI-functions.

Let MI and $\mathscr{M}$ be as in T5. Then $\mathscr{M}$ is defined on $\mathscr{E}^{\text{mol}}$ for the language $\mathscr{L}_1$ containing the denumerable set $D = \mathbf{N}$ as its individual index set, but containing only one family F of attributes. Let $\mathscr{E}_1$ be the class of molecular propositions for $\mathscr{L}_1$. For any $n > 0$, let $\mathscr{L}_1^n$ be the sublanguage of $\mathscr{L}_1$ restricted to the individual index set $D_n = \mathbf{N}_n$; let $\mathscr{E}_1^n$ be the class of molecular propositions on $\mathscr{L}_1^n$. Then $\mathscr{L}_1^n$ is a sublanguage of the first kind of $\mathscr{L}_1$ (D6-1). Therefore we shall apply rule R6-1; hence the following holds:

T11-7. The function $\mathscr{C}'$ for the sublanguage $\mathscr{L}_1^n$ of $\mathscr{L}_1$ has, for any propositions in $\mathscr{L}_1^n$ the same value that $\mathscr{C}$ has for the corresponding propositions in $\mathscr{L}_1$. The analogous result holds for $\mathscr{M}'$ and $\mathscr{M}$.

We introduce a convenient notation:

D11-4. For any function MI, for any $s \geqq 0$, MI^s is the subfunction of MI restricted to ${}^0\mathbf{N}^{k,s}$.

If MI is a symmetric MI-function, then, by virtue of the sum condition (D3a(2)), the values of MI are uniquely determined if those of a suitable subfunction of MI are given. The following theorem shows this for a specified subfunction.

T11-8. Let MI be a symmetric MI-function. Let MI′ be the subfunction of MI restricted to those k-tuples $\langle s_1, \ldots, s_k\rangle$ in which $s_k = 0$. If the values of MI′ are given, all values of MI are determined by the following recursive formula (from the sum condition D3a(2)). For any **s** in ${}^0\mathbf{N}^{s,k}$,

$$\mathrm{MI}^{s+1}(\mathbf{s}^k) = \mathrm{MI}^s(\mathbf{s}) - \sum_{j=1}^{k-1} \mathrm{MI}^{s+1}(\mathbf{s}^j).$$

If all values of MI^s for $s = 0, \ldots, n$ and all values of MI^{n+1} for $s_k = 0, \ldots, m$ are known, the given rule determines the values of MI^{n+1} for $s_k = m + 1$.

If $k = 2$, MI′ is restricted for any s to the one pair $(s, 0)$.

The following theorem says that, since MI^s is determined by MI^{s+1}, it is also determined by MI^{s+m} with any m.

T11-9. Let MI be a symmetric MI-function. The following holds for any $s \geqq 0$, any $\mathbf{s} = \langle s_1, \ldots, s_k\rangle$ in ${}^0\mathbf{N}^{k,s}$, any $s' \geqq 0$, any $\mathbf{s}' = \langle s'_1, \ldots, s'_k\rangle$ in ${}^0\mathbf{N}^{k,s'}$. (We take: $\mathbf{s} + \mathbf{s}' =_{\mathrm{Df}} \langle s_1 + s'_1, \ldots, s_k + s'_k\rangle$.)

a. $\mathrm{MI}^0(\mathbf{s}_0) = 1$. (From D3a(1).)

b. $\mathrm{MI}^s(\mathbf{s}) = \sum_j \mathrm{MI}^{s+1}(\mathbf{s}^j)$. (From D3a(2).)

c. $\mathrm{MI}^s(\mathbf{s}) = \sum \left[\frac{s'!}{s'_1! \ldots s'_k!} \mathrm{MI}^{s+s'}(\mathbf{s} + \mathbf{s}')\right]$

(the sum ranges over all $\mathbf{s}' \in {}^0\mathbf{N}^{k,s'}$). (From (b), by mathematical induction with respect to s'. Note that for any s'-sample the number of s.p.'s with the given k-tuple $\mathbf{s}'$ is

$$\frac{s'!}{s'_1! \ldots s'_k!}.)$$

Let MI be a symmetric MI-function. Let $\mathscr{B} = \{\mathrm{MI}^0, \mathrm{MI}^1, \mathrm{MI}^2, \ldots\}$ be the sequence of all its subfunctions MI^n $(n = 0, 1, \ldots)$. It is clear that, if all values of all functions of $\mathscr{B}$ are given, then all values of MI are determined. The same holds if any infinite subsequence of $\mathscr{B}$ is given, say, $\mathscr{B}' = \mathrm{MI}^{n_1}, \mathrm{MI}^{n_2}, \ldots,$ with index set $I' \in {}^0\mathbf{N}$, since any function MI^n in $\mathscr{B} - \mathscr{B}'$ can be determined by a function

MI^{n_1} in $\mathscr{B}'$ with $n_i > n$, according to T9c. We say that MI and $\mathscr{B}$ correspond to each other; and, for a given index set I', MI and $\mathscr{B}'$ correspond to each other. Suppose that $\mathscr{M}$ is the symmetric $\mathscr{M}$-function generated by MI and hence MI is the representative MI-function of $\mathscr{M}$. Then we say that $\mathscr{M}$ is generated by $\mathscr{B}$ and by $\mathscr{B}'$, that $\mathscr{B}$ is the *complete representative MI-sequence* for the function $\mathscr{M}$; and, for any given *proper* subset I' of $^0\mathbf{N}$, that $\mathscr{B}'$ is *the incomplete representative* MI-*sequence with the index set* I' for $\mathscr{M}$.

Consider now a sequence $\mathscr{B} = \{\mathrm{MI}^0, \mathrm{MI}^1, \ldots\}$ with index set $^0\mathbf{N}$ such that the functions MI^n are not defined on the basis of a given symmetric MI, but each MI^n is an arbitrary real-valued function on $^0\mathbf{N}^{k,n}$. We call $\mathscr{B}$ a *complete symmetric* MI-*sequence* if-if (a) $\mathrm{MI}^0(\mathbf{s}_0) = 1$; (b) any two consecutive functions in $\mathscr{B}$ satisfy T9b; (c) any value of any function is nonnegative. An infinite sequence $\mathscr{B}' = \{\mathrm{MI}^{n_1}, \mathrm{MI}^{n_2}, \ldots\}$ is said to be an *incomplete symmetric* MI-*sequence* if-if there is a complete symmetric MI-sequence $\mathscr{B}$ that contains $\mathscr{B}'$ as a subsequence. This is the case if-if $\mathscr{B}'$ (or, if $\mathscr{B}'$ does not contain MI^0, the sequence $\mathscr{B}''$ formed from $\mathscr{B}'$ by adding MI^0) fulfills the above conditions (a) and (c), and further (b′): for any pair of consecutive functions (including MI^0, MI^{n_1} in $\mathscr{B}''$) the relation specified in T9c holds. If $\mathscr{B}'$ fulfills these conditions, then there is exactly one complete sequence $\mathscr{B}$ containing $\mathscr{B}'$.

It is easily seen that $\mathscr{B}$ (or $\mathscr{B}'$) is a representative MI-sequence of some symmetric $\mathscr{M}$-function if-if it is a symmetric MI-sequence. An MI-sequence is called *regular* if-if all values of all its functions are positive.

Thus we have a one-to-one correspondence between the class of symmetric $\mathscr{M}$-functions and the class of complete symmetric MI-sequences; and likewise, for any infinite $I' \subset {}^0\mathbf{N}$, a one-to-one correspondence between the former class and the class of incomplete symmetric MI-sequences with index set I'. The same holds for regular, symmetric $\mathscr{M}$-functions and regular, symmetric MI-sequences.

C. MS- AND MD-FUNCTIONS

We shall now introduce *a second representative function* MS (these letters have been chosen because this function represents the $\mathscr{M}$-values of *structures*). Its use is often convenient as an alternative to the use of MI.

D11-5. Let MI be a symmetric MI-function.

a. For any $\mathbf{s} = \langle s_1, \ldots, s_k \rangle$ in $^0\mathbf{N}^{k,s}$,

$$\mathrm{MS}(\mathbf{s}) =_{\mathrm{Df}} \frac{s!}{s_1! \ldots s_k!} \mathrm{MI}(\mathbf{s}).$$

b. For any $s \geqq 0$, MS^s is the subfunction of MS restricted to ${}^0\mathbf{N}^{k,s}$.

T11-10. Let $\mathcal{M}$ be a symmetric $\mathcal{M}$-function. Let MI be representative of $\mathcal{M}$. Let MS and MS^s be defined as in D5. For any $s \geqq 0$ and any $\mathbf{s}$ in ${}^0\mathbf{N}^{k,s}$, let $E_{s,\mathbf{s}}$ be an s.p. of any s-sample with k-tuple $\mathbf{s}$. Let $S_{s,\mathbf{s}}$ be the structure corresponding to $E_{s,\mathbf{s}}$, hence with the same k-tuple $\mathbf{s}$.

a. For any s, and any $\mathbf{s}$ in ${}^0\mathbf{N}^{k,s}$,

$$\mathrm{M}s^s(\mathbf{s}) = \frac{s_1! \ldots s_k!}{s!}\,\mathrm{MS}^s(\mathbf{s}).$$

b. $\mathrm{MS}^0(\mathbf{s}_0) = 1$.

c. $\mathrm{MS}(\mathbf{s}) \geqq 0$. (From D3a(3).)

d. *Sum theorem for MS.*

$$\mathrm{MS}^s(\mathbf{s}) = \sum_j \left[\frac{s_j + 1}{s + 1}\,\mathrm{MS}^{s+1}(\mathbf{s}^j)\right]. \quad \text{(From T1c.)}$$

e. $\mathcal{M}(S_{s,\mathbf{s}}) = \mathrm{MS}^s(\mathbf{s})$. (From T1e.)

f. $\sum_{\mathbf{s}} \mathrm{MS}^s(\mathbf{s}) = 1$ (the sum ranges over ${}^0\mathbf{N}^{k,s}$). (From (e) and T10-4d.)

g. $\mathcal{M}(E_{s,\mathbf{s}}) = \dfrac{s_1! \ldots s_k!}{s!}\,\mathrm{MS}^s(\mathbf{s})$. (From (a), T1a.)

h. For any $s' > 0$, any $\mathbf{s}' = \langle s_1', \ldots, s_k' \rangle$ in ${}^0\mathbf{N}^{k,s'}$,

$$\mathrm{MS}^s(\mathbf{s}) = \sum_{\mathbf{s}'} \frac{\binom{s_1 + s_1'}{s_1} \cdots \binom{s_k + s_k'}{s_k}}{\binom{s + s'}{s}}\,\mathrm{MS}^{s+s'}(\mathbf{s} + \mathbf{s}')$$

(the sum ranges over ${}^0\mathbf{N}^{k,s'}$; for $\mathbf{s} + \mathbf{s}'$, see T9). (From (a) and T9c.)

T10a shows that MI is determined by MS. T10e shows that the values of MS represent $\mathcal{M}$-values of structures. Thus MS could be introduced, independently of MI, as a representative function of $\mathcal{M}$, defined by $\mathcal{M}(S_{s,\mathbf{s}})$ for the initial s-sample (in analogy to D1).

If two functions MI and MS have the relation stated by D5a (and by T10a), we say that they *correspond to each other*. If $\mathcal{M}$ is a symmetric $\mathcal{M}$-function, and MI is representative of $\mathcal{M}$ (and hence $\mathcal{M}$ is generated by MI), and MS corresponds to MI, then we say that MS is *the representative* MS-*function of* $\mathcal{M}$, and that $\mathcal{M}$ is *the* $\mathcal{M}$-*function generated by* MS.

We define now in analogy to D3:

D11-6. Let MS be a real-valued function on ${}^0\mathbf{N}^{k,s}$.

a. MS is a *symmetric* MS-*function* $=_{\mathrm{Df}}$ MS satisfies the following three conditions:

(1) $\mathrm{MS}^0(\mathbf{s}_0) = 1$.

(2) *Sum condition.* For any $s \geqq 0$, and any k-tuple $\mathbf{s} = \langle s_1, \ldots, s_k \rangle$ in ${}^0\mathbf{N}^{k,s}$,

$$\mathrm{MS}^s(\mathbf{s}) = \sum_j \left[\frac{s_j + 1}{s + 1} \mathrm{MS}^{s+1}(\mathbf{s}^j) \right].$$

(3) For any $\mathbf{s}$ in ${}^0\mathbf{N}^{k,s}$, $\mathrm{MS}(\mathbf{s}) \geqq 0$.

b. MS is a *regular*, *symmetric* MS-*function* $=_{\mathrm{Df}}$ MS satisfies the above conditions (1) and (2), and, instead of (3), the following stronger condition: (3′) For any $\mathbf{s}$ in ${}^0\mathbf{N}^{k,s}$, $\mathrm{MS}(\mathbf{s}) > 0$.

T11-11. Let MI and MS be real-valued functions on ${}^0\mathbf{N}^{k,s}$, corresponding to each other. Let $\mathscr{M}$ be generated by MI, and hence also by MS.

a. MS is a symmetric MS-function if-if MI is a symmetric MI-function.

b. MS is a regular, symmetric MS-function if-if MI is a regular, symmetric MI-function.

c. MS is a symmetric MS-function if-if $\mathscr{M}$ is a symmetric $\mathscr{M}$-function.

d. MS is a regular, symmetric MS-function if-if $\mathscr{M}$ is a regular, symmetric $\mathscr{M}$-function.

T11c and d are analogous to, and based upon, the earlier theorems T5a, b and T6j, k on MI-functions.

Thus we have here a one-to-one correspondence between the class of all symmetric $\mathscr{M}$-functions and the class of all symmetric MS-functions. This correspondence consists in the one direction in the relation of MS being the representative MS-function of $\mathscr{M}$, and in the other direction in the relation of $\mathscr{M}$ being generated by MS, which is the converse of the former relation.

In analogy to T8 we have here:

T11-12. Let MS be a symmetric MS-function. Let MS′ be the subfunction of MS restricted to those k-tuples $\langle s_1, \ldots, s_k \rangle$ in which $s_k = 0$.

If the values of MS′ are given, all values of MS are determined by the following recursive formula (from D6a(2)): for any **s** in ${}^0\mathbf{N}^{k,s}$,

$$\mathrm{MS}^{s+1}(\mathbf{s}^k) = \frac{s+1}{s_k+1}\,\mathrm{MS}^s(\mathbf{s}) - \sum_{j=1}^{k-1}\left[\frac{s_j+1}{s_k+1}\,\mathrm{MS}^{s+1}(\mathbf{s}^j)\right].$$

In the case $k = 2$ (a family consisting of an attribute and its negation), the function MS′ is, for any s, restricted to the one pair $\langle s, 0\rangle$. (This special function MS′ is de Finetti's function ω_n; his $\omega_r^{(n)}$ corresponds to our $\mathrm{MS}^n(r, n-r)$ for $k = 2$. See his [1937, pp. 27 f.] (or translation [1964, pp. 121 f.]) and [1938, p. 8].)

Here we can define the concepts of *symmetric* MS-*sequences* and of *regular* symmetric MS-sequences, either complete $\{\mathrm{MS}^0, \mathrm{MS}^1, \ldots\}$, or incomplete $\{\mathrm{MS}^{n_1}, \mathrm{MS}^{n_2}, \ldots\}$. We shall not state the definitions here, since they are quite analogous to those for symmetric MI-sequences (with reference to T10d and h). Clearly a symmetric MS-sequence defined on the basis of $\mathcal{M}$ may be regarded as a *representative* MS-*sequence* for $\mathcal{M}$.

In the investigation of symmetric $\mathcal{M}$-functions it is very convenient to use, instead of the $\mathcal{M}$-functions themselves, their numerical representative functions. It is inessential which of the two alternative forms is used, the MI-functions or the MS-functions. As we have seen, they are closely related, and it is easy to switch from one form to the other. I have dealt with MI-functions in greater detail because I have found them useful (they have a simpler sum condition, a simpler relation to the $\mathcal{C}$-functions and their representative C-functions, and a simpler relation to the de Finetti integral). I shall frequently use MI-functions in later sections of this article and in later articles. Others, however, may well prefer the MS-functions.

D11-7. **a.** $\mathbf{Q} =_{\mathrm{Df}}$ the set of all rational numbers.

b. $\mathbf{Q}^p =_{\mathrm{Df}}$ the set of all p-tuples of rational numbers. We use '**t**' as a variable for p-tuples of rational or real numbers.

c. For any $n > 0$, $\mathbf{Q}_n =_{\mathrm{Df}} \{r\colon r \in \mathbf{Q}$; for some m $(0 \leqq m \leqq n)$, $r = m/n\}$; these are the rationals in [0, 1] equal to fractions with denominator n.

d. $\mathbf{Q}_0 =_{\mathrm{Df}} \{0\}$.

e. For any $n > 0$ and any $k > 1$, $\mathbf{Q}_{(n)}^{k-1} =_{\mathrm{Df}} \{\mathbf{t}\colon \mathbf{t} \in \mathbf{Q}^{k-1}$; $\mathbf{t} = \langle x_1, \ldots, x_{k-1}\rangle$, where, for every $j < k$, $x_j \in \mathbf{Q}_{(n)}$; and $\sum_{j=1}^{k-1} x_j \leqq 1\}$.

f. $\mathbf{R} =_{\mathrm{Df}}$ the set of real numbers.

g. $\mathbf{R}^k =_{\mathrm{Df}}$ the set of k-tuples of real numbers.

h. For any two k-tuples of real numbers,
(1) $\langle v_1, \ldots, v_k \rangle = \langle u_1, \ldots, u_k \rangle =_{\text{Df}}$ for every $j \leqq k$, $v_j = u_j$.
(2) $\langle v_1, \ldots, v_k \rangle < \langle u_1, \ldots, u_k \rangle =_{\text{Df}}$ for every $j \leqq k$, $v_j < u_j$. Similarly with $\leqq$.

We shall now define some random variables on the space **Z**. (See D3-7; the first two r.v.'s here are analogous to D3-9a and b; the Z's here correspond to the earlier B_p's; the subscript 'Z' takes the place of the earlier 'p' for B_p; in the practical application, we often omit this subscript.)

D11-8. **a.** The *truth-value* TV of a proposition H in the model Z:

$$\text{TV}_Z(H) =_{\text{Df}} \begin{cases} 1 & \text{if-if } H \text{ holds (or is true) in the model } Z, \\ & \text{i.e., } Z \in H; \\ 0 & \text{otherwise.} \end{cases}$$

b. Let $\mathscr{A} = \{A_1, A_2, \ldots\}$ be a countable sequence of propositions A_n (not necessarily independent of each other). The *truth-frequency* TF of $\mathscr{A}$ in Z: $\text{TF}_Z(\mathscr{A}) =_{\text{Df}} \sum_n \text{TV}_Z(A_n)$ (the sum ranges over the indexes of the propositions in $\mathscr{A}$). (Here, the improper number ∞ is admitted as a possible value of TF for a denumerable sequence.)

c. *The number* (absolute frequency) *of individuals with the attribute* P_j in the initial s-sample in Z:

$$s_{j,Z}^{(s)} =_{\text{Df}} \text{TF}_Z(\{P_j a_i : 0 < i \leqq s\}).$$

d. $\mathbf{s}_Z^{(s)} =_{\text{Df}} \langle s_{1,Z}^{(s)}, s_{2,Z}^{(s)}, \ldots, s_{k,Z}^{(s)} \rangle$ in ${}^0\mathbf{N}^{k,s}$.

e. The relative frequency of the attribute P_j in the initial s-sample in Z:

$$r_{j,Z}^{(s)} =_{\text{Df}} s_{j,Z}^{(s)}/s.$$

f. The limit of the relative frequency of P_j in Z: $R_{j,Z} =_{\text{Df}} \lim_{s \to \infty} r_{j,Z}^{(s)}$.

g. The absolute frequency of P_j in Z:

$$N_{j,Z} =_{\text{Df}} \text{TF}_Z(\{P_j a_i : i \in \mathbf{N}\}).$$

(Here, as in (b), ∞ is admitted.)

h. (In analogy to (3-7b), but here on $\mathbf{Z}$. For any $s > 0$ and any

$$\mathbf{s}_Z^{(s)} = \langle s_{1,Z}^{(s)}, s_{2,Z}^{(s)}, \ldots, s_{k,Z}^{(s)} \rangle,$$

$$\mathbf{t}_{s,Z}^{(s)} =_{\mathrm{Df}} \langle r_{1,Z}^{(s)}, r_{2,Z}^{(s)}, \ldots, r_{k-1,Z}^{(s)} \rangle$$

in $\mathbf{Q}_{(s)}^{k-1}$.

i. (Analogous to (3-7c)). $\mathbf{t}_0 =_{\mathrm{Df}} \langle 0, \ldots, 0 \rangle$ in $\mathbf{Q}_0^{k-1}$.

I shall now introduce and briefly discuss three other kinds of functions. Although the functions of the first and the second kind could be used as representative functions in their own right, we shall not do so. Our main purpose for their introduction is their use as steps toward the third kind, the MD^∞-functions. These functions will be of importance later, in connection with the de Finetti representation theorem; this will be explained in Art. **3** by Richard Jeffrey.

D11-9. Let MS be a symmetric MS-function. (We will write '$r_j^{(s)}$' or simply 'r_j' for '$r_{j,Z}^{(s)}$'.)

a. For any $s \geqq 0$, for any $(k-1)$-tuple

$$\langle r_1^{(s)}, \ldots, r_{k-1}^{(s)} \rangle \text{ in } \mathbf{Q}_{(s)}^{k-1},$$

$\mathrm{MS}_{\mathrm{rf}}^s(r_1, \ldots, r_{k-1}) =_{\mathrm{Df}} \mathrm{MS}^s(sr_1, \ldots, sr_{k-1}, sr_k)$. (Here each argument sr_j is an integer (s_j), since $r_j \in \mathbf{Q}_{(s)}$. For r_k, see below.)

b. For any $s \geqq 0$, for any $(k-1)$-tuple $\langle u_1, \ldots, u_{k-1} \rangle$ in $\mathbf{R}^{k-1}$,

$$\mathrm{MD}^s(u_1, \ldots, u_{k-1}) =_{\mathrm{Df}} \sum \mathrm{MS}_{\mathrm{rf}}^s(r_1, \ldots, r_{k-1}),$$

where the sum ranges over the $(k-1)$-tuples $\langle r_1, \ldots, r_{k-1} \rangle$ in $\mathbf{Q}_{(s)}^{k-1}$ such that $\langle r_1, \ldots, r_{k-1} \rangle \leqq \langle u_1, \ldots, u_{k-1} \rangle$.

c. $\mathrm{MD}^\infty(u_1, \ldots, u_{k-1}) =_{\mathrm{Df}} \lim_{s \to \infty} \mathrm{MD}^s(u_1, \ldots, u_{k-1})$, provided that the limit exists.

$\mathrm{MS}_{\mathrm{rf}}^s$ differs from MS^s by taking as arguments the relative frequencies (therefore "rf") $r_j = s_j/s$ instead of the absolute frequencies s_j. MD^s is the *distribution function* (therefore "D") corresponding to $\mathrm{MS}_{\mathrm{rf}}^s$; see D3-8. MD^∞ is an important concept; it is the special form for language $\mathscr{L}_1$ of the distribution function Φ occurring in de Finetti's representation theorem. This concept will not be used in the present article. De Finetti ([1937] or translation [1964], chap. iii) has shown (for $k = 2$) that the limit does always exist and that the limit function MD^∞ is itself a distribution function. MD^∞ may alternatively be defined as follows: $MD^{\infty}(u_1, \ldots, u_{k-1})$ is the value $\mathscr{M}(A)$ for the proposition $A = \{Z\colon \text{for every } j \leqq k,\ R_{j,Z} \leqq u_j\}$.

Note that, for any given s, we have only $k - 1$ degrees of freedom for the arguments of MI^s, MS^s, MS^s_{rf}, because of the restricting conditions:

$$(1)\ \sum_j s_j = s;$$

$$(2)\ (\text{for } s > 0) \sum_j r_j = 1.$$

Thus the functions mentioned are essentially functions of $k - 1$ arguments, in contradistinction to MI and MS. It does not matter whether the functions are written with k or with $k - 1$ arguments. I have written MS^s and MI^s with k arguments, to make them similar to MS and MI, respectively, but MS^s_{rf}, MD^s, and MD^{∞} with $k - 1$ arguments. This seems convenient in the case of MD^s and MD^{∞}, because we have to apply to these functions the rules for $(k - 1)$-dimensional distribution functions, and to MD^{∞} a $(k - 1)$-fold integral. In contexts where we have the argument expression "$(r_1, \ldots, r_{k-1})$", we sometimes still use "r_k" or "s_k" (e.g., in the definitions of D9a); these symbols are then to be understood as defined in this way:

$$(3)\ s_k =_{Df} s - (s_1 + \ldots + s_{k-1}),$$

$$(4)\ r_k =_{Df} 1 - (r_1 + \ldots + r_{k-1}).$$

For the functions defined in D9, we have the following theorems, analogous to and derived from T10.

T11-13. Let $\mathscr{M}$, MS, MS^s, $E_{s,s}$ and $S_{s,s}$ be as in T10. Let MS^s_{rf}, MD^s, and MD^{∞} be defined as in D9.

a. $MS^0_{rf}(\mathbf{t}_0) = 1$.
b. $MS^s_{rf}(\mathbf{t}_s) \geq 0$.
c. If MS is, moreover, regular, then $MS^s_{rf}(\mathbf{t}_j) > 0$.
d. If the function MS^s_{rf} is given, MS^s is uniquely determined.
e. If MS^{s+1}_{rf} is given, then MS^s_{rf} is determined.
f. For any $m > 0$, if MS^{s+m}_{rf} is given, MS^s_{rf} is determined.
g. For any $s \geqq 0$, MD^s is a discrete $(k - 1)$-dimensional distribution function. It has jumps at some or all $(k - 1)$-tuples in $\mathbf{Q}^{k-1}_{(s)}$, and is level elsewhere. For any $(k - 1)$-tuple $\mathbf{t} = \langle u_1, \ldots, u_{k-1}\rangle$ in $\mathbf{R}^{k-1}$, the following holds:
(1) If some $u_j < 0$, $MD^s(\mathbf{t}) = 0$.
(2) For each of the $k - 1$ arguments, MD^s is continuous on the right.
(3) If every $u_j \geqq 1$, $MD^s(\mathbf{t}) = 1$.
h. For $s = 0$, MD^0 has exactly one jump from 0 to 1 at $\mathbf{t}^*_0$.
i. If the function MD^{s+m} $(m > 0)$ is given, MD^s is determined.

Suppose that a complete symmetric MS-sequence $\mathscr{B}_S = \{MS^0, MS^1, \ldots\}$ is given, and that the corresponding sequence $\mathscr{B}_{rf} = \{MS^0_{rf}, MS^1_{rf}, \ldots\}$ is defined by D9a. Then we say that $\mathscr{B}_{rf}$ is a complete *symmetric* MS_{rf}*-sequence*. Inversely, if $\mathscr{B}_{rf}$ is given, we can determine $\mathscr{B}_S$ (T13d), and hence MS, MI, and finally $\mathscr{M}$. From $\mathscr{B}_{rf}$ we can further determine the corresponding sequence $\mathscr{B}_D = \{MD^0, MD^1, \ldots\}$ by D9b; we call $\mathscr{B}_D$ a complete *symmetric* MD-*sequence*. Inversely, $\mathscr{B}_{rf}$ is determined by $\mathscr{B}_D$. Finally, from $\mathscr{B}_D$ we can define the function MD^∞ by D9c. As with MI-sequences and MS-sequences, we can also reconstruct $\mathscr{B}_{rf}$ from an infinite subsequence of it (T13e and f); and similarly with $\mathscr{B}_D$ (T13i). Thus we have a one-to-one correspondence between the class of all symmetric $\mathscr{M}$-functions and the class of all symmetric MS_{rf}-sequences, and further the class of all symmetric MD-sequences. Therefore sequences of these two kinds may be taken as *representative sequences* for symmetric $\mathscr{M}$-functions. The conditions of regularity for sequences of these kinds can likewise be stated easily.

If the function MD^∞ is given, the corresponding function MI can be determined directly (i.e., without using the long way back through $\mathscr{B}_D$, $\mathscr{B}_{rf}$, $\mathscr{B}_S$, and MS) with the help of de Finetti's integral. Moreover, de Finetti's theorem shows that any function Φ that, like MD^∞, satisfies the criterion of a distribution function, even if, unlike MD^∞, it had not been derived from a symmetric $\mathscr{M}$, is the representative function of a symmetric $\mathscr{M}$-function.

The representative functions, e.g., MI or MS, are especially useful in situations of the following kind. Suppose that we are looking for an inductive method, say, an $\mathscr{M}$-function, suitable for a given language form; we intend it to be symmetric and, moreover, to fulfill some additional requirements, depending on the language. Often the given requirements leave still some range of choice; in this case we wish to choose among the possible $\mathscr{M}$-functions one that is as simple as possible or, since we usually do not have an exact criterion of simplicity, at least one that is not clearly less simple than a known possible $\mathscr{M}$-function. To tackle a problem of this kind, and specifically, the task of determining either the class of all possible functions or at least some possible functions, and then to choose one of them, is considerably simpler if we focus our attention, not on the set function $\mathscr{M}$ itself, but on a numerical representative function for $\mathscr{M}$, say, MI or MS.

There is an essential difference in the problem situation, depending upon whether the language in question is finite or infinite. The problem is simple if we are concerned with a finite sublanguage $\mathscr{L}'$ of $\mathscr{L}_1$, restricted to an individual domain Ind_N of finite size N with the index set $\mathbf{N}_N$ (see §10). The number of structures for the total domain Ind_N

is $\tau = \binom{N+k-1}{N}$. Each of these τ structures has one of the τ k-tuples in ${}^0\mathbf{N}^{k,N}$. Here it is simple to specify the totality of possible symmetric $\mathscr{M}$-functions. Any arbitrary assignment of nonnegative real numbers $u_1, \ldots, u_\tau$, whose sum is 1, as values of $\mathrm{MS}^N(\mathbf{s})$ for the τ k-tuples $\mathbf{s}$ determines the function MS^N completely. Thereby MS^s for any s in ${}^0\mathbf{N}_N$ is determined; hence likewise MS itself for $\mathscr{L}'$, and thus $\mathscr{M}$ for all propositions $\mathscr{E}'$ in $\mathscr{L}'$ (T10-9). But here we must make sure that $\mathscr{M}$ fulfills the requirement of extensibility (see rule R6-2).

We shall, however, be interested mostly in a language like $\mathscr{L}_1$ itself, with a denumerable domain of individuals. Here MS is not determined by any MS^N, no matter how high an N we take. MS^N determines MS^s only if $s < N$; not if $s > N$, although in this case MS^N imposes some restrictions on MS^s (through the sum condition D3a(2)). The obstacle lies in the fact that for $\mathscr{L}_1$, in contrast with the finite language $\mathscr{L}'$, there is no maximum N and hence no highest function of the kind MS^N, nor of the kind $\mathrm{MS}^N_{\mathrm{rf}}$. If, however, we go over to the distribution functions, then, although there is no highest function MD^N in the MD-sequence, we have nevertheless the limit function MD^∞, which is in a sense the highest distribution function for $\mathscr{L}_1$. In analogy to the fact that MS^N or MD^N is sufficient for the determination of $\mathscr{M}$-values for all propositions in $\mathscr{L}'$, one might conjecture that MD^∞ may determine all $\mathscr{M}$-values for $\mathscr{L}_1$. According to the de Finetti representation theorem, this is indeed the case.

12
Representative Functions for $\mathscr{C}$

We have introduced several numerical functions as representative functions for symmetric $\mathscr{M}$-functions. Now we shall introduce a class of numerical functions as representatives for symmetric $\mathscr{C}$-functions. The following definition is analogous to D11-1.

D12-1. Let $\mathscr{C}$ be any real-valued function on $\mathscr{E}^{\text{mol}} \times (\mathscr{E}^{\text{mol}} - \{\varnothing\})$ for language $\mathscr{L}_1$. The k functions $C_1, \ldots, C_k$ are called *the representative C_j-functions* for $\mathscr{C}$, and the function C is called *the representative C-function* for $\mathscr{C}$, if-if they are defined as follows.

- **a.** For any j in $\mathbf{N}_k$, and any $\mathbf{s}$ in ${}^0\mathbf{N}^{k,s}$, $C_j(\mathbf{s}) =_{\text{Df}} \mathscr{C}(H_j' \mid E^*_{s,\mathbf{s}})$, where $E^*_{s,\mathbf{s}}$ is defined as in D11-1, and H_j' is the atomic proposition $P_j a_{s+1}$.
- **b.** $C(\mathbf{s}) =_{\text{Df}} \langle u_1, \ldots, u_k \rangle$, where $u_1 = C_1(\mathbf{s}), \ldots, u_k = C_k(\mathbf{s})$.
- **c.** For any $s \geqq 0$, for any j in $\mathbf{N}_k$, C_j^s is the subfunction of C_j, and C^s is that of C, both restricted to ${}^0\mathbf{N}^{k,s}$.

The function C with values in $\mathbf{R}^k$ is introduced merely for the formal convenience of representing $\mathscr{C}$ by one function instead of by the k functions C_j $(j = 1, \ldots, k)$.

Suppose that C is representative for $\mathscr{C}$, and C' for $\mathscr{C}'$. It is clear from the definition that, if C and C' are distinct, $\mathscr{C}$ and $\mathscr{C}'$ are distinct. The inverse does not generally hold.

The following definition is analogous to D1-11.

D12-2. Let MI and each of the functions C_j $(j = 1, \ldots, k)$ be a real-valued function on ${}^0\mathbf{N}^{k,s}$, and let C be the corresponding function on ${}^0\mathbf{N}^{k,s}$ with values in $\mathbf{R}^k$. Let MI^s be defined as in D11-4 and C_j^s as in D1c. MI and C (or the class $\{C_1, \ldots, C_k\}$) are **related** to each other $=_{\text{Df}}$ for any $s \geqq 0$, any $\mathbf{s}$ in ${}^0\mathbf{N}^{k,s}$, and any j in $\mathbf{N}_k$,

$$\text{MI}^{s+1}(\mathbf{s}^j) = \text{MI}^s(\mathbf{s})C_j^s(\mathbf{s}).$$

T12-1. Let $\mathscr{C}$ be a symmetric $\mathscr{C}$-function for $\mathscr{E}^{\text{mol}}$ in $\mathscr{L}_1$. Let $\mathscr{M}$ be related to $\mathscr{C}$ (D1-11), hence also symmetric. Let C be defined as representative of $\mathscr{C}$ (D1), and MI as representative of $\mathscr{M}$ (D11-1). Let Z' be a submodel for the initial s-sample (with index set $\mathbf{N}$), with the k-tuple $\mathbf{s}_{(s)} = \langle s_1, \ldots, s_k \rangle$ in ${}^0\mathbf{N}^{k,s}$. For any $n \leqq s$, let $Z'_{(n)}$ be the submodel of Z' restricted to $\mathbf{N}_n$ (the initial n-sample); let $\mathbf{s}_{(n)}$ be the k-tuple of $Z'_{(n)}$. Let E_s' be the s.p. corresponding to Z' (D10-2a), and let E_n' be the s.p. corresponding to $Z'_{(n)}$; let $E_0' = \mathbf{Z}$, and $\mathbf{s}_{(0)} = \mathbf{s}_0$. For any

$i \in \mathbf{N}_s$, let A_i be the atomic proposition $P_j a_i$ with $j = Z'(i)$. (Thus $E'_s = \bigcap_{i=1}^{s} A_i$, and $E'_n = \bigcap_{i=1}^{n} A_i$.) For any j, let H'_j be the atomic proposition $P_j a_{s+1}$. Let E_s be an s.p. for any arbitrary s-sample with the same k-tuple $\mathbf{s}_{(s)}$ as E'_s. For any j, let H_j be an atomic proposition $P_j a_{i'}$, with an i' not involved in E_s.

+a. For any $\mathbf{s}$ in $\mathbf{N}^k$,

(1) if $C(\mathbf{s}) = \langle u_1, \ldots, u_k \rangle$, then $\sum_j u_j = 1$;

(2) $\sum_j C_j(\mathbf{s}) = 1$. (From T10-3e.)

+b. $\mathscr{C}(H_j \mid E_s) = C_j(\mathbf{s}_{(s)})$. (From D1, since $\mathscr{C}$ is symmetric.)

c. For any n in $\mathbf{N}_s$, $\mathscr{C}(A_n \mid E'_{n-1}) = C_j(\mathbf{s}_{(n-1)})$ with $j = Z'(n)$.

d. For any j, $\mathscr{M}(E_s \cap H_j) = \mathscr{M}(E_s)\mathscr{C}(H_j \mid E_s)$. (From D1-11.)

+e. For any $s \geqq 0$, any $\mathbf{s}$ in ${}^0\mathbf{N}^{k,s}$, and any j in $\mathbf{N}_k$, $\mathrm{MI}^{s+1}(\mathbf{s}^j) = \mathrm{MI}^s(\mathbf{s})C_j^s(\mathbf{s})$. (From (d) and (b).) Thus MI and C are related to each other.

f. For any n in $\mathbf{N}_s$,

$$\mathscr{M}(E'_n) = \mathscr{M}(E'_{n-1} \cap A_n) = \mathscr{M}(E'_{n-1})\mathscr{C}(A_n \mid E'_{n-1}).$$

(From D1-11.)

g. $\mathscr{M}(E'_s) = \prod_{n=1}^{s} \mathscr{C}(A_n \mid E'_{n-1})$. (From (f), by mathematical induction with respect to n.)

+h. $\mathscr{M}(E'_s) = \mathrm{MI}(\mathbf{s}_{(s)}) = \prod_{n=1}^{s} C_{j_n}^{n-1}(\mathbf{s}_{(n-1)})$, where $j_n = Z'(n)$. (From (e), (c), and T11-1a.)

+i. *Product theorem.* For any $s \geqq 0$, any $\mathbf{s}$ in ${}^0\mathbf{N}^{k,s}$, and any j and l in $\mathbf{N}_k$,

$$C_j^s(\mathbf{s})C_l^{s+1}(\mathbf{s}^k) = C_l^s(\mathbf{s})C_j^{s+1}(\mathbf{s}^l).$$

Proof. Let H''_l be an atomic proposition $P_l a_i$ with an index i not involved in E_s or in H_j. Then, by the multiplication axiom A4 (in §1B):

$$\mathscr{C}(H_j \cap H''_l \mid E_s) = \mathscr{C}(H_j \mid E_s)\mathscr{C}(H''_l \mid E_s \cap H_j)$$
$$= \mathscr{C}(H''_l \cap H_j \mid E_s) = \mathscr{C}(H''_l \mid E_s)\mathscr{C}(H_j \mid E_s \cap H''_l).$$

Hence the assertion with (b). ■

+j. For any s, $\mathbf{s}$, j, if $\mathrm{MI}(\mathbf{s}) > 0$, thus in particular if $\mathscr{M}$ (and hence MI) is regular,

$$C_j^s(\mathbf{s}) = \frac{\mathrm{MI}^{s+1}(\mathbf{s}^j)}{\mathrm{MI}^s(\mathbf{s})}. \quad \text{(From (e).)}$$

+k. *Quotient theorem.* For any s, **s**, j, l, if both $C_j^s(\mathbf{s})$ and $C_l^s(\mathbf{s})$ are positive, thus in particular if $\mathscr{C}$ is regular,

$$\frac{C_l^{s+1}(\mathbf{s}^j)}{C_l^s(\mathbf{s})} = \frac{C_j^{s+1}(\mathbf{s}^l)}{C_j^s(\mathbf{s})}. \quad \text{(From (i).)}$$

l. For any s, **s**, j, l, if both $C_j^s(\mathbf{s})$ and $C_j^{s+1}(\mathbf{s}^l)$ are positive, thus in particular if $\mathscr{C}$ is regular,

$$\frac{C_l^{s+1}(\mathbf{s}^j)}{C_j^{s+1}(\mathbf{s}^l)} = \frac{C_l^s(\mathbf{s})}{C_j^s(\mathbf{s})}. \quad \text{(From (i).)}$$

T1h shows that, if the C_j-functions are given, MI can be defined. The inverse is in general not possible; but it is possible in the case of regular functions, as we see from T1j.

In D1 we introduced C as a representative function for a given $\mathscr{C}$. Now we shall define a class of C-functions merely by certain arithmetical conditions, without any reference to $\mathscr{C}$-functions. Thus this definition is similar in nature to the earlier definition of symmetric MI-functions (D11-3).

D12-3. Let C be a function on ${}^0\mathbf{N}^k$ with values in $\mathbf{R}^k$. For any j in $\mathbf{N}_k$, let C_j be the jth component function of C (i.e., if $C(\mathbf{s}) = \langle u_1, \ldots, u_k \rangle$, $C_j(\mathbf{s}) = u_j$). For any $s \geqq 0$, let C^s be the subfunction of C and C_j^s that of C_j, both restricted to ${}^0\mathbf{N}^{k,s}$.

a. C is a *symmetric C-function* and $C_1, \ldots, C_k$ are *symmetric C_j-functions* $=_{\text{Df}}$ the following three conditions are satisfied for any $s \geqq 0$ and any **s** in ${}^0\mathbf{N}^{k,s}$:

(1) *Sum condition.* $\sum_j C_j^s(\mathbf{s}) = 1$.

(2) *Product condition.* For any j and l in $\mathbf{N}_k$,

$$C_j^s(\mathbf{s})C_l^{s+1}(\mathbf{s}^j) = C_l^s(\mathbf{s})C_j^{s+1}(\mathbf{s}^l).$$

(3) For any j, $C_j^s(\mathbf{s}) \geqq 0$.

b. C is a *regular*, *symmetric C-function* and $C_1, \ldots, C_k$ are *regular*, *symmetric C_i-functions* $=_{\text{Df}}$ the above conditions (1) and (2) are satisfied, and, instead of (3), the following stronger condition: (3′) For any j, $C_j(\mathbf{s}) > 0$. In view of (3′), we can take here as an alternative of (2) either of the following two forms of the *quotient condition*. For any j and l in $\mathbf{N}_k$,

(2′)
$$\frac{C_l^{s+1}(\mathbf{s}^j)}{C_j^{s+1}(\mathbf{s}^l)} = \frac{C_l^s(\mathbf{s})}{C_j^s(\mathbf{s})};$$

or:

(2″)
$$\frac{C_l^{s+1}(\mathbf{s}^j)}{C_l^s(\mathbf{s})} = \frac{C_j^{s+1}(\mathbf{s}^l)}{C_j^s(\mathbf{s})}.$$

The following theorem shows that the conditions in D3a are indeed necessary for C being representative of a symmetric $\mathcal{C}$.

T12-2. Let $\mathcal{C}$ be a symmetric $\mathcal{C}$-function and C be the representative C-function of $\mathcal{C}$.

a. C is a symmetric C-function. (From D3a, T1a(2) and i.)

b. If $\mathcal{C}$ is moreover regular, then C is a regular, symmetric C-function.

The following theorems state some relations between symmetric C-functions and symmetric **MI**-functions.

T12-3. Let C be a symmetric C-function. Let MI be a real-valued function on ${}^0\mathbf{N}^k$ defined on the basis of C as follows (it is not assumed that MI is symmetric):

(1) For $s = 0$, $\mathrm{MI}^0(\mathbf{s}_0) =_{\mathrm{Df}} 1$.

(2) For any $s > 0$, for any $\mathbf{s}$ in ${}^0\mathbf{N}^{k,s}$,

$$\mathrm{MI}^s(\mathbf{s}) =_{\mathrm{Df}} \prod_{n=1}^{s} C_{j'}^{n-1}(\mathbf{s}_{(n-1)}),$$

where $j' = Z'_{\mathbf{s}}(n)$.

This is the same product as in T1h (we shall write here simply '$\prod$' for it), where $Z'_{\mathbf{s}}$ is defined as in D1, $Z'_{(n)}$ is the submodel of $Z'_{\mathbf{s}}$ restricted to $\mathbf{N}_n$, and $\mathbf{s}_{(n)}$ is the k-tuple of $Z'_{(n)}$.

a. Let π be any permutation for $\mathbf{N}_s$. Let $Z'' = \pi'(Z'_{\mathbf{s}})$ (thus for any i in $\mathbf{N}_s$, $Z'_{\mathbf{s}}(i) = Z''(\pi(i))$). For every n in $\mathbf{N}_s$, let $Z''_{(n)}$ be the submodel of Z'' restricted to $\mathbf{N}_n$; let $\mathbf{s}''_{(n)}$ be the k-tuple of $Z''_{(n)}$; let $\mathbf{s}''_{(0)} = \mathbf{s}_0$. Let

$$\prod{}'' = \prod_{n=1}^{s} C_{j_n}^{n-1}(\mathbf{s}''_{(n-1)}),$$

where $j_n = Z''(n)$. Then $\prod = \prod''$.

Proof. 1. Let π be merely a transposition of two consecutive indexes, i.e., for some p $(0 < p < s)$ $\pi(p) = p + 1$, and $\pi(p + 1) = p$, and for any i distinct from p and $p + 1$, $\pi(i) = i$. Then $Z''(p) = Z'(p + 1)$; let this be l. And $Z''(p + 1) = Z'(p)$; let this be l'. We have $\mathbf{s}_{(p-1)} = \mathbf{s}''_{(p-1)}$; let this be $\mathbf{s}'$. Let X_n be the nth factor in $\prod$, and X''_n that in $\prod''$. Except for $n = p$ and $n = p + 1$, $X_n = X''_n$. We have:

$$X_p X_{p+1} = C_{l'}^{p-1}(\mathbf{s}') C_l^p(\mathbf{s}'^{l'});$$

$$X''_p X''_{p+1} = C_l^{p-1}(\mathbf{s}') C_{l'}^p(\mathbf{s}'^{l}).$$

But these two products are equal by the product condition (D3a(2)). Therefore $\prod = \prod''$.—2. From this result, the assertion for an arbitrary permutation follows, since any finite permutation is equivalent to a series of transpositions of consecutive elements (T9-2a). ■

+b. C and MI are related to each other.

Proof. Let $Z'_{\mathbf{s},j}$ be defined on the basis of $\mathbf{s}^j$ as $Z'_{\mathbf{s}}$ is defined in D1 on the basis of **s**. Let Z'' be an extension of $Z'_{\mathbf{s}}$ to $\mathbf{N}_{s+1}$, with $Z''(s+1) = j$. Then Z'' has likewise the k-tuple $\mathbf{s}^j$ and thus is isomorphic to $Z'_{\mathbf{s},j}$. From (2):

$$\mathrm{MI}^{s+1}(\mathbf{s}^j) = \prod_{n=1}^{s+1} C^{n-1}_{j'}(\mathbf{s}_{(n-1)}), \quad \text{where} \quad j' = Z'_{\mathbf{s},j}(n);$$

Hence with (a):

$$= \prod_{n=1}^{s+1} C^{n-1}_{j''}(\mathbf{s}_{(n-1)}), \quad \text{where} \quad j'' = Z''_s(n);$$

$$= \prod_{n-1}^{s} C^{n-1}_{j''}(\mathbf{s}_{(n-1)}) C^s_j(\mathbf{s}).$$

Since Z'' is an extension of $Z'_{\mathbf{s}}$, the last product $= \prod = \mathrm{MI}^s(\mathbf{s})$. Hence:

(3) $\mathrm{MI}^{s+1}(\mathbf{s}^j) = \mathrm{MI}^s(\mathbf{s}) C^s_j(\mathbf{s})$. Thus the condition of D2 is satisfied for $s > 0$. It is easily seen that it holds also when $s = 0$. ■

c. For any $s \geqq 0$, and any **s** in ${}^0\mathbf{N}^{k,s}$,

$$\mathrm{MI}^s(\mathbf{s}) = \sum_j \mathrm{MI}^{s+1}(\mathbf{s}^j).$$

Proof. From (3) (in the preceding proof):

$$\sum_j \mathrm{MI}^{s+1}(\mathbf{s}^j) = \mathrm{MI}^s(\mathbf{s}) \sum_j C^s_j(\mathbf{s}).$$

Hence the assertion by D3a(1). ■

+d. MI is a symmetric MI-function.

Proof. Of the three conditions in D11-3a, (1) follows from (1) in T3; (2) from (c); (3) from (1) and (2) in T3 and D3a(3). ■

e. If C is a regular, symmetric C-function, then MI is a regular symmetric MI-function. (From D3b(3′), D11-3b(3′).)

T12-4. Let C and MI be symmetric and related to each other.

a. C and MI satisfy the conditions (1) and (2) in T3.

Proof. 1. (1) by D11-3a(1).—2. By D2, for any s, $\mathbf{s}$, j, $\mathrm{MI}^{s+1}(\mathbf{s}^j) = \mathrm{MI}^s(\mathbf{s})C_j^s(\mathbf{s})$. Let $Z_\mathbf{s}'$ (with the k-tuple $\mathbf{s}$) and $\mathbf{s}_{(n)}$ be as in T3. Then, for any n in $\mathbf{N}_s$, with $Z_\mathbf{s}'(n)$ for j': $\mathrm{MI}^n(\mathbf{s}_{(n)}^{j'}) = \mathrm{MI}^{n-1}(\mathbf{s}_{(n-1)})C_{j'}^{n-1}(\mathbf{s}_{(n-1)})$. Hence, with (1), by mathematical induction with respect to n, condition (2) follows. ■

b. If C is regular, MI is regular. (From (a) and T3e.)

c. If MI is regular, C is regular. (By D2.)

d. If MI is given and is regular, C is uniquely determined by MI as follows. For any s, $\mathbf{s}$, and j,

$$C_j^s(\mathbf{s}) = \frac{\mathrm{MI}^{s+1}(\mathbf{s}^j)}{\mathrm{MI}^s(\mathbf{s})}. \quad \text{(From D2.)}$$

From now on we shall usually apply the procedure of *forming representative C-functions (D1) only to those 𝒞-functions that are* not only symmetric but also *regular*. And among symmetric C-functions (defined in D3 without reference to 𝒞-functions) we shall mostly restrict our attention to the regular ones. The reason for this restriction lies in the following fact. If 𝒞 is a symmetric, but nonregular 𝒞-function, then there is still a unique symmetric function C, determined from 𝒞 by D1. In this case, however, there may be a function 𝒞′ distinct from 𝒞, such that the procedure of D1 when applied to 𝒞′ leads to the same function C. If this happens, then it is obviously impossible to reconstruct 𝒞 from C; thus in this case C is not genuinely representative of 𝒞. It is for this reason that we have so far not given a definition of the concept "the 𝒞-function generated by a given symmetric C", in analogy to D11-2. We shall soon do so, but only for regular, symmetric C-functions. From our point of view the restriction is not serious, because we have accepted the axiom of regularity (A5 in §7); and for good reasons, because a nonregular 𝒞-function is not strictly coherent (T8-6).

[A few remarks about *nonregular 𝒞-functions:* It seems that for certain kinds of these functions, a unique reconstruction from the representative function is possible. This holds, for example, for the 𝒞-function ${}^0\mathscr{C}$ characterized by the parameter value $\lambda = 0$ in the λ-system (in Part II). This is perhaps the most interesting among the nonregular 𝒞-functions. The values of its C-functions for $s > 0$ are $C_j^s(\mathbf{s}) = s_j/s$, which is the relative frequency in the observed sample. The estimate function corresponding to ${}^0\mathscr{C}$ gives as the estimate (expectation value) of the relative frequency of the attribute P_j in any future sample of any size likewise s_j/s (the "straight rule"). This estimate function, if interpreted as indicating reasonable betting quotients, is likewise not strictly coherent; in spite of this it is accepted by a great majority of statisticians. ${}^0\mathscr{C}$ satisfies the weaker regularity condition that I have taken as defining "*semiregular* $\mathscr{C}$-functions" (D7-2): for any $s > 0$, if s_j in **s** is positive, then $C_j^s(\mathbf{s}) > 0$. In contrast with some other nonregular $\mathscr{C}$-functions, ${}^0\mathscr{C}$ is uniquely determined by its representative function. (More exactly speaking, for any $\lambda > 0$, there is a representative function ${}^\lambda C$ for ${}^\lambda\mathscr{C}$; and any value ${}^\lambda\mathscr{C}(H \mid E)$ is uniquely determined in terms of ${}^\lambda C$. Then we define ${}^0\mathscr{C}(H \mid E) = \lim_{\lambda\to 0} {}^\lambda\mathscr{C}(H \mid E)$ and ${}^0C_j(\mathbf{s}) =_{\mathrm{Df}} \lim_{\lambda\to 0} {}^\lambda C_j(\mathbf{s})$; and this limit does always exist.) I do not know whether every semiregular $\mathscr{C}$-function is uniquely determined by its representative C-function. It would be of interest to examine this question, especially for those who would require, not regularity, but only semiregularity.]

The following theorem is analogous to T11-9. While the earlier theorem was stated for *all* symmetric MI-functions, however, the present theorem must be restricted to regular C-functions.

T12-5. Let C be a *regular*, symmetric C-function.

a. For any $s \geqq 0$, if all values of C^{s+1} are given, then thereby all values of C^s are determined as follows. For any l in $\mathbf{N}_k$, and any **s** in ${}^0\mathbf{N}^{k,s}$, $C_l^s(\mathbf{s}) = 1/\sum_j q_{jl}$, where $q_{jl} =_{\mathrm{Df}} C_j^{s+1}(\mathbf{s}^l)/C_l^{s+1}(\mathbf{s}^j)$, thus $q_{ll} = 1$.

Proof. Suppose that all values of C^{s+1} are given. Then all values of q_{jl} are determined. By the quotient condition D3b(2′), $C_j^s(\mathbf{s})/C_l^s(\mathbf{s}) = q_{jl}$; hence $C_j^s(\mathbf{s}) = C_l^s(\mathbf{s})q_{jl}$; $\sum_j C_j^s(\mathbf{s}) = C_l^s(\mathbf{s}) \sum_j q_{jl}$. By the sum condition D3a(1), the left-hand sum is 1; hence the assertion. ■

b. For any $s \geqq 0$ and any $m > 0$, if all values of C^{s+m} are given, then all values of C^s are uniquely determined. (From (a), by mathematical induction with respect to m.)

We found that, for any symmetric C, there is one and only one MI that is related to C; this MI is defined by a product of C-values (conditions (1) and (2) in T3). For *regular* functions also the inverse holds: for any regular MI, there is one and only one C that is related to MI; it is defined by a quotient of MI-values (T4d). Thus relatedness establishes a one-to-one correspondence between the regular C-functions and the regular MI-functions. This result is important. By combining it with earlier results of a one-to-one correspondence between MI-functions and $\mathscr{M}$-functions (here generally for symmetric functions, by T11-3 and T11-4) and a one-to-one correspondence between regular $\mathscr{M}$-functions and the related regular $\mathscr{C}$-functions (T7-5), we have now *a one-to-one correspondence between regular C-functions and regular $\mathscr{C}$-functions* which we need in order to assure for the C-functions the character as genuine representative functions for $\mathscr{C}$-functions.

We shall first define the $\mathscr{C}$- and $\mathscr{M}$-functions generated by a regular C-function. Then we have to show that this relation between $\mathscr{C}$ and C and the earlier relation of C being representative for $\mathscr{C}$ are converses of each other.

D12-4. Let C be a *regular*, symmetric C-function. Let $\mathscr{M}$ and $\mathscr{C}$ be real-valued functions on $\mathscr{E}^{\text{mol}}$ for $\mathscr{L}_1$.

a. $\mathscr{M}$ is *generated* by $C =_{\text{Df}} \mathscr{M}$ is generated (in the sense of D11-2) by the function MI related (D2) to C.

b. $\mathscr{C}$ is *generated* by $C =_{\text{Df}} \mathscr{C}$ is related (D1-11) to the function $\mathscr{M}$ generated (in the sense of (a)) by C.

From earlier results it is clear that, for any *regular*, symmetric C, there is one and only one $\mathscr{M}$-function generated by C, and there is one and only one $\mathscr{C}$-function generated by C.

Let us write temporarily, for informal discussions, "$R(\mathscr{C}) = C$" for "the representative function of $\mathscr{C}$ is C" (D1, but now restricted to regular $\mathscr{C}$); and "$G(C) = \mathscr{C}$" for "the $\mathscr{C}$-function generated by C is $\mathscr{C}$" (D4b). The operations R and G are analogous to the earlier operations r and g for MI and $\mathscr{M}$ ((11-1) and (11-2)). The next theorem shows that, for any regular C, $R(G(C)) = C$; in other words, if $G(C) = \mathscr{C}$, then $R(\mathscr{C}) = C$. This is the analogue to T11-3.

T12-6. We assume: (1) C is a regular, symmetric C-function; (2) $\mathscr{C}$ is generated (D4b) by C; (3) C' is the representative C-function of $\mathscr{C}$ (D1). Then the functions C' and C are identical, i.e., for any $s \geqq 0$, any j in $\mathbf{N}_k$, and any $\mathbf{s}$ in ${}^0\mathbf{N}^{k,s}$, $C'_j(\mathbf{s}) = C_j(\mathbf{s})$.

Proof. For the sake of an indirect proof, we assume that, for some s, j, $\mathbf{s}$, and some real number b, (4) $C'_j(\mathbf{s}) = b$, and (5) $C_j(\mathbf{s}) \neq b$. We shall show that this leads to a contradiction. By (2) and D4, there are functions MI and $\mathscr{M}$, both regular and symmetric, uniquely determined by C, such that (6) MI is related to C (D2); (7) $\mathscr{M}$ is generated by MI (D11-2); and (8) $\mathscr{C}$ is related to $\mathscr{M}$ (D1-11). By (4), (3), and D1a, $\mathscr{C}(H'_j \mid E^*_{s,\mathbf{s}}) = b$, where H'_j and $E^*_{s,\mathbf{s}}$ are as in D1a. Hence with (8) and T7-4a, $\mathscr{M}(E^*_{s,\mathbf{s}} \cap H'_j)/\mathscr{M}(E^*_{s,\mathbf{s}}) = b$. Hence, since MI is the representative MI-function of $\mathscr{M}$ (from (7) and T11-3), $\mathrm{MI}(\mathbf{s}^j)/\mathrm{MI}(\mathbf{s}) = b$. Then with (6), $C_j(\mathbf{s}) = b$, which is in contradiction to (5). ■

The next theorem shows that, for any symmetric and regular $\mathscr{C}$, $G(R(\mathscr{C})) = \mathscr{C}$; in other words, if $R(\mathscr{C}) = C$, then $G(C) = \mathscr{C}$; or again, two distinct regular $\mathscr{C}$-functions cannot have the same representative C-function. This theorem is the analogue to T11-4.

T12-7. Suppose that: (1) $\mathscr{C}$ is a regular, symmetric $\mathscr{C}$-function; (2) $\mathscr{C}$ is the representative C-function (D1) of $\mathscr{C}$ (hence by T2b, C is a regular, symmetric C-function); (3) $\mathscr{C}'$ is the $\mathscr{C}$-function generated (D4b) by C. Then the functions $\mathscr{C}$ and $\mathscr{C}'$ are identical.

Proof. By (1), there are functions $\mathscr{M}$, MI, C', uniquely determined by $\mathscr{C}$, each of them symmetric and regular, such that $\mathscr{M}$ is the $\mathscr{M}$-function related to $\mathscr{C}$ (D1-11); MI is the representative MI-function (D11-1) of $\mathscr{M}$; C' is the C-function related to MI (D2). Therefore (4) $\mathscr{C}$ is the $\mathscr{C}$-function generated by C' (D4b). Hence with T6, the representative C-function for $\mathscr{C}$ is C'; but by (2), it is C. Thus C' and C are identical. Hence with (4), the $\mathscr{C}$-function generated by C is $\mathscr{C}$; but by (3) it is $\mathscr{C}'$. Thus $\mathscr{C}$ and $\mathscr{C}'$ are identical. ■

The theorems T6 and T7 together say that the relation of C being representative of $\mathscr{C}$ is the converse of the relation of $\mathscr{C}$ being generated by C, provided that either C or $\mathscr{C}$ is symmetric and regular, and therefore the other one is, too. Thus:

+T12-8. Let $\mathscr{C}$ be a symmetric and regular $\mathscr{C}$-function, and C a function on ${}^0\mathbf{N}^{k,s}$ with values in $\mathbf{R}^k$. Then C is the representative C-function of $\mathscr{C}$ if-if $\mathscr{C}$ is generated by C.

We have seen that mutual relatedness (D2) constitutes a one-to-one correspondence between regular symmetric C-functions and MI-functions. If now C and MI are regular and related to each other, and MS is the MS-function corresponding to MI (which is likewise a one-to-one relation, see the remarks following T11-10), then we say that *C and MS are related to each other.*

If MS rather than MI is used as the main representative function for $\mathscr{M}$-functions, then it is convenient to have at hand some theorems about relations between C and MS. I shall give in T9 a few formulas. (Similar formulas, but only for $k = 2$, have been given by de Finetti [1937, p. 52] or [1964, p. 144].)

T12-9. Let C be a regular, symmetric C-function. Let MI be related to C, and MS be the MS-function corresponding to MI. (Hence MI and MS are regular, symmetric, and C and MS are related to each other.) The following holds for any $s \geqq 0$, any $\mathbf{s}$ in ${}^0\mathbf{N}^{k,s}$, and any j in $\mathbf{N}_k$.

a. $$C_j^s(\mathbf{s}) = \frac{(s_j + 1)\text{MS}^{s+1}(\mathbf{s}^j)}{(s + 1)\text{MS}^s(\mathbf{s})}. \qquad \text{(From T4d, T11-10a.)}$$

b. $$= \frac{(s_j + 1)\text{MS}^{s+1}(\mathbf{s}^j)}{\sum_{l=1}^{k} [(s_l + 1)\text{MS}^{s+1}(\mathbf{s}^l)]}. \qquad \text{(From (a), D11-6a(2).)}$$

c. $$= \frac{s_j + 1}{s_j + 1 + \sum_{l(\neq j)} \left[(s_l + 1) \frac{\text{MS}^{s+1}(\mathbf{s}^l)}{\text{MS}^{s+1}(\mathbf{s}^j)} \right]}. \qquad \text{(From (b).)}$$

d. $$= \frac{s_j + 1}{s + k + \sum_{l(\neq j)} \left[(s_l + 1) \left(\frac{\text{MS}^{s+1}(\mathbf{s}^l)}{\text{MS}^{s+1}(\mathbf{s}^j)} - 1 \right) \right]}. \qquad \text{(From (c).)}$$

I have explained earlier the usefulness of representative MI- or MS-functions for the task of finding an inductive method that is intended to satisfy certain requirements and, for the rest, is simple and its values are intuitively plausible. The main advantage of the representative C-functions lies in the last point. In the case of C-values, in other words, $\mathscr{C}$-values for a singular prediction H_j on the basis of a s.p. E_s, we have often a clear feeling whether or not a proposed value is intuitively acceptable, that is, reasonable as a betting quotient; and still more, whether $C_j^s(\mathbf{s})$ should be higher than $C_l^s(\mathbf{s})$, or lower, or equal to it, whether $C_j^s(\mathbf{s})$ should be higher or lower than $C_j^s(\mathbf{s}')$ (with another k-tuple), and the like.

Later, in connection with de Finetti's representation theorem [1964, chap. iii]; see Jeffrey, Art. **3**, §10, 'F'), we shall see that his representative function, the distribution function Φ, is a mathematically especially powerful tool for the construction of an inductive method. In the case of the simple language $\mathscr{L}_1$, Φ is the same as our MD^∞ (D11-9b). When we examine a function Φ or the corresponding density function φ, it is usually not difficult to ascertain whether the axioms and other mathematical requirements are fulfilled. But again, for testing intuitive plausibility, the best way is often to investigate values of the function C determined, via MI, from Φ or φ.

13
The Principle of Instantial Relevance

Consider an s.p. E_s for the initial s-sample, with k-tuple **s**. For any j, let H_j be the atomic proposition $P_j a_{s+1}$, and H'_j be $P_j a_{s+2}$. It certainly is one of the basic characteristics of customary inductive reasoning, that the probability of a singular prediction like H'_j is increased when we obtain, in addition to the original evidence E_s, the new observation result H_j which is an instance of the same attribute as H'_j:

(13-1) $$\mathscr{C}(H_j \mid E_s \cap H_j) > \mathscr{C}(H'_j \mid E_s).$$

We may call this the principle of the positive relevance of one instance for another instance of the same attribute, or, for short, the *principle of instantial relevance*. In the subsequent formulation of the principle, we shall, however, split it into two parts (a) and (b), which together say the same as (13-1), while (a) makes the weaker assertion that, under the conditions specified, the probability does not decrease.

P13-1. Principle of instantial relevance.

a. $\mathscr{C}(H'_j \mid E_s \cap H_j) \geqq \mathscr{C}(H'_j \mid E_s)$.

b. If $0 < \mathscr{C}(H'_j \mid E_s) < 1$, $\mathscr{C}(H'_j \mid E_s \cap H_j) \neq \mathscr{C}(H_j \mid E)$.

Let us write briefly 'c_2' for the first $\mathscr{C}$-expression in (a), and 'c_1' for the second. The reasons for inserting into (b) *the restricting condition* that c_1 be neither 0 nor 1 are as follows. If we presuppose regularity, as we usually do, then the conditional clause in (b) may, of course, be omitted. If someone presupposes only semiregularity (D7-2), then he may delete "0<" in (b), but he must keep the condition that $c_1 < 1$. For a semiregular $\mathscr{C}$, c_1 may be 1, and then by (a) $c_2 = 1$. If someone accepts not only the conditional statement (b), but even the corresponding statement (b′) without the conditional clause, then he must reject nonsemiregular $\mathscr{C}$-functions. In this case it seems to me preferable for him to express this rejection by stating an axiom of semiregularity, but to take in P1 the conditional formulation (b). This makes it possible to accept P1 also for those who wish to admit nonregular $\mathscr{C}$-functions.

Let us illustrate the situation by two examples of doubtful $\mathscr{C}$-functions, both of which have been proposed by prominent authors. The first is the function ${}^0\mathscr{C}$ in the extended λ-system, with $\lambda = 0$, based on the so-called straight rule. (${}^0\mathscr{C}$ is explained in [1952*a*, §14]; it was mentioned above, ahead of T12-5.) Let ${}^0C$ be the representative function of ${}^0\mathscr{C}$. For any $s > 0$, let $\mathbf{s} = \langle s, 0, \ldots, 0\rangle$ in ${}^0\mathbf{N}^{k,s}$. Then ${}^0C_1(\mathbf{s}) = 1$, and also ${}^0C_1(\mathbf{s}^1) = 1$. ${}^0\mathscr{C}$ is excluded by the axiom of regularity but not by P1, because of the conditional clause in P1b. The situation is different for the function ${}^{\infty}\mathscr{C}$ with $\lambda = \infty$ [1952*a*, §13] (this is the same function as $C\dagger$ in [1950, §110A]). This function is regular. But for its representative function ${}^{\infty}C$, for any given j, all values ${}^{\infty}C_j^s(\mathbf{s})$, for any s and any $\mathbf{s}$, are equal to ${}^{\infty}C_j^0(\mathbf{s}_0)$. Therefore ${}^{\infty}\mathscr{C}$ is excluded by P1b. It seems to me obvious that this function is inadmissible. But it has been accepted by C. S. Peirce, Keynes, and Wittgenstein (see [1950, p. 565], [1952*a*, p. 40]).

It is essential for the validity of the principle P1 that the prior evidence E_s does not involve the individuals involved in H_j and H_j'. If we take as prior evidence $E = E_s \cap A$, where A says something about the cardinal number s_j'' of P_j in the initial $(s + 2)$-sample, then H_j may very well be negatively relevant for H_j'. For example, suppose that A says that $s_j'' \leqq s_j + 1$ (s_j being the cardinal number in E_s). Then we have:

$$\mathscr{C}(H_j' \mid E \cap H_j) = 0 < \mathscr{C}(H_j' \mid E).$$

The following is an alternative formulation of the same principle, in terms of the representative function C.

P13-1′. For any $\mathbf{s}$ and any j:
a. $C_j(\mathbf{s}^j) \geqq C_j(\mathbf{s})$.
b. If $0 < C_j(\mathbf{s}) < 1$, $C_j(\mathbf{s}^j) \neq C_j(\mathbf{s})$.

We shall give a third formulation P1″ which refers to $\mathscr{M}$ by way of the representative MI-function. Note that

$$\mathscr{M}(E_s \cap H_j) = \mathscr{M}(E_s \cap H_j') = \mathrm{MI}(\mathbf{s}^j).$$

(13-2) *Notations.*
a. $\mathbf{s}^{jl} =_{\mathrm{Df}} (\mathbf{s}^j)^l$.
b. Recursive definition for $\mathbf{s}^{j^n}$:
(1) $\mathbf{s}^{j^0} =_{\mathrm{Df}} \mathbf{s}$; (2) $\mathbf{s}^{j^{n+1}} =_{\mathrm{Df}} (\mathbf{s}^{j^n})^j$.

P13-1″. For any $\mathbf{s}$ and any j:
a. $\mathrm{MI}(\mathbf{s})\mathrm{MI}(\mathbf{s}^{j^2}) \geqq [\mathrm{MI}(\mathbf{s}^j)]^2$.
b. If $0 < \mathrm{MI}(\mathbf{s}^j) < \mathrm{MI}(\mathbf{s})$, $\mathrm{MI}(\mathbf{s})\mathrm{MI}(\mathbf{s}^{j^2}) = [\mathrm{MI}(\mathbf{s}^j)]^2$.

In earlier publications I called attention to the importance of the principle of instantial relevance, which had always been used implicitly in inductive reasoning, but had never been stated either as an axiom or as a theorem. I proposed a special "axiom of instantial relevance", which was essentially the same as the present P1. [The axiom proposed in [1953*a*, p. 314] and [1959, p. 244, NA12] was more general than P1, by taking as the prior evidence an arbitrary molecular proposition. This more general statement can, however, be derived from P1; see T1a below. The axiom did not contain the conditional clause of P1b, because regularity was presupposed.] In the meantime, however, it has been found that this axiom is not necessary. Haim Gaifman proved in 1960 an important result, which is stated and proved in Art. **5**. In 1963, Jürgen Humburg found a considerably simpler proof, see Art. **4**. The result is essentially the following. On the basis of the axioms stated so far (the basic axioms, regularity, and symmetry) together with the following assumption, P1 can be proved.

(13-3) *Assumption*. For any $s > 0$, any $\mathbf{s}$ in ${}^0\mathbf{N}^{k,s}$, and any j in $\mathbf{N}_k$, if $C_j^s(\mathbf{s}) < 1$, then, for some (sufficiently large) n,

$$C_j^s(\mathbf{s}) \neq C_j^{s+n}(\mathbf{s}^{j^n}).$$

In our axiom system in this treatise, assumption (3) is provable with the help of the axiom A7 of convergence (Reichenbach), that we shall state in the section on the limit axioms in Part II (in Vol. II). If someone does not accept axiom A7, he will presumably still accept the statement (3), in view of its plausibility, either as an axiom or on the basis of his other axioms.

Although we do not give here the proof of the theorem, we shall at some places make use of the result by assuming that the principle P1 holds, and therefore we shall use also items of the following theorem T1.

We state some consequences of P1.

T13-1. Let $\mathscr{C}$ be a regular, symmetric $\mathscr{C}$-function on $\mathscr{E}^{\text{mol}}$ for $\mathscr{L}_1$ such that P1 holds for $\mathscr{C}$. Let C be representative of $\mathscr{C}$; hence P1′ holds for C. Let $\mathscr{M}$ be related to $\mathscr{C}$ (D1-11), and MI be representative of $\mathscr{M}$; hence P1″ holds for MI. Let E be *any molecular proposition* distinct from $\varnothing$ and from $\mathbf{Z}$. Let p be the number of the individual indexes involved in E; then p is positive and finite. Let D_p be the set of these indexes. For any given j in $\mathbf{N}_k$, let H and H' be the atomic propositions $P_j a_i$ and $P_j a_{i'}$, respectively, where i and i' are two distinct indexes not in D_p.

a. $\mathscr{C}(H' \mid E \cap H) > \mathscr{C}(H' \mid E)$.

Proof. For the proof we assume that $D_p = \mathbf{N}_p$; then the general theorem (a) follows immediately from the theorem for this special case by virtue of the symmetry of $\mathscr{C}$. Let $\mathscr{B}^{(p)}$ be the class of all s.p.'s for the initial p-sample (D3-6d), which has the index set D_p; and let $\mathscr{B}_E^{(p)}$ be defined as in D3-6e. Then we have (by T3-4e and f):

$$E = \bigcup \mathscr{B}_E^{(p)}$$

and

(1) $$\mathscr{M}(E) = \sum \mathscr{M}(B) \text{ (for all } B \in \mathscr{B}_E^{(p)}).$$

Let n be the cardinal number of $\mathscr{B}_E^{(p)}$; and let

$$\mathscr{B}_E^{(p)} = \{B_1, B_2, \ldots, B_n\}.$$

For every l ($l = 1, 2, \ldots, n$), let

(2) $$m_l = \mathscr{M}(B_l);\ m'_l = \mathscr{M}(B_l \cap H) = \mathscr{M}(B_l \cap H');$$
$$m''_l = \mathscr{M}(B_l \cap H \cap H').$$

We have from (1) $\left(\text{writing } `\sum\text{' for } `\sum_{l=1}^{n}\text{'}\right)$:

(3) $$\mathscr{M}(E) = \sum \mathscr{M}(B_l) = \sum m_l;$$

(4) $$\mathscr{M}(E \cap H) = \mathscr{M}(E \cap H') = \sum \mathscr{M}(B_l \cap H) = \sum m'_l;$$

(5) $$\mathscr{M}(E \cap H \cap H') = \sum \mathscr{M}(B_l \cap H \cap H') = \sum m''_l.$$

We have from P1, for every l ($l = 1, \ldots, n$):

$$\mathscr{C}(H' \mid B_l \cap H) > \mathscr{C}(H' \mid B_l);$$

hence

$$\frac{\mathscr{M}(B_l \cap H \cap H')}{\mathscr{M}(B_l \cap H)} > \frac{\mathscr{M}(B_l \cap H')}{\mathscr{M}(B_l)};$$

hence with (2):

(6) $$\frac{m''_l}{m'_l} > \frac{m'_l}{m_l}.$$

Since $\mathscr{M}$ is regular, we have:

(7) $$0 < m''_l < m'_l < m_l < 1;$$

hence with (6):

(8) $$(m'_l)^2 < m_l m''_l.$$

We now use the following purely algebraic lemma:

If each of n triples of real numbers m_l, m'_l, m''_l ($l = 1, \ldots, n$) satisfies the conditions (7) and (8), then

(9) $$[\sum m'_l]^2 < \sum m_l \sum m''_l.$$

This lemma can easily be proved by mathematical induction with respect to n. Then, since all terms and sums are positive:

$$\frac{\sum m''_l}{\sum m'_l} > \frac{\sum m'_l}{\sum m_l}.$$

Hence with (3), (4), (5):

$$\frac{\mathcal{M}(E \cap H \cap H')}{\mathcal{M}(E \cap H)} > \frac{\mathcal{M}(E \cap H')}{\mathcal{M}(E)}.$$

Hence the assertion. ■

b. $\mathcal{C}(H' \mid E \cap -H) < \mathcal{C}(H' \mid E)$.
c. $\mathcal{C}(-H' \mid E \cap H) < \mathcal{C}(-H' \mid E)$.

(b) and (c) follow from (a) by the well-known theorems that say that, if A is positively relevant for A' (with respect to given prior evidence), then (1) $-A$ is negatively relevant for A', and (2) A is negatively relevant for $-A'$ [1950, T65-6e and h].

Note the following distinction between the situations for $k = 2$ and for $k > 2$. For every j in $\mathbf{N}_k$, let $H_j = P_j a_i$ and $H_j' = P_j a_{i'}$. For $k = 2$, $-H_1 = H_2$; therefore by T1b:

(i) $$\mathcal{C}(H_1' \mid E \cap H_2) < \mathcal{C}(H_1' \mid E).$$

On the other hand, for $k = 3$, $-H_1 = H_2 \cup H_3$; here we have only:

(ii) $$\mathcal{C}(H_1' \mid E \cap (H_2 \cup H_3)) < \mathcal{C}(H_1' \mid E),$$

while (i) does not necessarily hold. When we obtain the additional information H_2, we might be tempted to think that thereby $\mathcal{C}$ must be decreased because, when we know H_2, we know also $H_2 \cup H_3$. But a reasoning of this kind is invalid; it violates the requirement of total evidence [1950, §45B], which demands the use of the total information at hand. It is possible that H_2 is positively relevant for H_1'; but in this case H_3 would be negatively relevant. In general, for arbitrary k, the following can be shown. By T1b, $H_2 \cup \ldots \cup H_k$ is negatively relevant for H_1'. Since the propositions $H_2, \ldots, H_k$ are pairwise disjoint, it follows that at least one of them is negatively relevant for H_1' [1950, T68-4a]. [The case that H_2 is positively relevant for H_1' occurs only under special conditions, namely, a sufficiently high degree of similarity between the attributes P_1 and P_2 referred to by H_1' and H_2, respectively. This "analogy influence" will be discussed in §16 (in Part II which will appear in Vol. II).]

3

Probability Measures and Integrals

BY RICHARD C. JEFFREY

1
Introduction

In its purely mathematical aspect, probability theory can be viewed as a part of the theory of measure and integration in abstract spaces. It would be a mistake to speak of the measure theoretic *interpretation* of probability. It is rather from its abstractness, i.e., its compatibility with a wide variety of interpretations of the concept of probability, that the measure theoretic approach derives its power: in a sense, it allows one to discuss probability without knowing exactly what one is talking about. Indeed, there is general satisfaction with the state of the mathematical theory while opinion about the meaning of probability statements is various and unsure.

The purpose of this article is to introduce and provide a convenient reference for the basic measure theoretic results used elsewhere in these volumes. There are many excellent textbooks on the theory of measure and integration which may be consulted for proofs and further details. The first hundred pages of Kolmogorov and Fomin [1961] contain most of the relevant measure theory and are quite lucid, as is Munroe [1953], which has more details. Halmos [1950] is an elegant exposition of abstract measure theory. For the application of measure theory to probability, some of the standard references are Kolmogorov [1933, 1956]; Doob [1953]; Loève [1963]. The early chapters of various statistics textbooks are also useful in this connection; see, e.g., Fraser [1957] and Lehmann [1959].

We shall use the terminology and notations of Art. **2**, §1, except that here, wherever there is no indication to the contrary, "probability measure" will always mean *countably additive probability measure*, and a *probability space* will always be a triple of the form $(Z, \mathscr{E}, \mathscr{P})$ in which $\mathscr{E}$ is a σ-field of subsets of Z, and $\mathscr{P}$ is a (countably additive) probability measure on $\mathscr{E}$.

Note that we now write "Z" in place of the boldface "$\mathbf{Z}$" of Art. **2**. The contrast between "$\mathbf{Z}$" and "Z" is not needed here, for we shall use lower case "z" as a variable for members of Z, e.g., we shall write "$z \in Z$" here in place of the "$Z \in \mathbf{Z}$" of Art. **2**.

The "points" (= members) of Z represent the ultimate possible cases, relative to the problem under discussion—ultimate, in the sense that any event (= proposition) whose probability interests us is represented by some subset, A, of Z, so that the event happens or not accordingly as the one member of Z which represents the actual case does or does not belong to A. It will make for fluency and should cause no confusion if we sometimes ignore the distinction between points in Z and the possible cases they represent, and between subsets of Z and the events they represent. Thus, we may say that if $A \in \mathscr{E}$, then the members of A *are* possible cases and A itself *is* an event. The relation between colloquial descriptions of events and their representation by subsets of Z is illustrated by the following example.

Example 1-1. *Idealized coin tossing*. An indestructible coin is to be tossed *ad infinitum*. Let Z be the set of all infinite sequences of zeros and ones, that is, let each $z \in Z$ be a function from the positive integers to the set $\{0, 1\}$ where $z(n)$, the value that z assumes for the argument n, is the nth member of the sequence. The point z represents the possible case in which the nth toss results in head or tail accordingly as $z(n)$ is 1 or 0. Let $\mathscr{E}$ be the σ-field generated by the sets in Z of form $H_n =_{\text{Df}} \{z: z(n) = 1\}$, i.e., by the events, *the first toss yields a head, the second toss yields a head*, ... Throughout this example, the variables 'l', 'm', and 'n' range over the positive integers.

(a) The event that all tosses yield heads is in $\mathscr{E}$, being represented by the set $\{z$: for all n, $z(n) = 1\}$, i.e., equivalently, by the set $\bigcap_n H_n$, which is the intersection of the countable collection of sets that generate $\mathscr{E}$.

(b) The event that some (= one or more) tosses yield heads is represented by $\{z$: for some n, $z(n) = 1\}$, i.e., equivalently, by the set $\bigcup_n H_n$ which, being the union of the countable class of sets that generate $\mathscr{E}$, is itself in $\mathscr{E}$.

(c) The event that infinitely many tosses yield heads is also in $\mathscr{E}$, since it is represented by a certain countable intersection of countable unions of sets that generate $\mathscr{E}$, namely, by the set $\{z$: for infinitely many n, $z(n) = 1\} = \{z$: for each m, there is an $n > m$ such that $Z(n) = 1\} = \bigcap_m \bigcup_{n>m} H_n$.

(d) The event that the limiting relative frequency of heads is $\frac{1}{2}$ belongs to $\mathscr{E}$, for let the relative frequency of heads in the first n tosses, in case z, be denoted by

(1-1) $$R_n(z) = \frac{1}{n}\sum_{i=1}^{n} z(i),$$

so that the limiting relative frequency of heads in case z is

(1-2) $$R(z) = \lim_n R_n(z),$$

if the sequence $R_1(z)$, $R_2(z)$, . . . converges. Now $\{z$: $R(z)$ exists and is $\frac{1}{2}\} = \{z$: for all l there is an m such that for all $n > m$, $|\frac{1}{2} - R_n(z)| < 1/l\} = \bigcap_l \bigcup_m \bigcap_{n>m} \{z: |\frac{1}{2} - R_n(z)| < 1/l\}$. Since the ranges of all three variables are countable, this set belongs to $\mathscr{E}$ if for each n and l, the set $\{z: |\frac{1}{2} - R_n(z)| < 1/l\}$ belongs to $\mathscr{E}$. That this is the case is shown as follows. For fixed n, $R_n(z)$ can only assume a finite number of different values, namely, 0, $1/n$, $2/n$, . . . , 1. Now the event that $|\frac{1}{2} - R_n(z)| < 1/l$ is a (necessarily finite) union of sets of the form $R_n^{-1}(0)$, $R_n^{-1}(1/n)$, $R_n^{-1}(2/n), \ldots, R_n^{-1}(1)$, where in general, $R_n^{-1}(i/n)$ is the set $\{z\colon R_n(z) = i/n\}$. Then it only remains to show that for each $i = 0, 1, \ldots, n$, $R_n^{-1}(i/n)$ is a member of $\mathscr{E}$. To see that this is the case, notice that $R_n^{-1}(i/n)$ is the union of the $\binom{n}{i}$ sets of the form $\{z\colon z(1) = a_1\} \cap \{z\colon z(2) = a_2\} \cap \ldots \cap \{z\colon z(n) = a_n\}$ that satisfy the condition $a_1 + a_2 + \ldots + a_n = i$, where each of the a's is either 0 or 1. Since each of the sets $\{z\colon z(j) = a_j\}$ is either one of the sets that generate $\mathscr{E}$ or the complement of such a set, $R_n^{-1}(i/n)$ must belong to $\mathscr{E}$.

(e) Similarly, one can show that the event that there is a limiting relative frequency of heads belongs to $\mathscr{E}$, for

$$\begin{aligned}\{z\colon R(z) \text{ exists}\} &= \{z\colon R_1(z), R_2(z), \ldots \text{ is a Cauchy sequence}\}\\ &= \textstyle\bigcap_l \bigcup_m \bigcap_{n>m} \{z\colon |R_m(z) - R_n(z)| < 1/l\},\end{aligned}$$

where $\{z\colon |R_m(z) - R_n(z)| < 1/l\}$ can be shown to belong to $\mathscr{E}$ by the method of (d).

Example 1-2. *Propositions expressible in a first-order language.* Given a fixed universe U over which the variables are to range, take Z to be the set of all first-order valuations of the sentences of the language, relative to the universe U, and take the proposition expressed by a sentence to be the set of all such valuations in which that sentence is true. Given a one-place predicate 'P', any such valuation induces an extension of 'P', namely, a function from U to the set $\{0, 1\}$ which takes the value 1 or 0 for an argument depending on whether the atomic sentence 'Px' is true or false in the given valuation when 'x' is assigned that argument as its value. Suppose that the language has as its sole extralogical constant the one-place predicate 'P', that U is the set of positive integers, and that the intended interpretation of 'P' is the function that takes the value 1 for an argument n if and only if a certain coin lands head up on the nth toss. With this choice of U, the proposition expressed by the sentence '$(x)Px$' (*all tosses yield heads*, in the intended interpretation) is the set $\bigcap_n H_n$ of example 1-1(a). (The terminology used in this example is roughly that of Smullyan [1968], IV, §2.)

2
Measures

The probability space $(Z, \mathscr{E}, \mathscr{P})$ is said to be *discrete* if Z is countable and $\mathscr{E}$ contains all of Z's subsets. In this case there is a particularly simple method for determining $\mathscr{P}$. Let p be a function that assigns a nonnegative real number to each member of Z in such a way that $\sum_z p(z) = 1$. The number $p(z)$ will be called the *weight* of the point z. Now, for each $A \subset Z$, define $\mathscr{P}(A)$ as the sum of the weights of the members of A. It is easily verified that $\mathscr{P}$ is then a probability measure of $\mathscr{E}$ and that conversely, if $\mathscr{P}$ is any probability measure on $\mathscr{E}$, then there is a weight function, p, given by

$$p(z) = \mathscr{P}(\{z\}),$$

such that for each $A \subset Z, \mathscr{P}(A)$ is the sum of the weights of the members of A. Even where Z is uncountably infinite, we call $\mathscr{P}$ discrete in case $\mathscr{E}$ has a countable subset $\mathscr{U}$ of unit sets, and for each $A \in \mathscr{E}$, $\mathscr{P}(A)$ is the sum of all terms of form $\mathscr{P}(U)$ where $U \subset A$ and $U \in \mathscr{U}$.

Example 2-1. *The St. Petersburg experiment* (Daniel Bernoulli [1738]). A coin is tossed repeatedly until a tail appears, at which point the experiment terminates. Let $Z = \{z_1, z_2, \ldots, z_\omega\}$. Each z_n with a positive integer n represents the case in which the experiment terminates on the nth toss, while z_ω represents the case where the experiment never terminates. Define $p(z_n) = 2^{-n}$ and $p(z_\omega) = 0$. Now $\mathscr{P}$ is completely determined on the class $\mathscr{E}$ of all subsets of Z, e.g., the probability that the experiment eventually terminates is $\mathscr{P}(\{1, 2, \ldots\}) = p(1) + p(2) + \ldots = 1$; the probability that the experiment terminates on an even-numbered toss is $\mathscr{P}(\{2, 4, \ldots\}) = \frac{1}{4} + \frac{1}{16} + \ldots = \frac{1}{3}$; and the probability that the experiment last no longer than n tosses is $\frac{1}{2} + \ldots + \frac{1}{2}^n = 1 - 2^{-n}$.

If Z is more than countably infinite, the device of determining $\mathscr{P}$ by way of a weight function, p, is not generally available: $\mathscr{P}(\{z\})$ may be 0 for all $z \in A$ while $\mathscr{P}(A)$ is positive. In such cases a standard procedure is to define $\mathscr{P}$ first for arguments of a simple sort, and then to extend the domain of definition of $\mathscr{P}$ by the technique that is illustrated in the following example.

Example 2-2. *Lebesgue measure on the unit square.* Let $Z = [0, 1]^2 =$ the set of all pairs of real numbers in the unit interval, end points included. A *rectangle* (= rectangle with sides parallel to the coordinate axes) is a Cartesian product of any pair of subintervals of the unit interval, i.e., if $0 \leq a_i \leq b_i \leq 1$, a rectangle is a set of points (x, y)

that either satisfy the two conditions

(2-1) $$a_1 \leq x \leq b_1, \qquad a_2 \leq y \leq b_2,$$

or satisfy the pair of conditions that result when some or all of the inequalities in (2-1) are replaced by strict inequalities. An *elementary set* is a union of finitely many disjoint rectangles. In particular, each rectangle itself counts as an elementary set. Define a function $\mathscr{P}_0$ on the class of rectangles by setting $\mathscr{P}_0(A) = (b_1 - a_1)(b_2 - a_2) =$ the area of the rectangle, where A is any one of the sixteen rectangles that are determined by the pairs of conditions that can be derived from (2-1). Extend $\mathscr{P}_0$ to a function $\mathscr{P}_1$ on the class of elementary sets by stipulating that if $A_1, \ldots, A_n$ are disjoint rectangles, then $\mathscr{P}_1(U_iA) = \mathscr{P}_0(A_1) + \ldots + \mathscr{P}_0(A_n)$. We now seek to extend $\mathscr{P}_1$ to a function $\mathscr{P}$ on the widest class of subsets of Z that can plausibly be said to have areas. Intuitively, if a subset of Z can be approximated with artibrary accuracy by elementary sets, its area may be identified with the limit of the areas of the approximating elementary sets. To apply this idea, observe that every subset of Z can be covered in at least one way by countably many rectangles, i.e., for each $A \subset Z$ there is a countable class $\mathscr{A}$ of rectangles such that $A \subset \bigcup \mathscr{A}$; the rectangles in $\mathscr{A}$ need not be disjoint. Now $\mathscr{P}^*(A)$, the *outer measure* of A, is defined as the infimum or greatest lower bound of the numbers

$$\Sigma_{E \subset \mathscr{A}} \mathscr{P}_0(E),$$

as '$\mathscr{A}$' ranges over all countable coverings of A by rectangles. Apparently if A can significantly be said to have an area, it will be no greater than $\mathscr{P}^*(A)$. Call a set $A \subset Z$ *Lebesgue measurable* if-if for all positive ϵ there is an elementary set, B, such that $\mathscr{P}^*(A \,\Delta\, B)$, the outer measure of the symmetric difference between A and B, (which is $(A - B) \cup (B - A)$), is less than ϵ. Now let $\mathscr{E}$ be the class of all Lebesgue measurable sets, and let $\mathscr{P}(A) = \mathscr{P}^*(A) =$ the *Lebesgue measure* of A, for each $A \in \mathscr{E}$. One can show that $\mathscr{E}$ is a σ-field of subsets of Z, and that $\mathscr{P}$ is countably additive, so that $(Z, \mathscr{E}, \mathscr{P})$ is indeed a probability space. (See Kolmogorov and Fomin [1961, §1].) Apparently, the Lebesgue measure of a unit set (and, in fact, of any countable set) is 0, so that we have $\mathscr{P}(Z) = 1$ even though $\mathscr{P}(\{z\}) = 0$ for all $z \in Z$.

The method of constructing probability spaces which is illustrated in example 2-2 is easily generalized. (Kolmogorov and Fomin [1961, chap. 1].) The class of rectangles, on which $\mathscr{P}$ is originally defined, is in general a *semiring* of subsets of a set Z, i.e., it is a set $\mathscr{S}$ such that

(2-2) (a) $\varnothing \in \mathscr{S}$.

(b) $A \cap B \in \mathscr{S}$ if $A, B \in \mathscr{S}$.

(c) If A and A_1 are in $\mathscr{S}$, and if $A_1 \subset A$, then there are disjoint sets $A_2, \ldots, A_n$ in $\mathscr{S}$ such that $A = A_1 \cup A_2 \cup \ldots \cup A_n$.

(Indeed, the null set is a rectangle, e.g., $\varnothing = (a, a]^2$; the intersection of any pair of rectangles is a rectangle, since all rectangles are understood to have sides parallel to the coordinate axes; and if a rectangle A_1 is included in a rectangle A, it is always possible to fill the intervening space $A - A_1$ with finitely many disjoint rectangles.) The class of elementary sets, i.e., the class of finite unions of members of the semiring $\mathscr{S}$, is in fact a *ring* of subsets of Z, i.e., it is nonempty and it is closed under the operations $\cap$ and Δ. Indeed, it can be shown to be identical with the ring $R(\mathscr{S})$ that is *generated* by $\mathscr{S}$, i.e., the intersection of all the rings of subsets of Z that include the semiring $\mathscr{S}$. (Kolmogorov and Fomin [1961, §2, theorem 3].)

A function M_0 is now defined on the semiring $\mathscr{S}$. In example 2-2, where $M_0 = \mathscr{P}_0$, $M_0((a_1, b_1] \times (a_2, b_2])$ was identified with the area, $(b_1 - a_1)(b_2 - a_2)$, of the rectangle. In general, where Z is an arbitrary nonempty set, M_0 is a (countably additive) *measure* on $\mathscr{S}$, i.e., a nonnegative, real-valued, countably additive function on $\mathscr{S}$. The requirement that M_0 be normalized is not essential to the construction, and has therefore been dropped.

The remainder of the construction proceeds as in example 2-2. By applying the property of additivity, M_0 is extended to a measure M_1 on the enlarged domain $R(\mathscr{S})$. The outer measure of an arbitrary subset, A, of Z, is defined as

(2-3)
$$M^*(A) = \inf_{\mathscr{A}} \sum_{E \subset \mathscr{A}} M(A),$$

where '$\mathscr{A}$' ranges over all countable coverings of A by members of the original semiring, $\mathscr{S}$. If M_0 is not normalized, we may have $M^*(A) = \infty$, i.e., there may be no real infimum in (2-3). A set $A \subset Z$ is said to be *measurable* in a generalized sense if-if for each real, positive ϵ there is a set B in the ring $R(\mathscr{S})$ such that $M^*(A \Delta B) < \epsilon$. If A is measurable, we set $M(A) = M^*(A)$.

Then, given a semiring $\mathscr{S}$ of subsets of a nonempty set Z, and a measure M_0 on $\mathscr{S}$, the extension procedure determines a unique class, $\mathscr{E}$, of measurable sets, and a unique measure, M, on $\mathscr{E}$. The resulting *measure space* $(Z, \mathscr{E}, M)$ is *complete* in the sense that every subset of a set of measure 0 is measurable (and, of course, has measure 0). Equivalently: if $A \subset Z$, if $B \in \mathscr{E}$, and if $M(A \Delta B) = 0$, then $A \in \mathscr{E}$ and in fact $M(A) = M(B)$.

Example 2-3. *Lebesgue measure on the plane.* Let $Z = R^2 =$ the set of all pairs (x, y) of real numbers. Let $\mathscr{S} =$ the set of all rectangles

$[a_1, b_1] \times [a_2, b_2]$, $(a_1, b_1) \times (a_2, b_2)$, $[a_1, b_1) \times (a_2, b_2]$, etc., with sides parallel to the coordinate axes, where $a_i \leq b_i$. If A is a rectangle of any one of these sixteen types, let $M_0(A)$ = the area of $A = (b_1 - a_1)(b_2 - a_2)$. Intuitively, the (Lebesgue) measurable sets are those that have finite area, and the (Lebesgue) measure of a set is its area. Here, "area" is construed very generously, so that, e.g., the set of all points with rational coordinates has an area, namely 0. But some sets fail to be measurable, either because (a) they have infinite area, or (b) they are so irregular that they cannot be approximated with arbitrary accuracy by finite unions of disjoint rectangles. An example of the first sort is the whole plane, R^2; for an example of the second sort, see Kolmogorov and Fomin [1961], p. 18.

The class of measurable sets which is determined by the extension procedure need not be a σ-field, for it need not be closed under the operation of forming countable unions. Thus, in example 2-3, Z is the union of the countable collection of disjoint rectangles $(m, m + 1] \times (n, n + 1]$ where m and n range over the integers. Each such rectangle is measurable, having measure 1; but we are forced to say that their union is not measurable. To avoid this limitation, we shall now classify countable unions of measurable sets as measurable, and we shall assign measure ∞ to each set that is measurable in the new sense but not in the old. $\mathscr{E}'$, the class of sets that are measurable in the new sense, can now be described as the *completion* (relative to M) of the σ-field $S(\mathscr{S})$ which is generated by the original semiring, $\mathscr{S}$; in other words, a set A belongs to $\mathscr{E}'$ if and only if there is a set B in $S(\mathscr{S})$ such that $M(A \Delta B) = 0$, in which case we have $M(A) = M(B)$.

Example 2-4. *Lebesgue measure on* R^n. Let $Z = R^n$ = the set of all n-tuples $(x_1, \ldots, x_n)$ of real numbers; let $\mathscr{S}$ be the semiring of all sets of form $A_1 \times A_2 \times \ldots \times A_n$, where each of the A_i is an interval of real numbers of one of the forms (a_i, b_i), $(a_i, b_i]$, $[a_i, b_i)$, $[a_i, b_i]$, with $a_i \leq b_i$. If A is such a set, let $M_0(A) = \prod_i (b_i - a_i)$ = the n-dimensional volume of A. M is now determined for all sets that are measurable in the extended sense, e.g., $M(R^n) = \infty$. In case $n = 1$, $\mathscr{S}$ is the semiring of all finite open, closed, or half-open intervals of real numbers, and the measure M_0 of such an interval is its length. M is then Lebesgue measure on the line, R.

If the original semiring $\mathscr{S}$ contains $\mathbf{Z}$, and if $M_0(Z)$ is real, then the extension procedure directly yields a σ-field $\mathscr{E}$ of measurable sets, i.e., the new and old senses of "measurable" coincide, and M is always finite. If $M_0(Z) = 1$, $(Z, \mathscr{E}, M)$ is a probability space; in such cases I shall generally write '$\mathscr{P}$' for 'M.' Where $\mathbf{Z} = R^n$ = the line, the plane, . . . , and $\mathscr{E}$ is the class of Lebesgue measurable subsets of Z, a probability measure $\mathscr{P}$ on $\mathscr{E}$ can always be determined by an n-dimensional *distribution function*, as in the following examples.

Example 2-5. *Lebesgue-Stieltjes probability measures on the line.* Let F be a *distribution function* on R, i.e., let F have the properties

(2-4) (a) $F(x) \leq F(y)$ if $x < y$ (*nondecreasing*)

(b) $\lim\limits_{y \downarrow x} F(y) = F(x)$ (*continuous on the right*)

(c) $\lim\limits_{x \to \pm\infty} F(x) = \begin{cases} 1 \\ 0 \end{cases}$

Let $\mathscr{S}$ be the class of finite intervals of real numbers. As a guide to the definition of M_0 on $\mathscr{S}$, think of $F(a)$ as the probability of the event that $z \leqq a$, i.e., as the probability of the set $(-\infty, a] = \{z: z \leqq a\}$. Then if $a \leq b$,

(2-5)
$$\mathscr{P}_0((a, b]) = F(b) - F(a)$$
$$\mathscr{P}_0((a, b)) = F(b^-) - F(a)$$
$$\mathscr{P}_0([a, b]) = F(b) - F(a^-)$$
$$\mathscr{P}_0([a, b)) = F(b^-) - F(a^-)$$

where $F(x^-) = \lim\limits_{y \uparrow x} F(x)$. After applying the extension procedure we have $P((-\infty, a]) = F(a)$. Various special cases are of interest.

a. *Probability concentrated at a point.* $F(x) = \begin{cases} 0, \text{ if } x < a \\ 1, \text{ if } x \geq a \end{cases}$. Here it is certain that $z = a$, i.e., in the probability space $(Z, \mathscr{E}, \mathscr{P})$ each event has probability 1 or 0 accordingly as it does or does not contain the point $z = a$.

b. *Discrete case: all probability concentrated at a countable number of points.* The situation in which there is a finite or infinite sequence of points $a_1 < a_2 < \ldots$ in $Z = R$ such that $P(\{a_1, a_2, \ldots\}) = 1$ while $P(\{a_i\}) = p_i > 0$ for each i is described by defining

$$F(x) = \begin{cases} 0 \text{ if } x < a_1 \\ p_1 \text{ if } a_1 \leq x < a_2 \\ p_1 + p_2 \text{ if } a_2 \leq x < a_3 \\ p_1 + p_2 + p_3 \text{ if } a_3 \leq x < a_4 \\ \vdots \end{cases}$$

The p's may be any positive numbers whose sum is 1. The St. Petersburg experiment (example 2-1) can be represented in this way (ignoring the point z_ω, which has probability 0), by setting $a_i = i$ and $p_i = 2^{-i}$ for each $i = 1, 2, \ldots$.

c. *The simplest continuous case: Lebesgue measure (uniform probability distribution) on the unit interval.* Define

$$F(x) = \begin{cases} 0 & \text{if } x < 0 \\ x & \text{if } 0 \leq x < 1 \\ 1 & \text{if } x \geq 1 \end{cases}$$

Then the (Lebesgue) measure of a measurable set A of reals coincides with the measure of $A \cap [0, 1]$, and the measure of a subinterval of the unit interval is its length.

d. *A mixed case.* Suppose that $\mathscr{P}(Z - [0, 1]) = 0$, that $\mathscr{P}(\{0\}) = \mathscr{P}(\{1\}) = \frac{1}{3}$, and that the probability of each subinterval of the unit interval is proportional to its length, so that $\mathscr{P}([a, b]) = (b - a)/3$ if $0 < a \leq b < 1$. Here we have

$$F(x) = \begin{cases} 0 & \text{if } x < 0 \\ (1 + x)/3 & \text{if } 0 \leq x < 1 \\ 1 & \text{if } x \geq 1 \end{cases}$$

The graph of this function is shown in figure 8-1(a), where it is evident that the choices of strict and weak inequalities in the three cases ensure that F is continuous on the right, as required in (2-4)(b).

e. *Density functions.* Where the distribution function F is everywhere continuous, and is differentiable throughout an interval (a, b) to which it assigns probability 1, $F(x)$ is often most conveniently described as the integral $\int_a^x f(x)\, dx$ of a probability density function f, where $f(x) = dF(x)/dx$:

$$F(x) = \begin{cases} 0 & \text{if } x < a \\ \int_a^x f(x)\, dx & \text{if } a \leq x < b \\ 1 & \text{if } x \geq b \end{cases}$$

Thus, in the simplest continuous case, example 2-5(c), we have $(a, b) = (0, 1)$ and $f(x) = 1$. Note, however, that where the distribution function F has discontinuities, the density function f will fail to be normalized, i.e., the condition $\int_a^b f(x)\, dx = 1$ will fail. Thus, in the mixed case (example 2-5(d)), $f(x) = \frac{1}{3}$ throughout the unit interval. Setting $f(x) = 0$ outside the unit interval, we then have $F(x) = F_s(x) + \int_{-\infty}^x f(x)\, dx$ where F_s is the step function graphed in figure 8-1(b) and the second term is the absolutely continuous component of the distribution, graphed in figure 8-1(c). The *normal distribution* with mean 0 and standard deviation σ provides a less trivial example: here the density function is $f(x) = \dfrac{1}{\sigma\sqrt{2\pi}} e^{-x^2/2\sigma^2}$ and F, being continuous, is given by $F(x) = \int_{-\infty}^{x} f(x)\,dx$ for all real x.

Example 2-6. *Lebesgue-Stieltjes probability measures on the plane.* The construction differs from that for Lebesgue measure on the plane only in that the measure of a rectangle need not be its area. In fact,

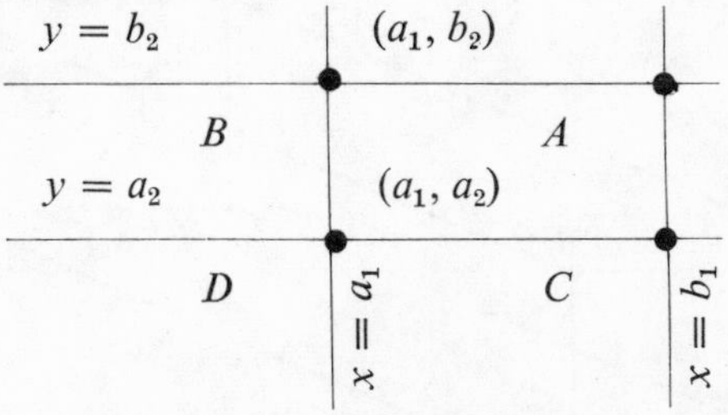

Fig. 2-1. Determining $\mathscr{P}(A)$ in terms of F.

the measure of a rectangle will depend on its location in the $X - Y$ plane, being determined by a two-dimensional distribution function, F, where $F(c, d)$ is interpreted as the probability of the event that $x \leq c$ and $y \leq d$; e.g., in figure 2-1, $F(a_1, b_2)$ is the measure of the quadrant $B \cup D$, and in general, $F(c, d)$ is the measure of the quadrant that lies below and to the left of the point (c, d). Then the probability of the rectangle $A = (a_1, b_1] \times (a_2, b_2]$ can be expressed in terms of the values that F assumes at each of the four corners of A:

(2-6) $$\mathscr{P}_0(A) = \mathscr{P}(A \cup B \cup C \cup D) - \mathscr{P}(B \cup D) - \mathscr{P}(C \cup D) + \mathscr{P}(D)$$
$$= F(b_1, b_2) - F(a_1, b_2) - F(b_1, a_2) + F(a_1, a_2).$$

Apparently, if a function F is to serve as a two-dimensional distribution function, i.e., if we are to have

(2-7) $$F(a, b) = \mathscr{P}((-\infty, a] \times (-\infty, b])$$

for some probability measure $\mathscr{P}$ on the Lebesgue measurable subsets of the plane, then F must have the following properties.

(2-8) **(a)** $F(b_1, b_2) - F(a_1, b_2) - F(b_1, a_2) + F(a_1, a_2) \geq 0$

provided $a_i \leq b_i \quad (i = 1, 2)$.

(b) $F(x^+, y) = F(x, y^+) = F(x, y)$.
(c) $F(-\infty, y) = F(x, -\infty) = 0$; $F(\infty, \infty) = 1$.

These requirements correspond to (2-4)(a)-(c) of the one-dimensional case (example 2-5). (2-8)(a) implies that F is nondecreasing in each variable; it is justified by (2-6). Conversely we can show that if F satisfies requirements (2-8), i.e., if F is a two-dimensional probability distribution, then (2-6) and its variants (cf. 2-5) determine a probability measure $\mathscr{P}_0$ on the class of rectangles, and the Lebesgue extension

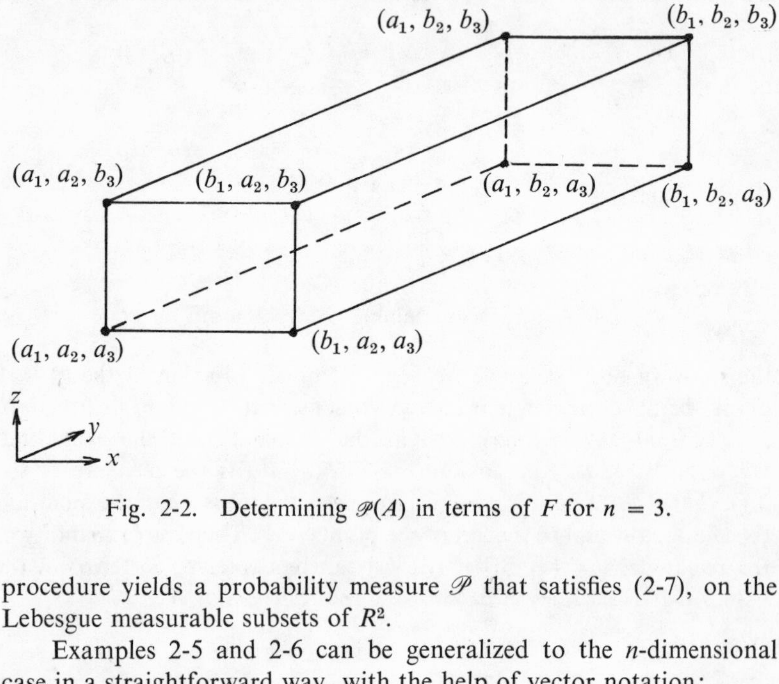

Fig. 2-2. Determining $\mathscr{P}(A)$ in terms of F for $n = 3$.

procedure yields a probability measure $\mathscr{P}$ that satisfies (2-7), on the Lebesgue measurable subsets of R^2.

Examples 2-5 and 2-6 can be generalized to the n-dimensional case in a straightforward way, with the help of vector notation:

(2-9) **(a)** $\vec{x} = (x_1, \ldots, x_n)$.
(b) $\vec{x} \leq \vec{y}$ if-if $x_i \leq y_i$ for each $i = 1, \ldots, n$.
(c) $(\vec{a}, \vec{b}] = \{\vec{x} : \vec{a} < \vec{x} \leq \vec{b}\}$.

Formula (2-6) is generalized by noticing that for $n = 3$ the interval $A = (\vec{a}, \vec{b}]$ is a rectangular parallelopiped, as in figure 2-2. The measure of A can be expressed in terms of the values that F assumes at the eight corners, i.e., in terms of the measures of the octants that lie left of, below, and before those corners. The required expression is the sum of some of these eight values of F with the negatives of the others, the signs being chosen so that everything but $\mathscr{P}(A)$ cancels out:

(2-10)
$$\mathscr{P}(A) = F(b_1, b_2, b_3) - F(b_1, b_2, a_3) - F(b_1, a_2, b_3) - F(a_1, b_2, b_3) + F(a_1, a_2, b_3) + F(a_1, b_2, a_3) + F(b_1, a_2, a_3) - F(a_1, a_2, a_3).$$

In the general n-dimensional case, $\mathscr{P}(A)$ will be the sum of the 2^n terms of the form

(2-11)
$$\pm F(c_1, \ldots, c_n),$$

where each c_i is either a_i or b_i, and the sign is $+$ or $-$ accordingly as the number of a's is even or odd. This sum will be written,

$$\Delta^n F,$$

where the dependence on the interval $(\vec{a}, \vec{b}]$ is not indicated in the notation. Now conditions (2-8) are easily generalized, yielding the following definition. An n-dimensional distribution function is a function, F, on R^n, satisfying the conditions,

(2-12) **(a)** $\Delta^n F \geq 0$ if $\vec{a} \leq \vec{b}$.

(b) F is continuous from the right in each coordinate.

(c) $F(\vec{x}) \to 0$ as any one coordinate $\to -\infty$.

$F(\vec{x}) \to 1$ as all coordinates $\to +\infty$.

Given an n-dimensional distribution function, the stipulation

(2-13)
$$\mathscr{P}((\vec{a}, \vec{b}]) = \Delta^n F$$

determines a unique probability measure $\mathscr{P}$ on the Lebesgue measurable subsets of R^n.

Many probabilistic situations are most conveniently represented in terms of Lebesgue-Stieltjes measures on the set R^∞ of all infinite sequences of real numbers, i.e., equivalently, the set of all real-valued functions, z, on the positive integers, where $z(n)$ is construed as the nth term of the sequence z. (Example 1-1 is a case in point where, however, the functions z can assume only the two values 0 and 1.) The initial semiring $\mathscr{S}$ consists of all the *finite-dimensional intervals*, i.e., all the sets of the form $A_1 \times A_2 \times \ldots$ where for all but a finite number of i's, $A_i = R$, and each of the remaining A's is a finite interval of real numbers. In analogy to the case of R^n for finite n, one may think of a distribution function, F, of an infinite sequence of arguments, which determines a probability measure, $\mathscr{P}$, such that if x is an infinite sequence, $x = (x(1), x(2), \ldots)$, then the probability of the ∞-dimensionally infinite interval $\bigtimes_{n=1}^{\infty} (-\infty, x(n))$ is $F(x)$. But the extension procedure assures us that $\mathscr{P}$ is determined for all such intervals by the values it assigns to the finite-dimensional intervals, so that all values of the function F are determined by the values it assumes when all but a finite number of its arguments are $\mathscr{P}$.

Now if $i_1, \ldots, i_n$ are positive integers where $i_1 < \ldots < i_n$, let $F_{i_1,\ldots,i_n}(x_1, \ldots, x_n)$ be the value that F assumes for an argument sequence all of whose members are ∞ except for the i_1st, . . . , i_nth, which have the respective values $x_1, \ldots, x_n$. Apparently each such $F_{i_1,\ldots,i_n}$ will be a distribution function on R_n, i.e., it will satisfy requirements (2-12). In addition, the infinite collection of all such functions must satisfy certain *consistency requirements*, namely, that for all $x_1, \ldots, x_m$,

(2-14) $$F_{i_1,\ldots,i_m}(x, \ldots, x_m) = F_{i_1,\ldots,i_m,\, i_{m+1},\ldots,i_n}(x_1, \ldots, x_m, \infty, \ldots, \infty)$$

Conversely, suppose that for each finite, increasing sequence $i_1, \ldots, i_n$ of positive integers we are given a function $F_{i_1,\ldots,i_n}$. It can be shown that the indexed set of all such functions determines a p.m. on the space of all Lebesgue measurable subsets of R^∞ if and only if each such function is a distribution function on R^n and the consistency requirements are satisfied, i.e., if and only if all conditions of forms (2-12) and (2-14) hold.

3
Measurable Functions

Not every subset of Z need belong to the σ-field, $\mathscr{E}$; those that do are said to be *measurable*, in the sense that it is to such sets that the measure, $\mathscr{P}$, assigns a probability. Derivatively, a real-valued "point" function, f, defined for all arguments in Z, is said to be measurable if-if the set $\{z: f(z) \leq x\}$ is measurable, for each real number, x; and more generally, f is said to be measurable *on* a set, A, in $\mathscr{E}$, if-if *f agrees on A with* some measurable function, g, in the sense that $f(z) = g(z)$ for all z in A. The special role played by the sets $\{z: f(z) \leq x\}$ in this definition is justified by the fact that all the usual probabilistic questions about point functions can be reduced to questions about sets in the σ-field generated by the class of all sets of that special form. This is a consequence of the fact that the property of measurability is preserved when point functions are subjected to the usual operations of analysis; in particular, sums, products, and absolute powers of measurable functions are measurable; every constant function is measurable; and limits of sequences of measurable functions are measurable if the limit function is defined for every point in Z.[1] Thus, the probability that the value of a function, f, is less than the real number x is the measure of one of the sets,

$$\{z: f(z) \leq x\},$$

that generate the σ-field mentioned above; and the probability that the sequence $f_1, f_2, \ldots$ converges pointwise to the function f is the measure of a set,

$$\bigcap_l \bigcup_m \bigcap_{n>m} \left\{z: |f(z) - f_n(z)| < \frac{1}{l}\right\},$$

in that σ-field.

Example 3-1. In the coin-tossing example, 1-1, taking Z to be the set of all functions from the positive integers to the set (0, 1), the point functions R, R_1, $R_2, \ldots$ are of interest, where $R_n(z)$ is the relative

---

[1] Munroe [1953], §20. If $f, g, f_1, f_2, \ldots$ are real-valued functions defined for all arguments in Z, and a is a real number, then the function, f, such that $f(z) = a$ for all $z \in Z$, is a *constant function;* $|f|^a$, the *a*th *absolute power* of the function f, is the function that assigns the value $|f(z)|^a$ to each point, z, in A; $f + g$ and fg, the *sum* and the *product* of f and g, are the functions that assign the values $f(z) + g(z)$ and $f(z)g(z)$ to each $z \in Z$; the sequence $f_1, f_2, \ldots$ is said to converge (pointwise) to the function f if-if for each z in Z, the sequence $f_1(z)$, $f_2(z), \ldots$ of real numbers converges to the real number $f(z)$; f is then said to be the limit, $\lim_{n\to\infty} f_n$, or $\lim_n f_n$, of the sequence $f_1, f_2, \ldots$.

frequency of heads in the first n tosses in case z, i.e.,

$$R(z) = \frac{1}{n}\sum_{i=1}^{n} z(i),$$

and R is the limit of the sequence $R_1, R_2, \ldots$. To make R_n measurable for each n, we define $\mathscr{E}$ to be the σ-field generated by the class $\mathscr{H} = \{H_1, H_2, \ldots\}$, where $H_n = \{z: z(n) = 1\}$ = the event that the nth toss yields a head. Notice that a point, z, in Z, although a *function* (of positive integers), is not a *point function* (= function on Z); but for each n, f_n and g_n are point functions, where we define

$$f_n(z) = z(n), \qquad g_n(z) = \frac{1}{n}.$$

Then we can write R_n as

$$R_n(z) = g_n(z)[f_1(z) + \ldots + f_n(z)],$$

i.e., as a product of a measurable (constant) function with a finite sum of measurable functions. Then $R_1, R_2, \ldots$ are all measurable, as will be their limit, R, provided it is defined for all z in Z. Unfortunately, it is not.[2]

The definitions of measurability for sets and functions that have been introduced so far make no mention of the measure, $\mathscr{P}$: questions of measurability are simply questions of membership in the σ-field, $\mathscr{E}$. It is convenient, however, to extend the notion by regarding as *almost measurable* any function, f, that agrees with some measurable function, g, "almost everywhere" (a.e.), i.e., except on a set to which $\mathscr{P}$ assigns measure 0. The interesting cases are those in which f is not defined everywhere on Z, but $\mathscr{P}$ assigns measure 0 to the set of points on which f fails to be defined. *Warning:* the term "almost measurable" is nonstandard.

---

[2] To see this, define complementary sets,

$$\begin{array}{llllll} H = \{1, & & 4, 5, 6, 7, & & 16 \ldots\} \\ T = \{ & 2, 3, & & 8, 9, 10, 11, 12, 13, 14, 15, & \ldots\} \end{array}$$

where positive integers are assigned to H or to T, depending in an obvious way on their relation to the members of the sequence

$$1, 2, 4, 8, 16, \ldots,$$

in which each term is twice its predecessor. There is a point, z, in Z, for which $z(n)$ is 1 or 0 accordingly as n belongs to H or T; with this point as argument, the sequence $R_1(z), R_2(z), \ldots$ fails to converge, since the subsequences $R_4(z), R_{16}(z), \ldots, R_{2^{2n}}(z), \ldots$ and $R_8(z), R_{32}(z), \ldots, R_{2^{2n+1}}(z), \ldots$ converge to different limits: 0 and 1.

Example 3-2. The set,

$$\bigcap_{l} \bigcup_{m} \bigcap_{n>m} \left\{ z : |R_m(z) - R_n(z)| < \frac{1}{l} \right\},$$

of points, z, for which the sequence $R_1(z)$, $R_2(z)$, . . . of real numbers converges, is measurable, relative to the σ-field, $\mathscr{E}$, defined in the preceding example. Suppose it has $\mathscr{P}$-measure 1 (as it will have, under the usual assumptions about coin-tossing). Then the function R, defined above as the limit of the sequence R_1, R_2, . . . of measurable functions, will be almost measurable, for since the nonempty set on which it fails to be defined has $\mathscr{P}$-measure 0, R agrees a.e. with a certain measurable function, R':

$$R'(z) = \begin{cases} R(z) & \text{if the sequence } R_1(z), R_2(z), \ldots \text{ converges;} \\ 0 & \text{otherwise.} \end{cases}$$

Real-valued point functions f and g that agree with each other a.e. are said to be *equivalent*: f and g are equivalent if-if $\{z : f(z) \neq g(z)\}$ is measurable and has measure 0. In these terms, to be almost measurable is to be equivalent to a measurable function.

Throughout this section, it is inessential that the measure $\mathscr{P}$ be normalized: all the definitions continue to make sense, and all the theorems continue to hold, if $(Z, \mathscr{E}, \mathscr{P})$ is assumed merely to be a *measure space* (= probability space, except that $\mathscr{P}$ is not required to be normalized). It was to achieve this result that "a.e." was defined, *except on a set of measure* 0, instead of, *on a set of measure* 1. In the sequel it is to be assumed only that $\mathscr{P}$ is a countably additive measure on $\mathscr{E}$. Where the restriction that $\mathscr{P}$ be normalized is intended, it is stated explicitly.

4
Integrals

A measurable function that takes on only finitely many different values as its argument ranges over Z is said to be *simple*. Thus, f is simple if-if it is measurable and there are only a finite number of distinct sets of the form $\{z : f(z) \leq x\}$, even though 'x' may take on any real value. Then if f is simple, there will be sets $A_1, \ldots, A_n$ in $\mathscr{E}$ and real numbers $y_1, \ldots, y_n$ such that for all z in Z, $f(z) = y_i$ if-if $z \in A_i$. The *integral* of f is then identified with the sum of the different values that f takes on, weighted by the measures of the sets on which it takes them:

(4-1) $$\int_Z f \, d\mathscr{P} = \sum_{i=1}^{n} y_i \mathscr{P}(A_i).$$

More generally, we may want to talk about the integral of the simple function, f, on some measurable subset, A, of Z.

(4-2) $$\int_A f \, d\mathscr{P} = \sum_{i=1}^{n} y_i \mathscr{P}(A_i \cap A).$$

In the ordinary (Riemann) theory of integration, the analogue of the set Z might be the unit interval $\{x : 0 \leq x \leq 1\}$; the analogues of the sets $A_1, \ldots, A_n$ are then disjoint subintervals that cover the unit interval; the analogues of the measures, $\mathscr{P}(A_1), \ldots, \mathscr{P}(A_n)$, of the A's are the lengths, $l_1, \ldots, l_n$, of these subintervals; the analogue of the simple function, f, is a "step" function, f, that assumes the constant values $y_1, \ldots, y_n$ on the successive subintervals; the integral,

$$\int_0^1 f(x) \, dx = \sum_{i=1}^{n} y_i l_i,$$

is then the analogue of $\int_Z f \, d\mathscr{P}$. (It is inessential that we write the integrand as 'f' rather than '$f(z)$': in Riemann's theory, too, it is the function, f, rather than the value, $f(x)$, which is being integrated, and the usual notation is mildly misleading on that account. And we write '$d\mathscr{P}$' instead, say, of 'dz', because we shall often wish to explicitly indicate the measure with respect to which the integration is performed, i.e., the measure that is used to determine the weights that are attached to $y_1, \ldots, y\epsilon_n$ in forming the sum that defines the integral. In Riemann integration, the measure is always the same, i.e., the weights of the y's are always the lengths of the corresponding intervals, so that there is no need for an explicit indication of the measure.)

The notion of integration can be extended to measurable functions generally by the following considerations. Any function, f, can be expressed in the form,

$$f = f^+ - f^-,$$

where $f^+(z)$ is $f(z)$ or 0, accordingly as $f(z)$ is positive or not, and $f^-(z)$ is $-f(z)$ or 0, accordingly as $f(z)$ is negative or not. Clearly, f^+ and f^- are both measurable, if f is. Then if we can define the notion of integration for nonnegative measurable functions, we can extend it to measurable functions generally by the stipulation,

(4-3) $$\int_A f\,d\mathscr{P} = \int_A f^+\,d\mathscr{P} - \int_A f^-\,d\mathscr{P}.$$

Of course, for the integral on the left to be well defined, at least one of the integrals on the right must be finite. But it is only when both are finite that f is called *integrable;* in general, f will be called *integrable on* A if-if $\int_A f\,d\mathscr{P}$ exists and is finite.

Any nonnegative measurable function, f, can be expressed as the limit of an infinite sequence of simple functions, $f_1, f_2, \ldots$, and in fact the sequence can always be chosen so as to be *nondecreasing* in the sense that for all z, $f_1(z) \le f_2(z) \le \ldots$.[1] (We may then write, '$f_1 \le f_2 \le \ldots$'.) The final move is to define the integral of f as the limit (if any) of the integrals of $f_1, f_2, \ldots$. This move is justified by the theorem that if two nondecreasing sequences of simple functions converge to the same limit, the limits of their integrals are the same.[2]

We now have the means to discuss *expectations* (= *expected values* = *probability integrals* = integrals with respect to *normalized measures*) of *random variables* (= *stochastic variables* = *measurable functions*.)

Example 4-1. An indestructible coin is to be tossed *ad infinitum;* after each toss (the nth, say), the player receives either nothing or $\frac{1}{2}^n$ units of an infinitely divisible currency, depending on whether the coin landed tail or head up. How much is it worth, to play this game? ("What is the value of this game?") Answer: the value of the game is the expected value of the player's gain. To find this value, let $g_n(z)$ be the player's net gain on the first n tosses in case z, and consider that

---

[1] Given f, such a sequence can be defined by setting $f_n(z)$ equal to n if $f(z) \ge n$, and to $(i-1)/2^n$ if $(i-1)/2^n \le f(z) < i/2^n$ for some $i = 1, 2, \ldots, n2^n$. See Munroe [1953], p. 155. The factor 2^n appears because each ordinate interval for f_i is to be divided into two equal ordinate intervals for f_{i+1}. Notice that if the nonnegative function f is unbounded, there will be no non*increasing* sequence of simple functions which converges to it.

[2] *Ibid.*, §23.

for each positive integer n, g_n is a simple function, where $g_n(z) = \sum_{i=1}^{n} z(i)/2^i$; here, we take Z to be the set of all functions from the positive integers to $\{0, 1\}$, and take $\mathscr{E}$ to be the σ-field generated by the sets $\{z: z(i) = 1\}$, as before. The sequence $g_1, g_2, \ldots$ is nondecreasing, and the function, g, to which it converges, assigns to each z in Z the amount the player would receive (= his gain) in case z. Then the value of the game is $\int_Z g\, d\mathscr{P} = \lim_n \int_Z g_n\, d\mathscr{P}$. To evaluate $\int_Z g_n\, d\mathscr{P}$, consider that the values of g_n other than 0 must be sums of some or all of the first n terms of the infinite sequence

$$\tfrac{1}{2}, \tfrac{1}{4}, \ldots, (\tfrac{1}{2})^n, \ldots,$$

and that each such sum can be obtained in only one way. More explicitly, the possible values of g_n are $0, 1/2^n, 2/2^n, \ldots, (2^n - 1)/2^n$, i.e., the first 2^n nonnegative integral multiples of the smallest possible positive value of f_n, and for each of these values, there is one and only one sequence of outcomes of the first n tosses that makes g_n assume it. Now

$$\int_Z g_n\, d\mathscr{P} = \sum_{i=0}^{2^n-1} (i/2^n)\mathscr{P}(\{z: g_n(z) = i/2^n\}),$$

and, as we have just observed, for each i there is a unique sequence, $a_1, \ldots, a_n$, of zeros and ones, for which

$$\{z: g_n(z) = i/2^n\} = \bigcap_{j=1}^{n} \{z: z(j) = a_j\}.$$

On the usual assumptions about coin tossing, the outcomes of different tosses are independent of one another, so that

$$\mathscr{P}\left(\bigcap_{j=1}^{m} \{z: z(j) = a_j\}\right) = \prod_{j=1}^{m} \mathscr{P}(\{z: z(j) = a_j\});$$

and on each toss, the two possible outcomes are equiprobable, so that

$$\mathscr{P}(\{z: z(j) = 0\}) = \mathscr{P}(\{z: z(j) = 1\}) = \tfrac{1}{2}.$$

Then

$$\mathscr{P}(\{z: g_n(z) = i/2^n\}) = (\tfrac{1}{2})^n,$$

and

$$\int_Z g_n \, d\mathscr{P} = \sum_{i=0}^{2^n-1} (i/2^n)(\tfrac{1}{2})^n$$

$$= (1/2^{2n}) \sum_{i=0}^{2^n-1} i = (1/2^{2n})(2^n - 1)2^{n-1} = \frac{2^n - 1}{2^{n+1}}.$$

Now

$$\int_Z g \, d\mathscr{P} = \lim_n \left(\frac{2^n - 1}{2^{n+1}}\right) = \lim_n \left(\frac{1}{2} - \frac{1}{2^{n+1}}\right) = \frac{1}{2}:$$

the value of the game is $\frac{1}{2}$.

5
Properties of the Integral

It often happens that a measurable function, f, is most naturally defined as the limit of a sequence, $f_1, f_2, \ldots$, of simple functions which fails to satisfy the condition, $f_1 \leq f_2 \leq \ldots$. It may nevertheless be that

(5-1)
$$\int_A f\,d\mathscr{P} = \lim_n \int_A f_n\,d\mathscr{P};$$

in particular, by Lebesgue's *dominated convergence theorem*,[1] this equality will hold whenever the sequence $|f_1|, |f_2|, \ldots$ is *dominated* a.e. by some integrable function, g, i.e., whenever

$$\mathscr{P}(\{z: |f_n(z)| < g(z)\}) = 1 \text{ for each } n.$$

If $f(z)$ is defined for "almost" all z in A, that is, for all z in $A - B$, where $\mathscr{P}(B) = 0$, we may identify $\int_A f\,d\mathscr{P}$ with $\int_{A-B} f\,d\mathscr{P}$, if the latter exists. In general, we set $\int_\varnothing f\,d\mathscr{P} = 0$.

Example 5-1. With $R_n(z) = \frac{1}{n}\sum_{i=1}^{n} z(i) =$ the relative frequency of heads in the first n tosses, as in example 1-1(d), $R = \lim_n R_n$ is defined a.e., and for each n, $|R_n(z)| = R_n(z) \leq 1$, for all z. Then the sequence $|R_1|, |R_2|, \ldots$ is dominated a.e. by the constant function, g, for which $g(z) = 1$ for all z. The function g is integrable; in fact since g is a (very) simple function, $\int_Z g\,d\mathscr{P} = 1\mathscr{P}(Z) = 1$, no matter what normalized measure $\mathscr{P}$ may be. Then $\int_Z R\,d\mathscr{P} = \lim_n \int_Z R_n\,d\mathscr{P}$. The values that R_n can assume are $0/n, i/n, \ldots, n/n$, so that

$$\int_Z R_n\,d\mathscr{P} = \sum_{i=0}^{n} (i/n)\mathscr{P}(\{z: R_n(z) = i/n\}).$$

And on the usual assumptions about coin tossing, each of the $\binom{n}{i}$ sequences of outcomes of the first n tosses in which there are exactly i heads has the same probability, $(\frac{1}{2})^n$. Then

$$\int_Z R_n\,d\mathscr{P} = \sum_{i=0}^{n}(i/n)\binom{n}{i}(\tfrac{1}{2})^n,$$

whence

$$\int_Z R\,d\mathscr{P} = \tfrac{1}{2}\lim_n \sum_{i=0}^{n}(i/n)\binom{n}{i}(\tfrac{1}{2})^{n-1} = \tfrac{1}{2},$$

---

[1] Loève [1963], pp. 125–126.

since

$$\sum_{i=0}^{n}(i/n)\binom{n}{i}(\tfrac{1}{2})^{n-1} = (\tfrac{1}{2})^{n-1}\sum_{i=1}^{n}\binom{n-1}{i-1} = (\tfrac{1}{2})^{n-1}(2^{n-1}) = 1.$$

The integral has the property of countable linearity: for any real numbers, $a_1, a_2, \ldots$, the equation

$$\text{(5-2)} \qquad \int_A \sum_n a_n f_n \, d\mathscr{P} = \sum_n a_n \int_A f_n \, d\mathscr{P}$$

holds, if both sides are well defined.

Example 5-2. *An easier way to find the value of the coin-tossing game in example 4-1.* Let $f_n(z) = z(n) = 1$ or 0 accordingly as the nth toss yields head or tail, and let $a_n = \frac{1}{2}^n =$ the gain from the nth toss, if it yields a head. Then for each n,

$$\int_Z f_n \, d\mathscr{P} = 1\mathscr{P}(\{z : z(n) = 1\}) + 0\mathscr{P}(\{z : z(n) = 0\})$$

$$= (1)(\tfrac{1}{2}) + (0)(\tfrac{1}{2}) = \tfrac{1}{2},$$

so that

$$a_n \int_A f_n \, d\mathscr{P} = \tfrac{1}{2}^{n+1} \quad \text{and} \quad \sum_n a_n \int_A f_n \, d\mathscr{P} = \tfrac{1}{2}\sum_n \tfrac{1}{2}^n = \tfrac{1}{2}.$$

The expected gain from the entire sequence of tosses in case z is $\sum_n a_n f_n(z)$, so that the value of the game $= \int_A \sum_n a_n f_n \, d\mathscr{P} = \frac{1}{2}$.

Where $\mathscr{P}$ is not required to be normalized, the integral is a generalization of the notion of a weighted sum, or nonnegative linear combination. Indeed, if f is a simple function or, more generally, an "elementary function" (= a measurable function that takes on only a countable set, $\{y_i, y_2, \ldots\}$, of distinct values), $\int_Z f \, d\mathscr{P}$ will be literally a weighted sum:

$$y_1 a_1 + y_2 a_2 + \ldots,$$

where the weight a_n, is $\mathscr{P}(\{z : f(z) = y_n\})$, i.e., the integral will be a linear combination of $y_1, y_2, \ldots$, in which the a's are required to be nonnegative. Where $\mathscr{P}$ is normalized (e.g., in the elementary case, where the weights, $a_1, a_2, \ldots$, add up to 1), we have a *convex* linear combination, or a weighted *average*. Thus, in the elementary case, if the y's are bounded, that is, if

$$l < y_1 < y_2 < \ldots < u,$$

then the requirement that the (nonnegative) a's sum to 1 means that

$$y_1 a_1 + y_2 a_2 + \ldots$$

will lie, like the y's severally, between l and u. And in general, if $\mathscr{P}$ is normalized and f is measurable and bounded both above and below, $\int_Z f\,d\mathscr{P}$ will exist and lie at or between the extreme values of f. In particular, the expected value (= probability integral) of an a.e. nonnegative measurable function, f, must be nonnegative.

Summarizing, if we write the *expectation* or *expected value* of f as

(5-3) $$E(f) = \int_Z f\,d\mathscr{P}$$

for normalized $\mathscr{P}$, we have the following properties of expectation for measurable functions f and g.[2]

(5-4) **(a)** $|E(f)| \leq E(|f|)$.
(b) $E(f) \leq E(g)$ if $0 \leq f \leq g$.
(c) $\inf(f) \leq E(f) \leq \sup(f)$.
(d) $E(af + bg) = aE(f) + bE(g)$.
(e) $E(\sum_n f_n) = \sum_n E(f_n)$ if $\sum_n E(|f_n|)$ converges.
(f) $E(f) = E(g)$ if $f = g$ a.e.
(g) $E(f)$ is real if f is bounded above and below.

---

[2] Kolmogorov [1956], p. 39. inf (f) is the infimum or greatest lower bound of the range of values of f; similarly, sup (f) is the supremum or least upper bound of the range of f.

6
Lebesgue-Stieltjes Integrals

The notion of integration in an abstract space arose as a generalization of Lebesgue's concept of integration in the n-dimensional spaces, R^n = the set of all ordered n-tuples of real numbers. Geometrically, R^1 is the real line; R^2 is the plane; R^3 is three-dimensional space. If Z is R^1, and $\mathscr{A}$ is the class of all sets of the form $[x, y) = \{z: x \leq z < y\}$, where $x \leq y$, the members of the σ-field that $\mathscr{A}$ generates are called *Borel Sets*. As we shall see in the following section, there is one and only one countably additive measure, μ, on $\mathscr{E}$, that assigns to each interval, $[x, y)$, in $\mathscr{A}$, its length, $y - x$, as measure. We can now *complete* $\mathscr{E}$, i.e., we can replace $\mathscr{E}$ by the class (in fact, a σ-field), $\mathscr{E}'$, of all sets of the form $A \cup B$, where B is a Borel Set and A is a subset of a Borel Set to which μ assigns measure zero. And we can complete μ, i.e., we can extend its domain of definition from $\mathscr{E}$ to $\mathscr{E}'$ by stipulation that with $A \cup B$ as above,

(6-1) $$\mu(A \cup B) = \mu(B).$$

The sets in $\mathscr{E}'$ are said to be *Lebesgue measurable*, and μ, completed, is called *Lebesgue measure*. In fact, $\mathscr{E}'$ is more inclusive than $\mathscr{E}$ but does not exhaust the subsets of R^1.[1] The integral $\int_A f\, d\mu$ is called the *Lebesgue integral* of f on $A \subset R^1$. If f is Riemann integrable on an interval $[a, b]$, its Riemann integral on $[a, b]$ coincides with its Lebesgue integral. And we have as a necessary and sufficient condition for Riemann integrability on $[a, b]$ that f be continuous a.e. on $[a, b]$, i.e., that the set of points of discontinuity of f on $[a, b]$ have Lebesgue measure zero.[2]

In general, with $Z = R^n$ = the set of all n-tuples of real numbers, let $\mathscr{A}$ be the class of sets of the form

(6-2) $$\bigcap_{i=1}^{n} \{z: x_i \leq z_i < y_i\}$$

for all real $x_i \leq y_i$; let $\mathscr{E}$ be the σ-field generated by $\mathscr{A}$, that is, the class of n-dimensional Borel Sets; and let μ be the countably additive measure that assigns to each n-dimensional interval in $\mathscr{A}$ its n-dimensional "volume" as measure:

(6-3) $$\mu\left(\bigcap_{i=1}^{n} \{z: x_i \leq z_i < y_i\}\right) = \prod_{i=1}^{n} (y_i - x_i).$$

---

[1] Munroe [1953], §18.

[2] *Ibid.*, Theorem 24.4, p. 174.

Complete $\mathscr{E}$ to get the class, $\mathscr{E}'$, of Lebesgue measurable subsets of R^n, and complete μ to get n-dimensional Lebesgue measure. Again, a function, f, on R^n, is Riemann integrable on an n-dimensional interval,

(6-4) $$A = \bigcap_{i=1}^{n} \{z : x_i \leq z_i \leq y_i\}$$

where $x_i \leq y_i$, if-if f is continuous a.e. on A, relative to n-dimensional Lebesgue measure; and if this is the case, the Riemann and Lebesgue integrals of f are the same.

For each positive integer n, let $\mathscr{E}_n$ be the class of all Lebesgue measurable subsets of R^n, and let μ_n be Lebesgue measure on $\mathscr{E}_n$. Then the triple $(R^n, \mathscr{E}_n, \mu_n)$ will be a *measure space*. Where m and n are positive integers, the measure space $(R^{m+n}, \mathscr{E}_{n+m}, \mu_{n+m})$ is said to be the *product* of the measure spaces $(R^m, \mathscr{E}_m, \mu_m)$ and $(R^n, \mathscr{E}_n, \mu_n)$, and the measure μ_{m+n} is said to be the product of the measures μ_m and μ_n. In general, if $(Z', \mathscr{E}', \mathscr{P}')$ and $(Z'', \mathscr{E}'', \mathscr{P}'')$ are measure spaces, their product is the space $(Z, \mathscr{E}, \mathscr{P})$ in which (a) $Z = Z' \times Z''$, that is, Z is the Cartesian product of Z' and Z'' (the set of all pairs, (z', z''), with z' in Z' and z'' in Z''), in which (b) $\mathscr{E}$ is the σ-field generated by the class of all sets of the form $A' \times A''$ with A' in $\mathscr{E}'$ and A'' in $\mathscr{E}''$, and in which (c) μ is the unique countably additive measure on $\mathscr{E}$ such that $\mu(A' \times A'') = \mu'(A')\mu''(A'')$ for all $A' \in \mathscr{E}'$ and $A'' \in \mathscr{E}''$.

According to a theorem of Cauchy, integration of any continuous function on an interval $\bigcap_{i=1}^{m+n} \{z : x_i \leq z_i \leq y_i\}$ in R^{m+n} can be reduced to successive integration on the intervals

$$\bigcap_{i=1}^{m} \{z : x_i \leq z_i < y_i\} \quad \text{and} \quad \bigcap_{i=m+1}^{m+n} \{z : x_i \leq z_i < y_i\}$$

in R^m and R^n; e.g., the integral of f, where $f(x, y) = xy$, on the unit square $[0, 1] \times [0, 1]$, can be replaced by two integrations on the unit interval:

$$\int_0^1 \left(\int_0^1 xy\, dx \right) dy = \int_0^1 (y/2)\, dy = \tfrac{1}{4}.$$

Lebesgue (1904) extended this theorem to all bounded Lebesgue measurable functions, and Fubini (1907) extended it further to all Lebesgue integrable functions. In its most general form the theorem refers to products $(Z, \mathscr{E}, \mathscr{P})$ of ordered pairs $(Z', \mathscr{E}', \mathscr{P}')$, $(Z'', \mathscr{E}'', \mathscr{P}'')$ of measure spaces, and uses only the hypothesis that $\mathscr{P}'$ and $\mathscr{P}''$ are *σ-finite:* that Z' and Z'', if not of finite measure relative to $\mathscr{P}'$ and $\mathscr{P}''$, are at least expressible as unions of countable classes of sets in $\mathscr{E}'$ and $\mathscr{E}''$ of finite measure.

Example 6-1. Lebesgue measure on R^1 is σ-finite, since $R^1 = \bigcup_i \{z: i \leq z < i + 1\}$ where 'i' ranges over the integers, which are countable, and each set in the union has finite Lebesgue measure, namely, 1.

To state Fubini's theorem in its abstract form we introduce the following notation. Let f be a function of two arguments, integrable relative to a product space $(Z, \mathscr{E}, \mathscr{P})$ of which the component spaces are $(Z', \mathscr{E}', \mathscr{P}')$ and $(Z'', \mathscr{E}'', \mathscr{P}'')$ in that order. Let f_1 and f_2 be functions that satisfy the conditions

$$f_1(z') = \int_{Z''} f(z', \quad) \, d\mathscr{P}'', \qquad f_2(z'') = \int_{Z'} f(\quad, z'') \, d\mathscr{P}',$$

for all z' in Z' and z'' in Z''. (Under the hypotheses of the theorem, such functions exist and are integrable relative to the respective component spaces.) In this notation, Fubini's theorem implies that

$$\text{(6-5)} \qquad \int_Z f \, d\mathscr{P} = \int_{Z'} f_1 \, d\mathscr{P}' = \int_{Z''} f_2 \, d\mathscr{P}''$$

if the three integrals exist, as they do if the first does, under the hypothesis that $\mathscr{P}'$ and $\mathscr{P}''$ are σ-finite. (The full theorem asserts (6-5) under somewhat weaker conditions: see Munroe [1953], p. 207.)

The notations 'f_1' and 'f_2' in (6-5) are nonstandard but clear. In a more common notation, (6-5) would be written as

$$\text{(6-6)} \quad \int_{Z' \times Z''} f \, d\mathscr{P} = \int_{Z'} \left(\int_{Z''} f \, d\mathscr{P}'' \right) d\mathscr{P}' = \int_{Z''} \left(\int_{Z'} f \, d\mathscr{P}' \right) d\mathscr{P}'',$$

in which the two parenthesized integrals are to be understood as f_1 and f_2, respectively. (Often, the parentheses are omitted.)

7

Extensions and Mixtures of Measures; Stationary, Symmetric, and Bernoullian Measures

We must now develop some facts about particular measures on the σ-field, $\mathscr{E}$. Often, $\mathscr{E}$ will be defined as the σ-field generated by some class, $\mathscr{A}$, of subsets of Z.

Example 7-1. When we are particularly interested in the behavior of a sequence $f_1, f_2, \ldots$ of point functions, $\mathscr{A}$ may be taken as the class of all sets of the form

$$\{z: x \leq f_i(z) < y\}$$

for positive integral i and real $x \leq y$. In such cases, a countably additive measure, $\mathscr{P}$, may be defined on $\mathscr{E}$ by first defining it on the *field*, $\mathscr{F}$, generated by $\mathscr{A}$, and then invoking the following theorem. (Notice that the σ-field generated by $\mathscr{F}$ is identical with $\mathscr{E}$, the σ-field generated by $\mathscr{A}$.)

Extension theorem. Let $\mathscr{E}$ be the σ-field generated by a field, $\mathscr{F}$, and let $\mathscr{P}'$ be a countably additive measure on $\mathscr{F}$. Then there exists one and only one countably additive measure, $\mathscr{P}$, on $\mathscr{E}$, that agrees with $\mathscr{P}'$ on $\mathscr{F}$.[1]

Further, to define $\mathscr{P}$ on $\mathscr{F}$, it is sufficient to determine the values it assigns to all finite intersections of members of $\mathscr{A}$, provided $\mathscr{P}(A)$ is finite for all A in $\mathscr{A}$. (The "intersection" of a single event is that event itself. Similarly, $\bigcup \{A\} = A$.)

Proof: any event in $\mathscr{F}$ other than $\varnothing$ can be expressed in disjunctive normal form as the union of some finite, disjoint class, $\mathscr{B}$, each member of which is a finite intersection of members of $\mathscr{A}$ and/or complements of members of $\mathscr{A}$. Then $\mathscr{P}(\bigcup \mathscr{B}) = \sum_{B \in \mathscr{B}} (B)$, where B is either an intersection of members of $\mathscr{A}$ (in which case the point is made), or is of the form $B' \cap \bar{A}$, where $A \in \mathscr{A}$. In the latter case, $\mathscr{P}(B) = \mathscr{P}(B') - \mathscr{P}(B' \cap A)$, where B' has one less complemented member of A as a component than B had. Proceeding in this way, one eventually expresses $\mathscr{P}(\bigcup \mathscr{B})$ as a linear combination of probabilities of finite intersections of members of $\mathscr{A}$.

---

[1] Kolmogorov [1956], p. 17.

Example 7-2.

$$\begin{aligned}\mathscr{P}((A_1 \cup \bar{A}_2) \cap (\bar{A}_1 \cup A_2)) &= \mathscr{P}(\bigcup \{A_1 \cap A_2, \bar{A}_1 \cap \bar{A}_2\}) \\ &= \mathscr{P}(Z) - \mathscr{P}(A_1) - \mathscr{P}(A_2) \\ &\qquad + 2\mathscr{P}(A_1 \cap A_2).\end{aligned}$$

If $\mathscr{P}(A)$ is finite for all A in $\mathscr{A}$, $\mathscr{P}((A_1 \cup \bar{A}_2) \cap (\bar{A}_1 \cup A_2))$ is well defined, and is finite if-if $\mathscr{P}$ is normalizable.

In the sequel, we shall often be interested in *symmetric* classes (or sequences) of events. A denumerable subclass, $\mathscr{A}$, of $\mathscr{E}$, is said to be symmetric, relative to $\mathscr{P}$ (and $\mathscr{P}$ may be said to be symmetric, relative to $\mathscr{A}$), if-if for each positive integer n, each intersection of n distinct members of $\mathscr{A}$ has the same probability, say p_n. Then if $\mathscr{E}$ is generated by $\mathscr{A}$, $\mathscr{P}$ can be determined on $\mathscr{E}$ by specifying the infinite sequence of numbers, $p_1, p_2, \ldots$. If A_n is thought of as the event that the nth trial of an experiment is successful, then symmetry of $\mathscr{A}$ implies constant probability of success from trial to trial. In the special ("Bernoullian") case where outcomes of different trials are independent, the entire sequence of p's is determined by p_1, since $p_n = (p_1)^n$. In the Bernoullian case, we shall write 'p' for p_1.

Suppose that $\mathscr{E}$ is generated by a denumerable class, $\mathscr{A}$, of events, and that for each real number, p, in the unit interval, $\mathscr{P}_x$ is the Bernoullian probability measure on $\mathscr{E}$ (relative to $\mathscr{A}$) for which $p = x$. Define a particular probability measure, $\mathscr{P}$, by the stipulation that for each E in $\mathscr{E}$,

(7-1)
$$\mathscr{P}(E) = \int_0^1 \mathscr{P}_x(E)\, dx.$$

In particular, if E is the intersection of n distinct events in $\mathscr{A}$, then

$$\mathscr{P}(E) = \int_0^1 x^n\, dx = 1/(n+1),$$

while if E is the intersection of n distinct events in $\mathscr{A}$ and the complements of m other, distinct events in $\mathscr{A}$,

$$\mathscr{P}(E) = \int_0^1 p^n(1-p)^m\, dp = \frac{n!m!}{(n+m+1)!}.$$

(cf. Carnap's $\mathscr{M}^*$).

Example 7-3. *Tossing a bent coin.* One who believes that outcomes of different tosses are independent, with constant but completely unknown probability, p, of getting a head on each toss, may have $\mathscr{P}$, as defined above, as his subjective probability measure. Here, $\mathscr{A}$ is the class of events of the form $H_n = \{z : z(n) = 1\}$ $(n = 1, 2, \ldots)$. Notice that $\mathscr{P}$, unlike any of the $\mathscr{P}_p$'s, allows one to learn from experience; e.g.,

$$\lim_n \mathscr{P}(H_{n+1} \mid H_1 \cap \ldots \cap H_n) = \lim_n (1/(n+2))/(1/(n+1)) = 1,$$

whereas

$$\lim_n \mathscr{P}_p(H_{n+1} \mid H_1 \cap \ldots \cap H_n) = \lim_n p^{n+1}/p^n = p = \mathscr{P}_p(H_{n+1}),$$

so that $\mathscr{P}_p$ "ignores" the evidence, $H_1 \cap \ldots \cap H_n$.

In general, mixtures (= convex linear combinations = probability integrals) of probability measures (= normalized, countably additive measures) on the same σ-field, $\mathscr{E}$, will again be probability measures on $\mathscr{E}$. There is some interest in formulating this statement exactly, and in proving it, both as an illustration of the generality of the notion of integration in an abstract space, and as a preparation for the ideas of §10, below.

Let Z' be the set of all possible probability measures, $\mathscr{P}$, on a certain σ-field, $\mathscr{E}$, of subsets of a possibility space, Z. Let $\mathscr{E}'$ be the σ-field generated by the class of subsets of Z' of the form

$$\{\mathscr{P} : \mathscr{P}(E) \leq x\},$$

where E may be any member of $\mathscr{E}$, and x may be any real number. And let $\mathscr{P}'$ be a probability measure on $\mathscr{E}'$. Corresponding to each event, E, in $\mathscr{E}$, define a point function, f_E, on Z', such that

$$f_E(\mathscr{P}) = \mathscr{P}(E).$$

Then f_E is measurable, since $\{\mathscr{P} : f_E(\mathscr{P}) \leq x\}$ is $\{\mathscr{P} : \mathscr{P}(E) \leq x\}$, which is one of the sets that generate $\mathscr{E}'$. Now define a set function, $\mathscr{Q}$, on $\mathscr{E}$, by the equation

$$\mathscr{Q}(E) = \int_{Z'} f_E \, d\mathscr{P}',$$

which is to hold for all E in $\mathscr{E}$. $\mathscr{Q}$ is normalized, nonnegative, and countably additive on $\mathscr{E}$ because each $\mathscr{P}$ in Z' has these properties on $\mathscr{E}$, because $\mathscr{P}'$ has them on $\mathscr{E}'$, and because the integral has the properties noted in §5. Normalized: since $f_Z(\mathscr{P}) = \mathscr{P}(Z) = 1$ for all $\mathscr{P}$ in Z', we have $\mathscr{Q}(Z) = \int_{Z'} f \, d\mathscr{P}' = 1\mathscr{P}'(Z) + 0\mathscr{P}'(\varnothing) = 1$. Nonnegative: $\mathscr{Q}(E) \geq 0$, because $f_E(\mathscr{P}) = \mathscr{P}(E) \geq 0$ for all $\mathscr{P}$ in Z'. Countably additive: if $\mathscr{A}$ is a disjoint, countable subclass of $\mathscr{E}$, then

$$f_{\bigcup \mathscr{A}}(\mathscr{P}) = \mathscr{P}(\bigcup \mathscr{A}) = \sum_{A \in \mathscr{A}} \mathscr{P}(A) = \sum_{A \in \mathscr{A}} f_A(\mathscr{P});$$

therefore,

$$\mathscr{Q}(\bigcup \mathscr{A}) = \int_{Z'} f_{\cup \mathscr{A}}\, d\mathscr{P}' = \int_{Z'} \sum_{A \in \mathscr{A}} f_A\, d\mathscr{P}'$$

$$= \sum_{A \in \mathscr{A}} \int_{Z'} f_A\, d\mathscr{P}' = \sum_{A \in \mathscr{A}} \mathscr{Q}(A).$$

Then mixtures of probability measures are always probability measures themselves. Furthermore, it is easy to show that if all the measures in the mixture are symmetric with respect to some denumerable subset, $\mathscr{A}$, of $\mathscr{E}$, then so is the mixture itself. For suppose Z', above, contains all and only the probability measures on $\mathscr{E}$ with respect to which $\mathscr{A}$ is symmetric. (Equivalently, we could have left Z' as before, but assumed instead that $\mathscr{P}'(\mathscr{S}) = 1$, where $\mathscr{S}$ is the set of all such measures.) Consider $\mathscr{Q}(A) = \int_{Z'} f_A\, d\mathscr{P}'$, where A is the intersection of some n distinct members of $\mathscr{A}$. By symmetry of $\mathscr{P}$, $f_A(\mathscr{P}) = \mathscr{P}(A) = p_n$, where p_n depends on $\mathscr{P}$ and on n, but not on the particular n sets whose intersection is A. Then $\mathscr{Q}(A) = \mathscr{Q}(B)$, where B is any other intersection of n distinct sets in $\mathscr{A}$, and $\mathscr{Q}$ is symmetric with respect to $\mathscr{A}$. It follows in particular that mixtures of Bernoullian measures are always symmetric (but not, in general, Bernoullian, as example 7-3 shows).

An infinite sequence, $A_1, A_2, \ldots$, of events in $\mathscr{E}$ is said to be *stationary* with respect to $\mathscr{P}$ if-if

$$\mathscr{P}(A_{i_1} \cap \ldots \cap A_{i_n}) = \mathscr{P}(A_{i_1+h} \cap \ldots \cap A_{i_n+h})$$

for all positive integers n and h, and all n-tuples, $i_1, \ldots, i_n$, of distinct positive integers. Thus, stationarity means invariance of $\mathscr{P}$ under all "translations" of $A_1, A_2, \ldots$ to the right. (In these terms, symmetry means invariance of $\mathscr{P}$ under all permutations of $A_1, A_2, \ldots$, and is clearly a special case of stationarity.) By an argument similar to the one in the last paragraph, one can prove that stationarity, like symmetry, is preserved under the operation of mixing probability measures.

The peculiar importance of the property of stationarity derives from the following *strong law of large numbers.*[2]

(7-2) If the sequence of events, $A_1, A_2, \ldots$, is stationary with respect to $\mathscr{P}$, and if $f_n(z)$ is 1 or 0 accordingly as z does or does not belong to A_n, then $\mathscr{P}\left\{z: \lim_n \frac{1}{n} \sum_{i=1}^{n} f_n(z) \text{ does not exist}\right\} = 0.$

---

[2] Doob [1953], pp. 464 ff.

Example 7-4. On the usual (Bernoullian) assumptions, coin tossing is a stationary process. If $A_n = H_n =$ the event that the nth toss yields a head, then $\frac{1}{n}\sum_{i=1}^{n} f_n(z) = R_n(z) =$ the relative frequency of heads in the first n tosses in case z, so that by the strong law of large numbers, R $(= \lim_n R_n =$ the limiting relative frequency of head) is defined a.e.

The notions of stationarity, symmetry, and "Bernoullianity" (independence, with constant probability of success) are easily generalized from sequences of events to sequences of measurable functions. The sequence $f_1, f_2, \ldots$ is said to be *stationary* with respect to $\mathscr{P}$ if-if for each positive integer n, for each n-tuple $(x_1, \ldots, x_n)$ of real numbers, for each n-tuple $(i_1, \ldots, i_n)$ of distinct positive integers, and for each individual positive integer h,

$$\text{(7-3)} \qquad \mathscr{P}\left(\bigcap_{j=1}^{n}\{z: f_{i_j}(z) < x_j\}\right) = \mathscr{P}\left(\bigcap_{j=1}^{n}\{z: f_{i_j+h}(z) < x_j\}\right).$$

The sequence $f_1, f_2, \ldots$ (and the set $\{f_1, f_2, \ldots\}$) is said to be *symmetric* with respect to $\mathscr{P}$ if-if for all $n, x_1, \ldots, x_n, i_1, \ldots, i_n$ as above, and for all permutations (= one-to-one mappings into themselves), $\prod$, of the positive integers,

$$\text{(7-4)} \qquad \mathscr{P}\left(\bigcap_{j=1}^{n}\{z: f_{i_j}(z) < x_j\}\right) = \mathscr{P}\left(\bigcap_{j=1}^{n}\{z: f_{\pi(i_j)}(z) < x_j\}\right).$$

The f's are said to be *independent and identically distributed* (or, *Bernoullian*) relative to $\mathscr{P}$ if-if for all $n, x_1, \ldots, x_n, i_1, \ldots, i_n, \prod$ as above,

$$\text{(7-5)} \qquad \mathscr{P}\left(\bigcap_{j=1}^{n}\{z: f_{i_j}(z) < x_j\}\right) = \prod_{j=1}^{n} \mathscr{P}(\{z: f_{\pi(i_j)}(z) < x_j\}).$$

Clearly, with respect to a measure, $\mathscr{P}$, every Bernoullian sequence of measurable functions is symmetric, and every symmetric sequence of measurable functions is stationary. Again, the strong law of large numbers holds: if $f_1, f_2, \ldots$ is stationary with respect to $\mathscr{P}$, and if $|f_1|$ is integrable, then

$$\text{(7-6)} \qquad \mathscr{P}\left(\left\{z: \lim_n \frac{1}{n}\bigcap_{i=1}^{n} f_i(z) \text{ does not exist}\right\}\right) = 0.$$

8
Indefinite Integrals and Derivatives

Any function, f, that is integrable in a measure space $(Z, \mathscr{E}, \mathscr{P})$ determines a set function, φ, on $\mathscr{E}$, by the condition that

$$\text{(8-1)} \qquad \varphi(E) = \int_E f \, d\mathscr{P}$$

for all E in $\mathscr{E}$. φ is then called the *indefinite integral* of f, and f is called a *Radon-Nikodym derivative* of φ. It is clear that φ is real-valued, countably additive, and *absolutely continuous* relative to $\mathscr{P}$ (i.e., φ vanishes wherever $\mathscr{P}$ does). Conversely, we have the

Radon-Nikodym theorem. If a set function, φ, on a σ-field, $\mathscr{E}$, is real-valued, countably additive, and absolutely continuous with respect to a σ-finite measure, $\mathscr{P}$, on $\mathscr{E}$, then φ is the indefinite integral of some function, f, i.e., there is an integrable function, f, such that for all E in $\mathscr{E}$,

$$\varphi(E) = \int_E f \, d\mathscr{P}.$$ [1]

A countably additive function, φ, on a σ-field, $\mathscr{E}$, of subsets of Z, is called *singular* relative to a measure, $\mathscr{P}$, on $\mathscr{E}$, if-if there is a set, E_0, in $\mathscr{E}$, of $\mathscr{P}$-measure 0, such that $\varphi(E) = 0$ if $E \subset Z - E_0$. (Only the constant function for which $\varphi(E) = 0$ for all E in $\mathscr{E}$ is both absolutely continuous and singular.) Any countably additive function, φ, on $\mathscr{E}$, has a unique *Lebesgue decomposition*, i.e., it can be expressed in one and only one way as the sum of an absolutely continuous function and a singular function, relative to $\mathscr{P}$.[2]

Example 8-1. *Tossing a bent coin.* In example 7-3 we supposed that the unknown probability of heads is equally likely to lie in either of any two equal subintervals of the unit interval. This assumption was formalized in (7-1), which is of form

$$\text{(8-2)} \qquad \mathscr{P}(E) = \int_0^1 \mathscr{P}_x \, dF(x)$$

with $F(x) = x$ in the unit interval, $F(x) = 0$ if $x \leq 0$, and $F(x) = 1$ if $x > 1$. Other hypotheses about the unknown probability of heads can be expressed by other assumptions about the behavior of F in the unit

---

[1] Munroe [1953], §27.
[2] Saks [1937], pp. 33–44.

interval. Thus, suppose we have $F(x) = (1 + x)/3$ for $0 \leq x < 1$, with $F(x) = 0$ if $x < 0$ and $F(x) = 1$ if $x \geq 1$. (See fig. 8-1(a).) (8-2) then determines a probability measure $\mathscr{P}$ that would express the views of a man who is convinced that the coin-tossing process is Bernoullian, and who regards the following three possibilities as equally likely. (a) The coin has two heads. (b) The coin has two tails. (c) The coin is as in example 7-3. The singular component of $\mathscr{P}$ is determined by the distribution function F_s where $F_s(x) = 0$ if $x < 0$, $F_s(x) = \frac{1}{3}$ for x in $[0, 1)$, and $F_s(x) = \frac{2}{3}$ if $x \geq 1$. (See fig. 8-1(b).) The absolutely continuous component of $\mathscr{P}$ is determined by the distribution function F_c

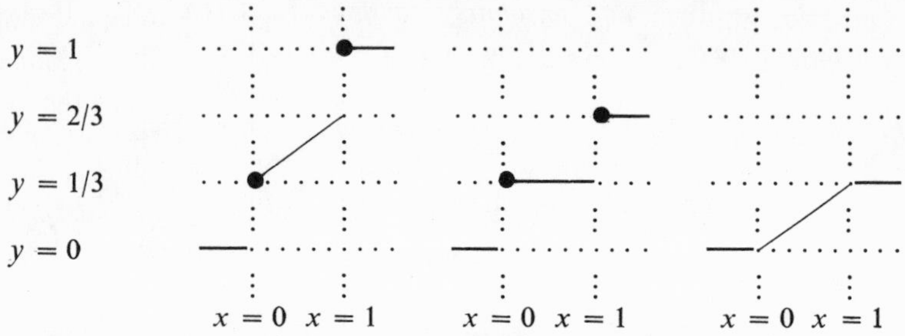

(a) $y = F(x)$ (b) $y = F_s(x)$ (c) $y = F_c(x)$

Fig. 8-1. Lebesgue decomposition of $F(x) = F_s(x) + F_c(x)$.

where $F_c(x) = 0$ if $x < 0$, $F_c(x) = x/3$ if x is in $[0, 1)$, and $F_c(x) = \frac{1}{3}$ if $x \geq 1$. (See fig. 8-1(c).)

Ordinarily, an absolutely continuous set function, φ, will have many derivatives, for if f is a derivative of φ, and g agrees a.e. with f, then g will also be a derivative of φ, since for all E in $\mathscr{E}$,

$$0 = \int_E (f - g)\, d\mathscr{P} = \int_E f\, d\mathscr{P} - \int_E g\, d\mathscr{P} = \varphi(E) - \int_E g\, d\mathscr{P},$$

so that

$$\varphi(E) = \int_E g\, d\mathscr{P}.$$

But the result of differentiation, if not unique, is "almost" unique, i.e., any two derivatives of the same set function, φ, will agree a.e. This near uniqueness is rather weak: typically, if z is a point in Z, $\mathscr{P}(\{z\}) = 0$, so that for any real number, there will be a Radon-Nikodym derivative of φ which assumes that number as its value, for the argument z.

The derivative of an absolutely continuous function, φ, can also be defined by a limiting process reminiscent of the definition of the derivative in elementary calculus. The basic idea is that the derivative of φ, with respect to $\mathscr{P}$, at a point z, ought to be $\varphi(\{z\})/\mathscr{P}(\{z\})$, if $\mathscr{P}(\{z\})$ is positive. If (as usual) this is not the case, the derivative is to be defined as a limit of such quotients: choose a sequence $\mathscr{S} = (E_1, E_2, \ldots)$ of sets in $\mathscr{E}$ such that $E_{n+1} \subset E_n$ for $n = 1, 2, \ldots$ and such that $\bigcap_n E_n = \{z\}$, and define the derivative of φ at z as $\lim_n \varphi(E_n)/\mathscr{P}(E_n)$. Unfortunately, the result will ordinarily depend on the particular sequence $\mathscr{S}$ chosen, so that one cannot speak simply of *the* derivative of φ at z; one must in effect mention $\mathscr{S}$.

Suppose, then, that $\mathscr{P}$ is σ-finite, and that $(Z, \mathscr{E}, \mathscr{P})$ is a measure space. A *net* in this space is defined as a countable division of Z in which the individual sets ("meshes") all belong to $\mathscr{E}$ and have finite measure. A sequence, $\mathscr{N} = (\mathscr{N}_1, \mathscr{N}_2, \ldots)$, of nets is called *monotone* if-if for each positive integer n, $\mathscr{N}_{n+1}$ is a *refinement* of $\mathscr{N}_n$ in the sense that every member of $\mathscr{N}_n$ is the union of certain members of $\mathscr{N}_{n+1}$. For each z in Z, let $[z]_n$ be the mesh of $\mathscr{N}_n$ that contains z. Relative to a countably additive function, φ, on $\mathscr{E}$, we define a sequence $d_1, d_2, \ldots$ of point functions:

(8-3)
$$d_n(z) = \begin{cases} \varphi([z]_n)/\mathscr{P}([z]_n) & \text{if} \quad \mathscr{P}([z]_n) > 0, \\ \infty \quad \text{if} \quad \varphi([z]_n) \geq 0 & \text{and} \quad \mathscr{P}([z]_n) = 0, \\ -\infty \quad \text{if} \quad \varphi([z]_n) < 0 & \text{and} \quad \mathscr{P}([z]_n) = 0. \end{cases}$$

The derivative of φ at z, relative to $\mathscr{P}$ and $\mathscr{N}$, is defined as the real limit (if any) of the sequence $d_1(z), d_2(z), \ldots$, and denoted by

(8-4)
$$D_{\varphi,\mathscr{P},\mathscr{N}}(z).$$

In general, if $\mathscr{M}$ and $\mathscr{N}$ are different monotone sequences of nets, there is no assurance that $D_{\varphi,\mathscr{P},\mathscr{M}}$ and $D_{\varphi,\mathscr{P},\mathscr{N}}$ will be the same, where they both exist. But if $\mathscr{M}$ and $\mathscr{N}$ are both *regular* on each set in $\mathscr{E}$, in a sense defined below,[3] and if φ is absolutely continuous with respect to $\mathscr{P}$, then these two derivatives are defined and equal a.e. In that case, each of them is a Radon-Nikodym derivative of φ, i.e., for all E in $\mathscr{E}$,

$$\varphi(E) = \int_E D_{\varphi,\mathscr{P},\mathscr{M}}\, d\mathscr{P} = \int_E D_{\varphi,\mathscr{P},\mathscr{N}}\, d\mathscr{P}.$$

$\mathscr{N}$ is said to be regular on $E \in \mathscr{E}$ with respect to $\mathscr{P}$ if-if for each positive real number, ϵ, there is a sequence $N_1, N_2, \ldots$ of meshes of

[3] Regularity of sequences of nets is completely unrelated to regularity of $\mathscr{C}$-functions, in Carnap's sense.

nets in $\mathscr{N}$ such that $\bigcup_n N_n$ "almost" subsumes E, in the sense that

(8-5) $$\mathscr{P}\left(E - \bigcup_n N_n\right) = 0,$$

and such that

(8-6) $$\mathscr{P}\left(\bigcup_n N_n\right) - \mathscr{P}(E) \leq \epsilon.$$

These two conditions say that E can be approximated arbitrarily closely, "almost" from without, by unions of countable subsets of $\bigcup_n \bigcap_n$.[4]

To make use of the notion of regularity, we need ways of recognizing it. In case $\mathscr{P}$ is defined on $\mathscr{E}$ by the method described at the beginning of §4, we have a useful criterion:[5] $\mathscr{N}$ is regular one very set in $\mathscr{E}$ if it is regular on every set in the class, $\mathscr{A}$, on which $\mathscr{P}$ was initially defined.

Where Z is construed as a metric space, the situation is equally simple.[16] Call a sequence of nets *metrically regular* if-if it is monotone, and the suprema of the diameters of the meshes of successive nets in the sequence converge to 0. Metrically regular sequences of nets exist in Z if-if Z is *separable*, i.e., if-if every open sphere in Z contains points in a certain fixed denumerable subset of Z. (Such a subset is said to be *everywhere dense* in Z.) Now if φ is countably additive on $\mathscr{E}$, if $\mathscr{P}$ is σ-finite, and if $\mathscr{M}$ and $\mathscr{N}$ are two metrically regular sequences of nets in Z, then $D_{\varphi,\mathscr{P},\mathscr{M}} = D_{\varphi,\mathscr{P},\mathscr{N}}$ a.e.; and if E is the set of points on which these derivatives fail to be both defined, or, if defined, fail to be equal, then $\varphi(A) = 0$ for every subset, $A \in \mathscr{E}$, of E.[17] And if φ is absolutely continuous, relative to $\mathscr{P}$, then $D_{\varphi,\mathscr{P},\mathscr{M}}$ and $D_{\varphi,\mathscr{P},\mathscr{N}}$ will both be Radon-Nikodym derivatives of φ.

---

[4] Munroe [1953], §43.

[5] *Ibid.*

[6] Z is a *pseudo-metric space*, relative to a *pseudo-metric*, or *pseudo-distance function*, d, if-if $d(z, z) = 0$ for every z in Z, and $d(z, z') \leq d(z'', z) + d(z'', z')$ for every z, z', and z'' in Z. If-if, in addition, $d(z, z') = 0$ only if $z = z'$, the qualification "pseudo-" can be dropped. For our purposes it is sufficient to suppose that Z is a pseudo-metric space in which the pseudo-metric, d, is related to $\mathscr{P}$ by the condition that $\mathscr{P}(A \cup B) = \mathscr{P}(A) + \mathscr{P}(B)$ if $d(A, B) \neq 0$, if A and B are in $\mathscr{E}$. Here, $d(A, B)$ is defined as the infimum of the distances between points in A and points in B. Similarly, the *diameter* of a subset of Z is understood to be the supremum of the distances between points in that subset. The *closed sphere* with center z and radius x is $\{z' : d(z, z') \leq x\}$; to obtain the definition of *open sphere*, replace '$\leq$' αy '$<$'.

[7] Saks [1937], p. 152.

Example 8-2. Let Z be R^3, let $\mathscr{P} = \mu =$ Lebesgue measure on R^3, and let d be the usual Euclidean metric on R^3, i.e., $d(x, y) = \sqrt{\sum_{i=1}^{3} (x_i - y_i)^2}$. Then open spheres relative to d are literally (interiors of) spheres. R^3 is separable, since the set of all ordered triples of rational numbers is countable, and everywhere dense in R^3. The simplest metrically regular sequences of nets in R^3 are those in which the meshes are cubes, $\bigcap_{i=1}^{3} \{x: a < x_i \leq b\}$, where $a < b$.

9

Conditioning: Probabilities and Expectations as Random Variables

When $\mathscr{P}(A)$ is positive, the conditional probability $\mathscr{P}(E \mid A)$ is determined as the ratio $\mathscr{P}(E \cap A)/\mathscr{P}(A)$, but when $\mathscr{P}(A)$ is zero we have more latitude: We may assign no denotation at all to the expression '$\mathscr{P}(E \mid A)$,' or we may assign it a value chosen with an eye to (say) continuity, setting $\mathscr{P}(E \mid A) = \lim_n \mathscr{P}(E \mid A_n)$ where $A_1, A_2, \ldots$ is some appropriate nested sequence of propositions of positive probability whose intersection is A.

Example 9-1. A might be the event that a certain random variable f assumes the value a, i.e., $A = \{z: f(z) = a\}$. If f's distribution function is continuous and increasing at the argument a, and if $I_1, I_2, \ldots$ is a nested sequence of open intervals whose intersection is $\{a\}$, then we might set $A_n = \{z: f(z) \in I_n\}$. $\mathscr{P}(A_n)$ is then positive for each n, and the limit $\lim_n \mathscr{P}(E \mid A_n)$ exists and has the same value, no matter what particular intervals may have been chosen.

To get an overview of the situation it is useful to generalize the concept of conditional probability, following Kolmogorov [1933] and Doob [1953]. (The present exposition is based on Billingsley [1965].) The result is a concept of probability *conditioned on the outcome of an experiment or observation* or, more generally, on a random set of propositions, namely, the propositions that the experiment or observation establishes as true. Abstractly, the experiment is represented by a sub-σ-field $\mathscr{F}$ of $\mathscr{E}$, and one speaks of the probability $\mathscr{P}(E \parallel \mathscr{F})z$ of E *relative to* (or *conditioned by* or *conditionally on*) $\mathscr{F}$ in world z. The thought is that in possible world z, the propositions established as true on the basis of the experiment are the propositions in $\{F: z \in F \in \mathscr{F}\}$, for which we (here, nonstandardly) adopt the abbreviation,

$$\mathscr{F}_z = \{F: z \in F \in \mathscr{F}\}.$$

Then $\mathscr{P}(E \parallel \mathscr{F})$ itself is a random variable that assumes the value $\mathscr{P}(E \parallel \mathscr{F})z$ at possible world z as argument. In an unorthodox variant of this notation, we might write the argument as a subscript on '$\mathscr{F}$,'

$$\mathscr{P}(E \parallel \mathscr{F}_z) = \mathscr{P}(E \parallel \mathscr{F})z,$$

where in the notation at the left above, we interpret '$\mathscr{F}_z$' quite literally as the set $\{F: z \in F \in \mathscr{F}\}$ of propositions established as true in world z by the experiment (or whatever) that $\mathscr{F}$ represents.

Example 9-2. In the simplest cases, $\mathscr{F}$ is generated by a countable partition $\{F_1, F_2, \ldots\} \subset \mathscr{E}$. In such cases, the partition itself would serve to represent the experiment, since the outcome of the experiment in world z would be represented by whichever member F_n of the partition contains z. $\mathscr{F}_z$ would then be determined by F_n:

$$\mathscr{F}_z = \{F\colon F_n \subset F \in \mathscr{F}\}.$$

Example 9-3. Suppose that the function $f\colon Z \to R$ is measurable, relative to the σ-field $\mathscr{E}$; that f represents some physically measurable magnitude; and that an (idealized) experiment is to be performed to determine the precise value that f assumes in the real world. Here we might think of representing the experiment by the uncountable partition of Z whose members are the sets $\{z\colon f(z) = x\}$ where x is any real number, but the σ-field generated by this partition is too poor for our purposes: f is not measurable, relative to it. Then instead, we represent the experiment by the σ-field $\mathscr{F}$ that is generated by all sets $\{z\colon f(z) \leq x\}$. (Here we may require that x be rational, so that there will be a countable number of generators; but the generators do not then form a partition of Z.)

At world z, the random variable $\mathscr{P}(E \parallel \mathscr{F})$ assumes the value $\mathscr{P}(E \parallel \mathscr{F})z$ or $\mathscr{P}(E \parallel \mathscr{F}_z)$, namely, the credence in E which is appropriate for someone whose credence function was $\mathscr{P}$ before he learned the outcome of the experiment, and who then learns that the true propositions in $\mathscr{F}$ are the members of $\mathscr{F}_z$. Note that in learning this he need not learn that the actual world is z; rather, he learns certain consequences of that fact, namely, all consequences that are expressible by propositions in $\mathscr{F}$. (Typically, there will be further consequences, expressed by propositions in $\mathscr{E} - \mathscr{F}$, which he does not learn when he learns that every proposition in $\mathscr{F}_z$ is true.) Note that we may have $\{F\colon z \in F \in \mathscr{F}\} = \{F\colon z' \in F \in \mathscr{F}\}$ even though $z \neq z'$: knowledge of the membership of $\mathscr{F}_z$ is not tantamount to knowledge of the identity of z.

Following Billingsley [1965], p. 98 (with minor modifications), we interpret $\mathscr{P}(E \parallel \mathscr{F})z$ as a conditional betting quotient in a manner parallel to our earlier interpretation (§8) of $\mathscr{P}(E \mid F)$. To emphasize the parallelism, we give both interpretations at once:

(9-1) $\begin{matrix}\mathscr{P}(E \mid F) \\ \mathscr{P}(E \parallel \mathscr{F})z\end{matrix}$ is the subjectively fair betting quotient on E for a man whose credence function is $\mathscr{P}$, provided the bet is conditional on $\dfrac{F}{\mathscr{F}_z}$, i.e., provided the bet is called off unless $\dfrac{F}{\mathscr{F}_z}$ is true.

(Here we understand a set of propositions to be true if-if each of its members is true.) In this interpretation, truth of F or of $\mathscr{F}_z$ is truth *tout court*: truth in the actual world.

Using an interpretation very much like this, Billingsley derives the following condition on the random variable $\mathscr{P}(E \parallel \mathscr{F})$:

(9-2) $$\int_F \mathscr{P}(E \parallel \mathscr{F})\, d\mathscr{P} = \mathscr{P}(F \cap E) \quad \text{for all} \quad F \in \mathscr{F}.$$

(The condition is the standard one, but Billingsley's justification of the condition in terms of betting is novel.)

Proof that (9-1) *implies* (9-2). (Billingsley [1965], p. 98, with minor modifications.) Consider a bet on E for a stake of \$1, conditionally on $\{F\} \cup \mathscr{F}_z$, at the subjectively fair betting quotient $\mathscr{P}(E \parallel \mathscr{F})z$. (To see that the betting quotient is subjectively fair, note that since F is in $\mathscr{F}$ we must have either $F \in \mathscr{F}_z$, in which case F is part of the evidence-set in $\mathscr{P}(E \parallel \mathscr{F}_z)$, or $Z - F \in \mathscr{F}_z$, in which case the bet is off since $z \notin F$.) The gain $g(z)$ from this bet in world z is given by

$$g(z) = \begin{cases} 0 & \text{if} \quad z \notin F \\ 1 - \mathscr{P}(E \parallel \mathscr{F})z & \text{if} \quad z \in F \cap E \\ -\mathscr{P}(E \parallel \mathscr{F})z & \text{if} \quad z \in F - E \end{cases}$$

($g(z)$ is the gain from the bet, computed on the assumption that z is the real world, in which case simple truth of F or of $\mathscr{F}_z$ is equivalent to truth-in-z.) For subjective fairness we must have $0 = E(g) = \int_Z g\, d\mathscr{P}$. Attending to the three cases in the expression for $g(z)$, this means that

$$\begin{aligned} 0 &= \int_F 0\, d\mathscr{P} + \int_{F\cap E} (1 - \mathscr{P}(E \parallel \mathscr{F}))\, d\mathscr{P} - \int_{F-E} \mathscr{P}(E \parallel \mathscr{F})\, d\mathscr{P} \\ &= \int_{F\cap E} 1\, d\mathscr{P} - \int_{F\cap E} \mathscr{P}(E \parallel \mathscr{F})\, d\mathscr{P} - \int_{F-E} \mathscr{P}(E \parallel \mathscr{F})\, d\mathscr{P} \\ &= \mathscr{P}(F \cap E) - \int_F \mathscr{P}(E \parallel \mathscr{F})\, d\mathscr{P}, \end{aligned}$$

which yields (9-2).

Then we want $\mathscr{P}(E \parallel \mathscr{F})$ to be a random variable that satisfies the condition (9-2). That such random variables do exist can be seen by applying the Radon-Nikodym theorem to the function $\mathscr{P}(E \cap \quad)$. This function is a measure on $\mathscr{F}$ (nonnormalized, unless $\mathscr{P}(E) = 1$) which is absolutely continuous relative to $\mathscr{P}$, i.e., $\mathscr{P}(E \cap F) = 0$ if $\mathscr{P}(F) = 0$. Then by the Radon-Nikodym theorem there is an integrable function f, measurable with respect to $\mathscr{F}$, such that $\int_F f\,d\mathscr{P} = \mathscr{P}(E \cap F)$ for any F in $\mathscr{F}$. Typically, indeed, there will be an infinity of such functions, for if f is one and $g = f$ a.e., then g is another. Our notation '$\mathscr{P}(E \parallel \mathscr{F})$' must be understood to denote some one of the functions that satisfy condition (9-2).

Example 9-4. If $\mathscr{F}$ is generated by a finite partition $\{F_1, \ldots, F_n\}$ of Z where $\mathscr{P}(F_i)$ is positive for each i, then the intuitively simplest function that satisfies (9-2) is a simple function in the technical sense: $\mathscr{P}(E \parallel \mathscr{F})z = \mathscr{P}(E \mid F_i)$ if $z \in F_i$. To see this, note that with $\mathscr{P}(E \parallel \mathscr{F})$ so defined, (4-2) yields

$$\int_F \mathscr{P}(E \parallel \mathscr{F})\, d\mathscr{P} = \sum_i \mathscr{P}(E \mid F_i)\mathscr{P}(F_i \cap F)$$

$$= \sum_i \mathscr{P}(E \cap F_i)\mathscr{P}(F \mid F_i) = \mathscr{P}(E \cap F)$$

since $\mathscr{P}(F \mid F_i) = 1$ for each i (since F is in $\mathscr{F}$, of which the F_i are atoms.) But there may well be messier functions that satisfy (9-2): messier "versions of $\mathscr{P}(E \parallel \mathscr{F})$" as we shall say. Thus, suppose $\mathscr{E}$ contains a nonempty set G of probability zero. ($\mathscr{E}$ may contain uncountably many such sets.) Then any integrable function that agrees with the function $\mathscr{P}(E \parallel \mathscr{F})$ defined above, except at the points in G, will also satisfy (9-2) and will serve as a version of the conditional probability of E relative to $\mathscr{F}$.

Much depends on the richness of the sub-σ-field $\mathscr{F}$ relative to which $\mathscr{P}(E \parallel \mathscr{F})$ is defined. At one extreme (complete poverty), $\mathscr{F} = \{\varnothing, Z\}$, and we have $\mathscr{P}(E \parallel \mathscr{F})z = \mathscr{P}(E)$ unless z is in some exceptional set A of measure 0, where the composition of A is determined by the particular version of $\mathscr{P}(E \parallel \mathscr{F})$ that has been chosen. At the other extreme, $\mathscr{F} = \mathscr{E}$, and (except on some set A of measure 0) $\mathscr{P}(E \parallel \mathscr{F})z$ is 1 or 0 depending on whether $E \in \mathscr{F}_z$ or $Z - E \in \mathscr{F}_z$. (Of course, in each case, the exception may be specious: we may have $A = \varnothing$, and indeed that would be the most natural choice of the function $\mathscr{P}(E \parallel \mathscr{F})$.) Note that in any case $\mathscr{P}(E \parallel \mathscr{F})z$ is either 0 or 1 when E is in $\mathscr{F}$. (Intuitively, the propositions in $\mathscr{F}$ are those whose truth values are decided by the experiment.) Between these extremes lie the cases for which the theory was invented.

Example 9-5. Where f is a random variable, define $E(x) = \{z : f(z) = x\}$ and $L(x) = \{x : f(z) < x\}$. Choose $\mathscr{F}$ as the σ-field generated by all propositions $L(x)$, and choose a version of $\mathscr{P}(E \parallel \mathscr{F})$ as follows. Where $\mathscr{P}(E(x))$ is positive, set $\mathscr{P}(E \parallel \mathscr{F})z = \mathscr{P}(E \mid E(x))$

for each z in $E(x)$; otherwise, set

$$\mathscr{P}(E \parallel \mathscr{F})z = \lim_n \mathscr{P}(E \mid L(x + 1/n) - L(x - 1/n)).$$

More compactly, the definition can be written as $\mathscr{P}(E \parallel \mathscr{F})z = \lim_n \mathscr{P}(E \mid L(f(z) + 1/n) - L(f(z) - 1/n))$. This version of the conditional probability random variable is constant on each set $E(x)$, so that it is natural to define conditional probabilities in the old sense, where the condition has the form $E(x)$, by setting $\mathscr{P}(E \mid E(x)) = \mathscr{P}(E \parallel \mathscr{F})z$ for some z in $E(x)$.

One can show (see, e.g., Billingsley [1965], pp. 103–104) that the distinct random variables $\mathscr{P}(Z \parallel \mathscr{F})$, $\mathscr{P}(E \parallel \mathscr{F})$, $\mathscr{P}(E_1 \parallel \mathscr{F}), \ldots$ resemble probability measures on $\mathscr{E}$ in the sense that each of the defining conditions of a probability measure is satisfied for "almost" all z in Z, i.e., we have, for any particular versions of these variables,

(9-3)(a) $\mathscr{P}(Z \parallel \mathscr{F})z = 1$ unless $z \in N_Z$ where $\mathscr{P}(N_Z) = 0$,

$\mathscr{P}(E \parallel \mathscr{F})z \geq 0$ unless $z \in N_E$ where $\mathscr{P}(N_E) = 0$,

$$\mathscr{P}\left(\bigcup_n E_n \parallel \mathscr{F}\right)z = \sum_n \mathscr{P}(E_n \parallel \mathscr{F})z \text{ if } E_i \cap E_j = 0$$

for all $i \neq j$ unless $z \in N_{E_1, E_2, \ldots}$ where $\mathscr{P}(N_{E_1, E_2, \ldots}) = 0$.

Here the exceptional sets N_Z, N_E, etc. depend on the particular versions of the conditional probability random variables *and on the propositions* Z, E, etc. If we are concerned only with some countable subfield of $\mathscr{E}$, the union of all these exceptional sets will still have probability 0, and for almost all z in Z, the set function $\mathscr{P}(\quad \parallel \mathscr{F})z$ will be a probability measure on the countable subfield in question; but this need not be the case on $\mathscr{E}$ itself. (See Doob [1953], chap. i, §9, for a complete discussion.)

We can be assured that $\mathscr{P}(\quad \parallel \mathscr{F})z$ will be a probability measure on $\mathscr{E}$ if z is a point to which $\mathscr{P}$ in effect assigns positive probability, i.e., if $\mathscr{P}(E)$ is positive whenever $z \in E \in \mathscr{E}$ (Billingsley [1965], p. 106); but again, there is no such assurance in general.

Kolmogorov [1933] introduced a notion of conditional expectation that bears the same relation to ordinary expectation that conditional probability as a random variable bears to ordinary probability. $E(f \parallel \mathscr{F})z$ is your expectation from the random variable f, conditionally on an experiment that we represent by a sub-σ-field $\mathscr{F}$ of $\mathscr{E}$, in world z. Billingsley [1965], p. 107, offers essentially this interpretation:

> If your credence function is $\mathscr{P}$ and $F \in \mathscr{F}$, \$$E(f \parallel \mathscr{F})z$ is your subjectively fair buying price, once you know that $\mathscr{F}_z$ is true, for a ticket worth \$$f(z)$ if $z \in F$ and worth the buying price if $z \notin F$.

As the gain from this arrangement in world z is given by

$$g(z) = \begin{cases} f(z) - E(f \,\|\, \mathscr{F})z & \text{if} \quad z \in F, \\ 0 & \text{if} \quad z \notin F, \end{cases}$$

your expected gain will be $\int_Z g \, d\mathscr{P} = \int_F (f - E(f \,\|\, \mathscr{F})) \, d\mathscr{P}$, which will vanish, as required by subjective fairness, if-if we have

$$\text{(9-4)} \qquad \int_F E(f \,\|\, \mathscr{F}) \, d\mathscr{P} = \int_F f \, d\mathscr{P}.$$

That there are functions $E(f \,\| \quad)$ that satisfy equation (9-4) for all F in $\mathscr{F}$ can be shown by applying the Radon-Nikodym theorem to the function $\mathscr{Q}$, where $\mathscr{Q}(F) = \int_F f \, d\mathscr{P}$ for all F in $\mathscr{F}$. One can show (Billingsley [1965], pp. 109 ff.) that $E(f \,\|\, \mathscr{F})$ has various of the key properties of an expectation almost everywhere.

10
De Finetti's Representation Theorem

It is fairly easy to verify, as in §7, that mixtures of probability measures on $\mathscr{E}$ which are symmetrical relative to $\mathscr{S} = \{E_1, E_2, \ldots\}$ are themselves symmetrical relative to $\mathscr{S}$. In particular, for each x in the unit interval, let $\mathscr{P}_x$ be a probability measure on $\mathscr{E}$ relative to which $E_1, E_2, \ldots$ are independent in pairs, triples, and so on, with constant probability $\mathscr{P}_x(E_n) = x$. Then $\mathscr{P}$ is a probability measure on $\mathscr{E}$ which is symmetrical relative to $\mathscr{S}$, where

(10-1) $$\mathscr{P}(E) = \int_0^1 \mathscr{P}_x(E)\, dF(x),$$

F being any distribution function on the unit interval. ($\mathscr{P}$ will be Bernoullian relative to $\mathscr{S}$ if F assumes only the values 0 and 1.) De Finetti [1931, 1937] proved the converse:[1]

(10-2) *De Finetti's representation theorem* (*two-valued case*)*:* Every probability measure on $\mathscr{E}$ which is symmetrical relative to $\mathscr{S}$ is a mixture (10-1) of probability measures on $\mathscr{E}$ which are Bernoullian relative to $\mathscr{S}$.

One can put the matter as follows (Loève [1960], pp. 364–365): *symmetry = conditional Bernoullianity. Explanation:* Let $\mathscr{F}$ be the σ-field that is generated by $\mathscr{S}$. $\mathscr{F}$ contains each of the propositions $R(x) = \{z$: the limiting relative frequency of truths in world z in the sequence $E_1, E_2, \ldots$ exists and equals $x\}$, and one can show that the set on which that limit fails to exist has probability 0 relative to the symmetrical measure $\mathscr{P}$. (See (7-2), and recall that symmetry implies stationarity.) For each E there will be a version of $\mathscr{P}(E \,\|\, \mathscr{F})$ which is constant on each set $R(x)$; and in fact, using these versions, we have for almost all z a set function $\mathscr{P}(\;\;\|\, \mathscr{F})z$ which is a Bernoullian probability measure on $\mathscr{E}$. In particular, if $z \in R(x)$ then $\mathscr{P}(\;\;\|\, \mathscr{F})z$ is $\mathscr{P}_x$. *Intuitively:* $\mathscr{P}$ is symmetrical if-if it is Bernoullian, conditionally on the "experiment" of discovering the limiting relative frequency of truths in the sequence $E_1, E_2, \ldots$.

If the predicates $P_1, \ldots, P_N$ form a family, and the individuals are $a_1, a_2, \ldots$, then for each $n = 1, 2, \ldots$ we have a random variable f_n that assumes the value i in world z if-if individual a_n has the property P_i in world z. The random variables $f_1, f_2, \ldots$ are said to be symmetrical (relative to $\mathscr{P}$) if-if their joint distribution function, F (corresponding

[1] See *Bibliographical Remarks*, below.

to $\mathscr{P}$) is a symmetrical function of its arguments: $F_{i_1,\ldots,i_m} = F_{1,\ldots,m}$ for any $m = 1, 2, \ldots$ and any increasing sequence $i_1, \ldots, i_m$ of positive integers. As was pointed out in §7, a formally identical definition will serve for symmetry of random variables $f_1, f_2, \ldots$ in general (where, so to speak, N may be uncountably infinite). In its general form, de Finetti's representation theorem asserts the identity of *symmetry* and *conditional independence with common distribution function* for sequences of random variables which need not be simple functions.

To understand the general theorem, begin by thinking about its converse, as follows. Let D be the set of all distribution functions of a single argument, and let $(D, \mathscr{D}, \mathscr{Q})$ be a probability space. (In objectivistic terms, one might imagine a nondeterministic process of choosing a function F out of D, where the probability that the chosen F will lie in a member X of $\mathscr{D}$ is given by $\mathscr{Q}(X)$.) The chosen function F is to be the common distribution function of all the random variables $f_1, f_2, \ldots$, which are furthermore to be independent in the sense that $F_{i_1,\ldots,i_m}(x_1, \ldots, x_m) = F(x_1) \ldots F(x_m)$ for all increasing i's and all x's. The f's are measurable relative to a sub-σ-field $\mathscr{F}$ of $\mathscr{E}$, and each choice of F determines a definite probability measure $\mathscr{P}_F$ on $\mathscr{E}$ relative to which the f's are independent and have F as their common distribution function. Now the probability measure $\mathscr{P}$ on $\mathscr{E}$ which is defined by the condition

(10-3) $$\mathscr{P}(E) = \int_D \mathscr{P}_F(E)\, d\mathscr{Q} \quad \text{for all} \quad E \in \mathscr{E}$$

will be symmetrical, relative to the f's. The general form of de Finetti's theorem states the converse.

(10-4) *De Finetti's representation theorem* (*general case*): Every probability measure on $\mathscr{E}$ relative to which the random variables f_1, $f_2, \ldots$ are symmetrical is a mixture (10-3) of probability measures on $\mathscr{E}$ relative to which the f's are independent and identically distributed.

De Finetti has further generalized the theorem to the case of *partial symmetry* ("équivalence partielle") in de Finetti [1938]; see also de Finetti [1959].

We conclude with some illustrations of the use of the two-valued case.

Example 10-1. If E is the event $E_{i_1} \cap \ldots \cap E_{i_s} \cap \bar{E}_{i_{s+1}} \cap \ldots \cap \bar{E}_{i_{s+t}}$ that, of a certain $s + t$ "trials", a particular s were successes and the rest were failures, then $\mathscr{P}_x(E) = x^s(1 - x)^t$ and (10-1) becomes

(10-5) $$\mathscr{P}(E) = \int_0^1 x^s(1 - x)^t\, dF(x).$$

With $t = 0$ and $F(x) = x$ in the unit interval, we have $\mathscr{P}(E) = 1/(s+1)$.

Example 10-2.

$$\mathscr{P}(E_1 \mid E_2 \cap \ldots \cap E_n) = \int_0^1 x^n \, dF(x) \Big/ \int_0^1 x^{n-1} \, dF(x) = \frac{n}{n+1}$$

if $F(x) = x$ in the unit interval, and in any case $\rightarrow 1$ as $n \rightarrow \infty$ unless $F(x) = 1$ for some $x < 1$.

Example 10-3. With E as in example 10.1 and $F(x) = x$ in the unit interval, the general expression for $\mathscr{P}(E)$ is

$$\int_0^1 x^s(1-x)^t \, dx$$

$$= \int_0^1 \left(\sum_{k=0}^{t} (-1)^k \binom{t}{k} x^{s+k} \right) dx$$

$$= \sum_{k=0}^{t} (-1)^k \binom{t}{k} \left(\frac{1}{s+k+1} \right) = \frac{t!}{(s+1)(s+2)\ldots(s+t+1)}$$

$$= \frac{s!t!}{(s+t+1)!}$$

(Cf. Carnap [1950], p. 566, equation (4) with $\kappa = 2$, $N_1 = s$, $N_2 = t$, $N = s + t$, $m^* = \mathscr{P}$, $\xi_i = E$.)

Example 10-4. Let $p(s, t)$ be the probability that $\mathscr{P}$ assigns to the proposition $E_1 \cap \ldots \cap E_s \cap \bar{E}_{s+1} \cap \ldots \cap \bar{E}_{s+t}$; since $\mathscr{P}$ is symmetrical, we have $\mathscr{P}(E) = p(s, t)$ with E as in example 10.1. Now suppose that on the first $s + t$ "trials", a certain s were "successes" and the rest were "failures", where success and failure on "trial" n correspond to truth of E_n and $\bar{E}_n$, respectively. Given this information, what is the probability that of the next $i + j$ tosses, a certain i will be "successes" and the rest "failures"? The answer is

$$\frac{p(s+i, t+j)}{p(s,t)} = \frac{\int_0^1 x^{s+i}(1-x)^{t+j} \, dF(x)}{p(s,t)} = \int_0^1 x^i(1-x)^j \, dG(x)$$

where

$$dG(x) = \frac{x^s(1-x)^t \, dF(x)}{p(s,t)}$$

or

(10-6) $$G(x) = \frac{1}{p(s,t)} \int_0^x x^s(1-x)^t \, dF(x).$$

Then de Finetti's theorem allows us to represent the accumulation of evidence by a change in the probability distribution function. Before observing the first $s + t$ trials, the probability of success on a particular i of the following $i + j$ trials and failure on the other j is

$$\int_0^1 x^i(1 - x)^j \, dF(x).$$

After observing success on a particular s of the first $s + t$ trials and failure on the rest, the corresponding (conditional) probability is

$$\int_0^1 x^i(1 - x)^j \, dG(x),$$

where the effect of the observation is reflected entirely in the difference between the prior and posterior distribution functions, F and G, with G determined by F, s, and t as in (10-6). One can show that as $s + t$ increases, G approaches a step function, $G(x)$ being small to the left of $x = s/(s + t)$ and large to the right.

Bibliographical Remarks

De Finetti [1937] (translated and somewhat revised in Kyburg and Smokler [1964]) remains the best general discussion of the representation theorem and its significance from a subjectivistic point of view. A more compact presentation can be found in Savage [1954], §3.7, from the same point of view. The present treatment distorts de Finetti's and Savage's ideas in two respects. First, the point of the theorem, from de Finetti's perspective, is to show how one can *avoid* talk of objective probabilities, whereas in the present treatment we have reversed the perspective, pointing out that any symmetrical subjective probability measure can be viewed as a weighted average of objective Bernoullian measures (where the weights are subjective). Second, both de Finetti and Savage deplore the widespread tendency to build countable additivity into the definition of probability, for they find it pointlessly restrictive to rule out finitely additive measures $\mathscr{P}$ on denumerable sets Z for which we have $\mathscr{P}(A) = 0$ if A is a finite subset of Z but $\mathscr{P}(Z) = 1$. (Finite additivity allows the measure of the whole to be greater than the sum of the measures of its parts.) The present treatment uses countable additivity simply because all standard textbooks of measure theory do; and they, in turn, use countable additivity because it is thought that proofs are simpler that way, or because theorems about countably additive measures tend to have simpler formulations than the corresponding theorems about finitely additive measures. For a case in point, compare a standard statement and proof of the Radon-Nikodym theorem with the statements and proofs of the corresponding "finitized" theorem by Bochner [1939], Bochner and Phillips [1941], or de Finetti [1955]; but note, on the finitist side, the elementary proof given by Dubins [1969].

For standard treatments of de Finetti's theorem, see Khinchin [1932], Ryll-Nardzewski [1957], Loève [1963], Feller [1966], and Révész [1968]. Fenstad [1968] treats the theorem from a different point of view, in which (as in Carnap's earlier writings) logical probabilities have sentences of formalized languages as their arguments. Finally, see Braithwaite [1957] for an elementary exposition of the basic idea, coupled with criticism from an objectivistic point of view.

Some Recent History

The framework for probability theory which we have been describing is essentially that of Kolmogorov [1933], which derived its novel generality from the application of work by Fréchet [1915] and Nikodym [1930] on the abstract Lebesgue integral—especially, from the application of the Radon-Nikodym theorem to the notions of conditional probability and expectation. Throughout the thirties, Kolomogorov's ideas lay outside the ken of all statisticians but the most mathematically sophisticated; but by now (especially since the work of Doob [1953] and Loève [1955]) they form the basis of the theoretical part of the normal statistics curriculum. It was primarily for this reason that, in 1960, Carnap decided to reformulate his theory of inductive probability within the measure theoretic framework: it was a matter of easing contact with the main body of work going on in mathematical statistics and probability theory. Meanwhile, Loś [1963], Gaifman [1964], Scott and Krauss [1966], and others were showing how the virtues of the measure theoretic approach are obtainable within a framework in which (as in Carnap [1950]) probabilities are attributed to sentences of formalized languages. But the new framework goes beyond those of Kolmogorov [1933] and Carnap [1950] in important respects—especially, in attributing probabilities to open sentences in a very fruitful way. The work by Gaifman and Krauss was inspired by their work with Carnap, but was largely informed by the model-theoretic atmosphere at Berkeley. Subsequently, Fenstad [1967, 1968] has used the polyadic logic of Halmos [1962] in a new treatment of earlier work, and Scott and Krauss [1966] have treated the subject from the point of view of infinitary languages.

The present state of this new framework seems to be like that of the Kolmogorov framework in the thirties: highly satisfactory, still under development, and still little understood outside the circle of specialists. For this reason it still seems appropriate to use the measure theoretic formulation in these papers; and since in any event the new framework makes liberal use of measure theory, the sort of information conveyed in the present article is prerequisite to its understanding. But the new framework deserves to be more widely understood: it has (anyway for those schooled in recent logic) a certain transparency and suggestive power.[1]

---

[1] An exposition of the new point of view is projected for a later volume.

4

The Principle of Instantial Relevance

BY JÜRGEN HUMBURG

[EDITOR'S NOTE: This article and the next prove the same basic facts about instantial relevance, for example, that axioms A1–A7, listed below, imply the principle of positive instantial relevance, namely, P13-1 of Art. **2**, or (2) below. The proofs in the next article were found by Gaifman in 1960, using a method suggested by Kemeny in 1959; the proofs in this article were found independently by Humburg in 1963. Both sets of proofs are published here, since the two approaches have complementary virtues: see Art. **5**, §0.]

Basic Axioms: Art. **2**, §1B.

A1. *Lower Bound*: $\mathscr{C}(H \mid E) \geq 0$.

A2. *Self-conformation*: $\mathscr{C}(E \mid E) = 1$.

A3. *Complement:* $\mathscr{C}(H \mid E) + \mathscr{C}(-H \mid E) = 1$.

A4. *Multiplication*: $\mathscr{C}(H \cap H' \mid E) = \mathscr{C}(H \mid E)\mathscr{C}(H' \mid E \cap H)$ *if* $E \cap H \neq 0$.

In A1–A4 we assume that the second arguments of $\mathscr{C}$ are *nonnull* in the sense that $\mathscr{M}$ assigns them positive values, where we define $\mathscr{M}(E) = \mathscr{C}(E \mid E \cup -E)$.

Axiom of Regularity: Art. **2**, §7.

A5. $\mathscr{M}(E) > 0$ *if E is molecular and* $E \neq \varnothing$.

Axiom of Symmetry: Art. **2**, §9.

A6. $\mathscr{C}(H' \mid E') = \mathscr{C}(H \mid E)$ *if* H' *and* E' *are obtained from H and E by the same finite permutation of the (infinite) domain of individuals.*

Axiom of Convergence ("The Reichenbach Axiom"): Vol. II.

A7. *Let* $b_1, b_2, \ldots$ *be an infinite sequence of individuals,*
let $Q_1, Q_2, \ldots$ *be a family of attributes, and*
let $E_1, E_2, \ldots$ *be a sequence of propositions, where*
(a) *Each* E_n *has the structure* $E_n = Q_{i_1}b_1 \cap \ldots \cap Q_{i_n}b_n$ *and*
(b) $E_{n+1} \subseteq E_n$ *for each* $n = 1, 2, \ldots$.
Let $s_j(n)$ *be the number of occurrences of* Q_j *in* E_n. *Then*
(c) $\lim_{n\to\infty} (\mathscr{C}(Q_jb_{n+1} \mid E_n) - s_j(n)/n) = 0$.

The principle of instantial relevance concerns the simplest sort of inductive reasoning. Given distinct individuals a, b, a molecular attribute M, and a non-null proposition E corresponding to a molecular sentence in which neither a nor b is named, we compare the inductive probability of the hypothesis Ma on the evidence E with the inductive probability of that hypothesis on the evidence $E \cap Mb$. *The principle of nonnegative instantial relevance* says that

(1) $\mathscr{C}(Ma \mid E \cap Mb) \geq \mathscr{C}(Ma \mid E)$, ("Nonnegative relevance"),

i.e., the inductive probability of the hypothesis does not decrease when an additional instance of M is observed. *The principle of positive instantial relevance* (what Carnap, Art. **2,** §13, calls simply "instantial relevance") says that

(2) $\mathscr{C}(Ma \mid E \cap Mb) > \mathscr{C}(Ma \mid E)$, ("Positive relevance"),

i.e., the inductive probability increases with every instance. Positive relevance is the conjunction of nonnegative relevance with the following principle,

(3) $\mathscr{C}(Ma \mid E \cap Mb) \neq \mathscr{C}(Ma \mid E)$, ("Bare relevance")

according to which each instance of M is either positively or negatively relevant to the hypothesis.

We now study the conditions under which these three principles hold, beginning with two theorems on principle (1).

Theorem 1. The principle (1) of nonnegative relevance follows from the basic axioms A1–A4 together with the axiom A6 of symmetry.

Proof. By symmetry (including the assumption that the domain of individuals is infinite) de Finetti's representation theorem (Art. **3**, §10) applies to $\mathscr{C}$. In particular, since E is a molecular sentence in which neither a nor b is named (so that E is independent of Ma and of $Ma \cap Mb$, relative to the Bernoullian measure $\mathscr{P}_x$) we have

(4)
$$\text{(a) } \mathscr{C}(Ma \mid E) = \int_0^1 x \, dF(x),$$
$$\text{(b) } \mathscr{C}(Ma \cap Mb \mid E) = \int_0^1 x^2 \, dF(x)$$

where F is some cumulative probability distribution over the unit interval. If $\mathscr{C}(Ma \mid E) = 0$, (1) holds by $A1$. If $\mathscr{C}(Ma \mid E) \neq 0$, we must also have $\mathscr{C}(Mb \mid E) \neq 0$ by A6, symmetry. Then by A4 we may replace the left-hand side of (1) by $\mathscr{C}(Ma \cap Mb \mid E)/\mathscr{C}(Mb \mid E)$. Using (4), we now find that (1) is equivalent to

(5)
$$\left(\int_0^1 x \, dF(x)\right)^2 \leq \int_0^1 x^2 \, dF(x),$$

which is a case of the Cauchy-Schwartz inequality. This completes the proof of theorem 1.

Theorem 2. Theorem 1 fails if we drop the assumption that the domain of individuals is infinite, in A6.

Proof. Let the domain consist of the two distinct individuals a, b, and consider a single family of two attributes, P and $-P$. Define

$$\mathscr{M}(Pa \cap Pb) = \mathscr{M}(-Pa \cap -Pb) = \tfrac{1}{20}$$

and

$$\mathscr{M}(Pa \cap -Pb) = \mathscr{M}(-Pa \cap Pb) = \tfrac{9}{20},$$

so that there is a strong bias against uniformity. If we define $\mathscr{C}(H \mid E) = \mathscr{M}(H \cap E)/\mathscr{M}(E)$ then the function $\mathscr{C}$ satisfies A1–A5 and satisfies what remains of A6 when we drop the assumption that the domain of individuals is infinite; but $\mathscr{C}$ violates (1), for with $M = P$ and $E = Z =$ the necessary proposition, we have

$$\mathscr{C}(Ma \mid E \cap Mb) = \tfrac{1}{10} < \mathscr{C}(Ma \mid E) = \tfrac{1}{2}.$$

This proves theorem 2.

Observe that the function $\mathscr{M}$ defined in the proof of theorem 2 on the field generated by $\{Pa, Pb\}$ cannot be extended to the field generated by $\{Pa, Pb, Pc\}$ without violating either symmetry or one of the basic axioms. To see this, note that any symmetry-preserving extension would yield $\mathscr{M}(P\ \ \cap P\ \ ) = \frac{1}{20}$, $\mathscr{M}(-P\ \ \cap -P\ \ ) = \frac{1}{20}$, $\mathscr{M}(P\ \ \cap -P\ \ ) = \frac{9}{20}$ whenever the two blanks in each equation are filled by different names, 'a', 'b', or 'c'. Then by the elementary probability calculus (i.e., by the basic axioms) we have

$$\begin{aligned}\mathscr{M}(Pa \cup Pb \cup Pc) &= \mathscr{M}(Pa) + \mathscr{M}(-Pa \cap Pb) \\ &\quad + \mathscr{M}(-Pa \cap -Pb \cap Pc) \\ &= \tfrac{1}{2} + \tfrac{9}{20} + \mathscr{M}(-Pa \cap -Pb \cap Pc),\end{aligned}$$

or

(6) $\mathscr{M}(Pa \cup Pb \cup Pc) = \frac{19}{20} + \mathscr{M}(-Pa \cap -Pb \cap Pc).$

We also have

(7) $\mathscr{M}(-Pa \cap -Pb \cap Pc) + \mathscr{M}(-Pa \cap Pb \cap Pc) = \frac{9}{20},$

(8) $\mathscr{M}(Pa \cap Pb \cap Pc) + \mathscr{M}(-Pa \cap Pb \cap Pc) = \frac{1}{20}.$

Subtracting (8) from (7) we have $\mathscr{M}(-Pa \cap -Pb \cap Pc) = \frac{8}{20} + \mathscr{M}(Pa \cap Pb \cap Pc)$, and combining this with (6) we have

$$\mathscr{M}(Pa \cup Pb \cup Pc) = \tfrac{27}{20} + \mathscr{M}(Pa \cap Pb \cap Pc) > 1,$$

in contradiction of the basic axioms.

We now turn to Carnap's formulation of the relevance principles in Art. **2,** §13. Recall the definitions (Art. **2,** §§11, 12) of the representative functions MI and C_j: If $P_1, \ldots, P_k$ is a family of attributes and $s_1, \ldots, s_k$ are natural numbers whose sum, s, is positive, an *initial sample proposition* with the given numbers is a conjunction $P_{i_1}a_1 \cap \ldots \cap P_{i_s}a_s$ in which each P_j occurs exactly s_j times. (By symmetry, any s distinct individuals might replace $a_1, \ldots, a_s$, without changing the $\mathscr{M}$ value of the proposition.) Now, where E is an initial sample proposition with the numbers $s_1, \ldots, s_k$, we define

$$\mathrm{MI}(s_1, \ldots, s_k) = \mathscr{M}(E)$$

and

$$C_j(s_1, \ldots, s_k) = \mathscr{C}(P_j a_{s+1} \mid E),$$

so that with $j = 1$ we have $C_1(s_1, \ldots, s_k) = \mathrm{MI}(s_1 + 1, \ldots, s_k)$ $\mathrm{MI}(s_1, \ldots, s_k)$. (In the sequel we consistently take $j = 1$ as a notational convenience which results in no real loss of generality.)

We shall be concerned with the special cases of (1)–(3) in which M is P_1, E is an initial sample proposition with numbers $s_1, \ldots, s_k$, a is a_{s+2}, and b is a_{s+1}. In this case we may write the principles as

$$\textbf{(9)}\quad C_1(s_1 + 1, \ldots, s_k) \overset{\geq}{\underset{\neq}{>}} C_1(s_1, \ldots, s_k), \quad \begin{array}{l}\text{(Nonnegative relevance)}\\ \text{(Positive relevance)}\\ \text{(Bare relevance)}\end{array}$$

or, in terms of the function MI, as

$$\textbf{(10)}\quad \mathrm{MI}(s_1 + 1, \ldots, s_k)^2 \overset{\leq}{\underset{\neq}{<}} \mathrm{MI}(s_1, \ldots, s_k)\mathrm{MI}(s_1 + 2, \ldots, s_k). \quad \begin{array}{l}\text{(Nonnegative)}\\ \text{(Positive)}\\ \text{(Bare)}\end{array}$$

We can bestow the right sort of sense on (9) when the sample is vacuous (when $s = 0$) by identifying the initial sample proposition which has the numbers $0, \ldots, 0$ with Z, the necessary proposition. Thus, when $s = 0$, (9) says that

$$\textbf{(11)(a)}\quad \mathscr{C}(P_1a_2 \mid P_1a_1) \overset{\geq}{\underset{\neq}{>}} \mathscr{M}(P_1a_1)$$

and (10) says that

$$\textbf{(11)(b)}\quad \mathscr{M}(P_1a_1)^2 \overset{\leq}{\underset{\neq}{<}} \mathscr{M}(P_1a_1 \cap P_1a_2).$$

By A6, symmetry, we may apply the de Finetti theorem to get

$$\textbf{(12)}\quad \mathrm{MI}(s_1, \ldots, s_k) = \int_\Delta x_1^{s_1} \ldots x_k^{s_k}\, d\mu$$

where Δ is the set of all k-tuples of nonnegative reals which sum to 1 and μ is a k-dimensional Lebesgue-Stieltjes measure for which $\mu(\Delta) = 1$. Defining

(13) $$d\nu = x_1^{s_1} \ldots x_k^{s_k}\, d\mu$$

we obtain

(14) $$\left(\int_\Delta x_1\, d\nu\right)^2 \leq \int_\Delta d\nu \int_\Delta x_1^2\, d\nu$$

by the Cauchy-Schwartz inequality. By (12), (14) is equivalent to form (10) of the principle of nonnegative relevance, and we have reproved the following special case of theorem 1:

> The basic axioms together with the axiom of symmetry imply the principle of nonnegative relevance in the weak form, (9).

The case of equality in (14) is precisely the case in which form (10) of the principle of bare relevance is violated. We use this observation in the following proof.

Theorem 3. Assume A1—A6. If form (9) of the principle of bare relevance is violated, i.e., if we have

$$C_1(s_1 + 1, \ldots, s_k) = C_1(s_1, \ldots, s_k)$$

for some k-tuple $s_1, \ldots, s_k$ of natural numbers, then we have

$$C_1(s_1' + 1, \ldots, s_k') = C_1(s_1', \ldots, s_k')$$

for every k-tuple $s_1', \ldots, s_k'$ of natural numbers in which $s_i' \neq 0$ whenever $s_i \neq 0$.

Proof. Equality holds in (14) if and only if x_1 (i.e., the function f for which $f(x_1, \ldots, x_k) = x_1$ identically) is constant except on a subset of Δ to which ν assigns measure 0. Here, ν is the measure determined by (13) when $\langle s_1, \ldots, s_k\rangle$ is a particular k-tuple for which equality holds in (14). Let Δ' be the subset of Δ on which we have $x_j > 0$ if $s_j > 0$, for each $j = 1, \ldots, k$. Then for each $\langle x_1, \ldots, x_k\rangle$ in Δ' we have $x_1^{s_1} \ldots x_k^{s_k} > 0$. Now let $\langle s_1', \ldots, s_k'\rangle$ be a k-tuple for which we have $s_j' > 0$ if $s_j > 0$ $(j = 1, \ldots, k.)$ For $\langle x_1, \ldots, x_k\rangle$ in $\Delta - \Delta'$ we have $x_1^{s_1'} \ldots x_k^{s_k'} = 0$, so that

$$\mathrm{MI}(s_1', \ldots, s_k') = \int_\Delta x_1^{s_1'} \ldots x_k^{s_k'}\, d\mu = \int_{\Delta'} x_1^{s_1'} \ldots x_k^{s_k'}\, d\mu$$

$$= \int_{\Delta'} \frac{x_1^{s_1'} \ldots x_k^{s_k'}}{x_1^{s_1} \ldots x_k^{s_k}}\, d\nu.$$

If c is the constant value of x_1 (i.e., of the function f) on Δ (except for a subset of ν-measure 0) then we may move the factor $x_1^{s_1'}$ or $c^{s_1'}$ out in front of the integral, to get

$$\mathrm{MI}(s_1', \ldots, s_k') = c^{s_1'} \int_{\Delta'} x_2^{s_2'} \ldots x_k^{s_k'}\, d\mu$$

via (13). Then we have

$$C_1(s_1', \ldots, s_k') = \frac{c^{s_1'+1} \int_{\Delta'} x_2^{s_2'} \ldots x_k^{s_k'}\, d\mu}{c^{s_1'} \int_{\Delta'} x_2^{s_1'} \ldots x_k^{s_k'}\, d\mu} = c,$$

and theorem 3 is proved.

Theorem 3 concerns the special case (9) of the principle (3) of bare relevance. A similar result, which is in some sense stronger, concerns the general form (3) of the principle.

Theorem 4. Assume A1–A6. If (3) is violated then it is "globally" violated, that is, if (3) fails for particular M, a, b, E, if $b_1, b_2, \ldots$ is a sequence of individuals, none of which is mentioned in E, and if E' is a proposition of structure $E' = Mb_1 \cap \ldots \cap Mb_n \cap -Mb_{n+1} \cap \ldots \cap -Mb_s$, then we have $\mathscr{C}(Mb_{s+1} \mid E \cap E') = \mathscr{C}(Mb_{s+1} \mid E)$.

Proof. By the de Finetti theorem, $\mathscr{C}(E' \mid E) = \int_0^1 x^n(1-x)^{s-n} dF(x)$ where F is a distribution concentrated on the unit interval. If (3) fails then A1–A5 imply $\mathscr{C}(Ma \cap Mb \mid E) = \mathscr{C}(Ma \mid E)\mathscr{C}(Mb \mid E)$ or, by (4),

$$\left(\int_0^1 x\, dF(x)\right)^2 = \int_0^1 x^2\, dF(x).$$

This last equation holds if and only if there is a real number r for which we have $x = r$ almost everywhere in the unit interval, relative to F. In other words, F is a step function, with $F(x)$ being 0 for $x < r$ and 1 for $x > r$. Then

$$\mathscr{C}(E' \mid E) = \int_0^1 x^n(1-x)^{s-n}\, dF(x) = r^n(1-r)^{s-n}.$$

To complete the proof, note that

$$\mathscr{C}(Mb_{s+1} \mid E \cap E') = \frac{\mathscr{C}(Mb_{s+1} \cap E' \mid E)}{\mathscr{C}(E' \mid E)}$$

$$= \frac{r^{n+1}(1-r)^{n-s}}{r^n(1-r)^{s-n}} = r = \mathscr{C}(Mb_{s+1} \mid E).$$

We can now prove that, given the first six axioms, the Reichenbach axiom implies the principle of bare relevance.

Theorem 5. A1–A7 imply (3).

Proof. (a) Assume that (3) fails. Then it fails "globally" in the sense defined in the statement of theorem 4, and we have $\mathscr{C}(Mb_{s+1} \mid E \cap E') = \mathscr{C}(Mb_{s+1} \mid E) = r$, a constant. (b) Apply the Reichenbach axiom, A7, to the family $\{M, -M\}$, with $E_n = Mb_1 \cap \ldots \cap Mb_n$. Then $\mathscr{C}(Mb_{s+1} \mid E_s) \to 1$ as $s \to \infty$. (c) Therefore we have

$$\mathscr{C}(Mb_{s+1} \cap E \mid E_s)/\mathscr{C}(E \mid E_s) \to 1$$

as well. (*Proof:*

$$\begin{aligned}\mathscr{C}(E \mid E_s) - \mathscr{C}(Mb_{s+1} \cap E \mid E_s) &= \mathscr{C}(-Mb_{s+1} \cap E \mid E_s)\\ &= \mathscr{C}(-Mb_{s+1} \mid E_s)\mathscr{C}(E \mid E_s \cap -Mb_{s+1}) \to 0\end{aligned}$$

because the first factor $\to 0$ by (b).) Finally (d)

$$r = \mathscr{C}(Mb_{s+1} \mid E \cap E_s) = \mathscr{C}(Mb_{s+1} \cap E \mid E_s)/\mathscr{C}(E \mid E_s) \to 1$$

by (c). Since r is a constant, we must then have $r = 1$, in contradiction to the axiom A5 of regularity, and the assumption (a) is refuted.

By theorems 1 and 5, the seven axioms A1–A7 imply both (1), nonnegative relevance, and (3), bare relevance. Since the conjunction of (1) and (3) is equivalent to (2), positive relevance, we have the principal result,

A1–A7 imply (2), the principle of positive instantial relevance.

5

Applications of de Finetti's Theorem to Inductive Logic

BY HAIM GAIFMAN

§0. The results of §1 and §2 were obtained while the author was a research assistant to Carnap during 1959 and 1960. The basic concepts are those that were introduced in the preceding articles in this volume. Some of the concepts, together with the notation used here, are explained in §1, while §2 contains the actual results and the proofs; §3 contains further results concerning Reichenbach's axiom.

Carnap and his assistants have noticed that one can construct examples of confirmation functions, for finite domains of individuals, in which the axiom of nonnegative relevance is violated. The violations became "weaker and weaker," however, as the number of individuals increased. It was guessed then that the axiom holds for infinite domain and Kemeny suggested using de Finetti's theorem to prove it. This theorem plays the central part in the present paper. Working on lines suggested by Kemeny I succeeded in proving the axiom of nonnegative relevance. I also succeeded in characterizing completely the cases in which the stronger axiom of positive relevance fails. Three years later, Humburg, applying de Finetti's theorem in a cleverer way, gave a much shorter proof of the main result. I present the original proofs not only because of historical interest, but because I think the original approach, in which the behavior of the probability function is investigated in a more direct way, although leading to lengthier calculations, gives a better all around view of the behavior of the function and is suggestive in the discovery of new features. I wish to reemphasize the major part played by de Finetti's theorem. This theorem, of which a special case is used here, allows one to represent probability functions satisfying certain requirements of symmetry in the form of a certain integral (see the beginning of §2). Once this is set forth, the main properties of the functions can be analyzed using the representation.

§1. Consider a family of k attributes $M_1, \ldots, M_k$ and an infinite sequence of individuals $a_1, a_2, \ldots$. Let $\mathscr{C}$ be a confirmation function defined for all the molecular propositions that are formed using the attributes and the individuals (with propositional operations and without quantifiers). We assume that $\mathscr{C}$ satisfies the axioms A1–A6, Art. **4** (A1–A4 are first stated in Art. **2,** §1B, A5 in Art. **2,** §7, and A6 in Art. **2,** §9). The probability function $\mathscr{M}$ is defined by: $\mathscr{M}(E) = \mathscr{C}(E \mid E \vee \neg E)$, where E is any molecular proposition, $\vee$ is the disjunction operation, and $\neg$ the negation operation. $\mathscr{C}$ is determined by $\mathscr{M}$ through the equation $\mathscr{C}(E \mid H) = \mathscr{M}(E \wedge H)/\mathscr{M}(H)$. The function

$\mathcal{M}$ is uniquely determined by its values for those propositions that are conjunctions of atomic propositions and their negations, since any proposition is equivalent to a disjunction of such, mutually exclusive, propositions (the disjunctive normal form).

Now by a "family of attributes" it is understood that the attributes are mutually disjoint and their union is the whole universe. This means that, for any a_i we have $\mathcal{M}(M_p(a_i) \wedge M_q(a_i)) = 0$, if $p \neq q$, and $\mathcal{M}(M_1(a_i) \vee \ldots \vee M_k(a_i)) = 1$. From this it follows that $\mathcal{M}$ is completely determined by its values for propositions that are conjunctions of atomic propositions. The axiom of symmetry, A6, means that the value of $\mathcal{M}$ for the conjunction $M_{i_1}(a_{i_1}) \wedge \ldots \wedge M_{i_n}(a_{i_n})$ is unchanged if we replace every a_i by a_j, provided that the mapping $a_{i_l} \to a_{j_l}$ is a one-to-one mapping of $\{a_{i_1}, \ldots, a_{i_n}\}$ onto $\{a_{j_1}, \ldots, a_{j_n}\}$. Hence, the value of $\mathcal{M}$ for the proposition depends only on the tuple $(s_1, \ldots, s_k)$, where s_j is the number of different i_l's for which $M_j(a_{i_l})$ occurs in the conjunction. *Let this value be* $m(s_1, \ldots, s_k)$. A partition of the set $\{a_{i_1}, \ldots, a_{i_n}\}$ into k subsets, which correspond to the k attributes, is called *a sample*.

If s_j individuals fall under the attribute M_j, $j = 1, \ldots, k$, then $(s_1, \ldots, s_k)$ is the *distribution of the sample*. Thus, $m(s_1, \ldots, s_k)$ is the probability of each of the propositions that describe a sample with the distribution $(s_1, \ldots, s_k)$. The axiom of symmetry makes this definition possible by making the probability depend on the distribution alone.

Given a sample with the distribution $(s_1, \ldots, s_k)$, the probability that a new individual, not in the sample, will belong to the attribute M_j is $\mathscr{C}(M_{i_l}(a_{i_l}) \wedge \ldots \wedge M_{i_n}(a_{i_n}) \wedge M_j(b) \mid M_{i_l}(a_{i_l}) \wedge \ldots M_{i_n}(a_{i_n}))$, where b is the name of the new individual. This probability is $m(s_1, \ldots, s_{j-1}, s_j + 1, s_{j+1}, \ldots, s_k)/m(s_1, \ldots, s_k)$ and we denote it by $c_j(s_1, \ldots, s_k)$. The *axiom of nonnegative instantial relevance* is that, for fixed $s_1, \ldots, s_{j-1}, s_{j+1}, \ldots, s_k$, c_j is a nondecreasing monotone function of s_j, that is,

$$c_j(s_1, \ldots, s_k) \leq c_j(s_1, \ldots, s_{j-1}, s_j + 1, s_{j+1}, \ldots, s_k).$$

The axiom of *positive instantial relevance* is obtained by replacing $\leq$ by $<$.

We will now sketch the original proof that, under our assumptions, the axiom of nonnegative relevance holds, and we will characterize those cases in which the stronger axiom of positive relevance fails.

§2. Assume that each attribute M_j is given an a priori probability, r_j, $0 \leq r_j \leq 1$ and $\sum_{j=1}^{k} r_j = 1$, and that the probability of $M_j(a_i)$ does not depend on any information concerning other individuals. In that case $m(s_1, \ldots, s_k) = r_1^{s_1} \cdot r_2^{s_2} \cdot \ldots \cdot r_k^{s_k}$. (We make the convention that $0^0 = 1$.) Now, a theorem by de Finetti states that the general case of a symmetric probability, in which the events described by $M_j(a_i)$, $i = 1, 2, \ldots$, $j = 1, \ldots, k$, are not necessarily independent, can be described as a "mixture of independent cases" in the following sense:

Let Δ be the set of all points $(r_1, \ldots, r_k)$ such that $0 \leq r_j \leq 1$ and $\sum_{j=1}^{k} r_j = 1$. Given any symmetric probability function, there is a measure μ on Δ such that the Borel subsets of Δ are measurable-μ, $\mu(\Delta) = 1$, and we have, for each distribution $(s_1, \ldots, s_k)$,

$$m(s_1, \ldots, s_k) = \int_\Delta r_1^{s_1} \cdot \ldots \cdot r_k^{s_k} \, d\mu(r_1, \ldots, r_k). \tag{1}$$

This will be the basic equation on which we will rely from now on.

Note that the right side of (1) is defined for all nonnegative $s_1, \ldots, s_k$, hence we can extend the definition of m to the case in which $s_1, \ldots, s_k$ are any nonnegative real numbers, not necessarily integers.

We have to show that $c_j(s_1, \ldots, s_k)$ is a monotone nondecreasing function of s_j. Take, for simplicity, $j = 1$.

Put $r = (r_1, \ldots, r_k)$, $s = (s_1, \ldots, s_k)$ and $r^s = r_1^{s_1} \cdot \ldots \cdot r_k^{s_k}$. We get:

$$c_1(s) = \int_\Delta r_1 \cdot r^s \, d\mu(r) \Big/ \int_\Delta r^s \, d\mu(r). \tag{2}$$

For $s_1 > 0$, we can differentiate with respect to s_1 under the integral (this is easily verifiable), and we get:

$$\frac{\partial c_1}{\partial s_1}(s) = \left[\int_\Delta r_1 \cdot r^s \log r_1 \, d\mu(r) \cdot \int_\Delta r^s \, d\mu(r) - \int_\Delta r_1 r^s \, d\mu(r) \int_\Delta r^s \log r_1 \, d\mu(r)\right] \cdot \left(\int_\Delta r^s \, d\mu(r)\right)^{-2}. \tag{3}$$

The second factor on the right side is always greater than 0, hence the sign of $\dfrac{\partial c_1}{\partial s_1}$ is determined by the sign of the first factor. Let us denote this factor by $f(s)$.

Put $\Delta^* = \Delta \times \Delta$ and let $\rho = (\rho_1, \ldots, \rho_k)$ be another variable ranging over Δ. Let μ^* be the product measure $\mu \times \mu$, defined on Δ^*.

Evaluating $f(s)$ with the help of Fubini's theorem, we get:

$$f(s) = \int_{\Delta^*} r_1 r^s \rho^s (\log r_1 - \log \rho_1) \, d\mu^*(r, \rho). \tag{4}$$

Here, as r and ρ range each over Δ, (r, ρ) ranges over Δ^*. Put

$$\Delta_1^* = \{(r, \rho) \in \Delta^* : r_1 > \rho_1\},$$

$$\Delta_{1'}^* = \{(r, \rho) \in \Delta^* : r_1 < \rho_1\}$$

and

$$\Delta_{1''}^* = \{(r, \rho) \in \Delta^* : r_1 = \rho_1\}.$$

The integral on the right side of (4), when taken over $\Delta_{1''}^*$, vanishes, hence:

$$\textbf{(5)}\quad f(s) = \int_{\Delta_1^*} r_1 r^s \rho^s (\log r_1 - \log \rho_1)\, d\mu^*(r, \rho) + \int_{\Delta_{1'}^*} r_1 r^s \rho^s (\log r_1 - \log \rho_1)\, d\mu^*(r, \rho)$$

Using the transformation $(r, \rho) \to (\rho, r)$ and the fact that it is measure preserving, we get:

$$\textbf{(6)}\quad \int_{\Delta_{1'}^*} r_1 r^s \rho^s (\log r_1 - \log \rho_1)\, d\mu^*(r, \rho) = \int_{\Delta_1^*} \rho_1 \rho^s \cdot r^s (\log \rho_1 - \log r_1)\, d\mu^*(r, \rho).$$

Substituting this in (5) we find by evaluating the expression:

$$\textbf{(7)}\qquad f(s) = \int_{\Delta_1^*} r^s \rho^s (r_1 - \rho_1)(\log r_1 - \log \rho_1)\, d\mu^*(r, \rho).$$

This is, obviously, nonnegative. It follows that c_1, as a function of s_1, has a nonnegative derivative in $(0, \infty)$, hence it is continuous and nondecreasing in $(0, \infty)$.

To see what happens in the case $s_1 = 0$, consider the right side of (2) as a function of s_1, where $s_1 \in [0, \infty)$. The numerator is continuous and for the denominator we have:

$$\textbf{(8)}\qquad \int_\Delta r^s\, d\mu(r) = \int_{\Delta'} r^s\, d\mu(r) + \int_{\Delta''} r^s\, d\mu(r)$$

where $\Delta' = \{r \in \Delta : r_1 > 0\}$ and $\Delta'' = \{r \in \Delta : r_1 = 0\}$. The first summand is continuous in $[0, \infty)$. The second summand is 0 whenever $s_1 > 0$, and for $s_1 = 0$ it is greater or equal to 0 (it is greater than 0 only if $\mu(\Delta'') > 0$). These considerations, together with what is known already of the behavior of c_1, imply that $c_1(0, s_2, \ldots, s_k) \leq c_1(s_1, s_2, \ldots, s_k)$, for all $s_1 \geq 0$. This proves the axiom of nonnegative relevance.

We will now check the fulfillment of the axiom of positive relevance. We first check the behavior of $c_1(t, s_2, \ldots, s_k)$, as a function of t, for $t > 0$.

From (7) it follows that $\frac{\partial c_1}{\partial s_1}$ is a continuous function of s_1 in $(0, \infty)$. This, with our previous observations, implies that, for all $t > 0$,

(9) $c_1(t, s_2, \ldots, s_k) < c_1(t + 1, s_2, \ldots, s_k)$ if and only if there exists s_1, $t < s_1 < t + 1$, such that $\frac{\partial c_1}{\partial s_1}(s_1, s_2, \ldots, s_k) > 0$.

Hence, for $t > 0$, $c_1(t, s_2, \ldots, s_k) = c_1(t + 1, s_2, \ldots, s_k)$, if and only if the right side of (7) vanishes for all s_1 such that $t < s_1 < t + 1$. The function under the integral vanishes if and only if there occurs in the product a term that is equal to 0; such a term can be either of the form $r_j^{s_j}$ or $\rho_j^{s_j}$, where $j \neq 1$, $s_j > 0$ and r_j, or ρ_j, is equal to 0, or of the form $\rho_1^{s_1}$ with $\rho_1 = 0$ (since $s_1 > 0$ the product $\rho_1^{s_1} \log \rho_1$, will vanish for $\rho_1 = 0$). Consequently, we look for those j's for which $s_j > 0$.

Put: $\Delta_1^*(s) = \{(r, \rho) \in \Delta_1^*: r_j > 0$ and $\rho_j > 0$ for each j such that $s_j > 0\}$. The function under the integral in (7) is greater than 0 if $(r, \rho) \in \Delta_1^*(s)$ and vanishes if $(r, \rho) \in \Delta_1^* - \Delta_1^*(s)$.

Hence, for $s_1 > 0$, we have

(10) $c_1(s_1 + 1, s_2, \ldots, s_k) = c_1(s_1, s_2, \ldots, s_k) \Leftrightarrow \mu^*(\Delta_1^*(s)) = 0$.

Define $\Delta_{1'}^*(s)$ and $\Delta_{1''}^*(s)$ in a similar way to that of $\Delta_1^*(s)$, with Δ_1^* replaced by $\Delta_{1'}^*$ and $\Delta_{1''}^*$, respectively. Put:

$$\Delta(s) = \{r \in \Delta: r_j > 0 \text{ for each } j \text{ such that } s_j > 0\}.$$

Obviously,

$$\Delta_1^*(s) = \{(r, \rho) \in \Delta(s) \times \Delta(s): r_1 > \rho_1\},$$

$$\Delta_{1'}^*(s) = \{(r, \rho) \in \Delta(s) \times \Delta(s): \rho_1 < r_1\}$$

and

$$\Delta_{1''}^*(s) = \{(r, \rho) \in \Delta(s) \times \Delta(s): r_1 = \rho_1\}.$$

Now, since $\Delta_1^*(s)$ and $\Delta_{1'}^*(s)$ are obtained from each other by interchanging r and ρ, they have the same μ^*-measure. Hence, $\mu^*(\Delta_1^*(s)) = 0$ if and only if the whole measure of $\Delta(s) \times \Delta(s)$ is concentrated in $\Delta_{1''}^*(s)$. Thus, for $s_1 > 0$, we get:

(11) $$c_1(s_1, \ldots, s_k) = c_1(s_1 + 1, s_1, \ldots, s_k) \Leftrightarrow \mu^*(\Delta(s) \times \Delta(s)) = \mu^*(\{(r, \rho) \in \Delta(s) \times \Delta(s): r_1 = \rho_1\}).$$

The condition on the right side means that the product measure of $\Delta(s) \times \Delta(s)$ is concentrated in the diagonal that is determined by: $r_1 = \rho_1$.

It is not difficult to show that this condition is equivalent to the condition that there exists an α such that the whole measure of $\Delta(s)$ is concentrated in $\{r \in \Delta(s): r_1 = \alpha\}$. (In fact, such an equivalence is true for a very general class of probability spaces, among which are all the spaces that are subsets of Euclidean spaces with every Borel set measurable.)

If $r \notin \Delta(s)$ then $r^s = 0$, hence, from (2), we have:

$$c_1(s) = \int_{\Delta(s)} r_1 r^s \, d\mu(r) \Big/ \int_{\Delta(s)} r^s \, d\mu(r). \tag{12}$$

In order that $c_1(s)$ should be defined we must have $\mu(\Delta(s)) > 0$. Hence, if $\mu(\Delta(s)) = \mu(\{r \in \Delta(s): r_1 = \alpha\})$, it follows, since $s_1 > 0$, that $\alpha > 0$; for otherwise the set on the right side would be empty. Substituting on the right side of (12) $\{r \in \Delta(s): r_1 = \alpha\}$ for $\Delta(s)$, we find at once that $c_1(s) = \alpha$. Moreover, whenever $\Delta(s') \subseteq \Delta(s)$ we will get $c_1(s') = \alpha$ (provided that $c_1(s')$ is defined). Hence, if s' is such that $s'_j > 0$ for each j such that $s_j > 0$, then $c_1(s') = c_1(s) = \alpha$.

Considering now the remaining case, where $c_1(0, s_2, \ldots, s_k) = c_1(1, s_2, \ldots, s_k)$. Assuming this equality, it follows that

$$\frac{\partial c_1}{\partial s_1}(s_1, s_2, \ldots, s_k) = 0$$

for every s_1 such that $0 < s_1 < 1$, and this, as before, implies that the measure of $\Delta(s)$, where $s = (s_1, s_2, \ldots, s_k)$ and $s_1 > 0$, is concentrated in $\{r \in \Delta(s): r_1 = \alpha\}$, for some $\alpha > 0$. This implies, as before, that $c_1(s') = \alpha$ for all s' such that $s_j > 0$ implies $s'_j > 0, j = 1, \ldots, k$.

Consider now the right side of (12) as a function of $s = (s_1, s_2, \ldots, s_k)$, with $s_2, \ldots, s_k$ the fixed given ones and s_1 varying over $[0, \infty)$. The numerator is continuous for $s_1 \in [0, \infty)$. The denominator can be split into a sum: $\int_{\Delta'(s)} r^s \, d\mu(r) + \int_{\Delta''(s)} r^s \, d\mu(r)$, where $\Delta'(s) = \{r \in \Delta(s): r_1 > 0\}$ and $\Delta''(s) = \{r \in \Delta(s): r_1 = 0\}$. Obviously, $\Delta''(s)$ is empty, unless $s_1 = 0$. The first summand is continuous for $s_1 \in [0, \infty)$.

It follows that if $\mu(\Delta''(0, s_2, \ldots, s_k)) = 0$ then c_1 is continuous at the point $s_1 = 0$. On the other hand, if $\mu(\Delta''(0, s_2, \ldots, s_k)) > 0$, then, since $r^s > 0$ for all $r \in \Delta(s)$, there will be a jump in $c_1(s)$ at the point 0, that is: $c_1(0, s_2, \ldots, s_k) < \lim_{s_1 \to 0+0} c_1(s_1, s_2, \ldots, s_k)$.

Consequently, assuming $c_1(0, s_2, \ldots, s_k) = c_1(1, s_2, \ldots, s_k)$, it follows that $\mu(\{r \in \Delta(0, s_2, \ldots, s_k): r_1 = 0\}) = 0$. This implies that the measure of $\Delta(0, s_2, \ldots, s_k)$ is concentrated in the subset obtained by fixing r_1 to be α.

On the other hand, if

$$\mu(\Delta(0, s_2, \ldots, s_k)) = \mu(\{r \in \Delta(0, s_2, \ldots, s_k): r_1 = \alpha\}),$$

then, since $\alpha > 0$, it follows that $\mu(\Delta''(0, s_2, \ldots, s_k)) = 0$. Hence, c_1 is continuous for $s_1 \in [0, \infty)$. We know already that it has the constant value α for $s_1 \in (0, \infty)$; therefore, it assumes also this value for $s_1 = 0$.

These considerations show that for $s_1 = 0$, as well, $c_1(s_1, \ldots, s_k) = c_1(s_1 + 1, s_2, \ldots, s_k)$ if and only if, for some $\alpha > 0$, $\mu(\Delta(s)) = \mu(\{r \in \Delta(s): r_1 = \alpha\})$; in which case c_1 will have the constant value α for all $s_1 \in [0, \infty)$.

The following theorem sums up the results:

Say that positive relevance for the ith attribute is violated at $s = (s_1, \ldots, s_k)$ if

$$c_i(s_1, \ldots, s_k) = c_i(s_1, \ldots, s_{i-1}, s_i + 1, s_{i+1}, \ldots, s_i).$$

Theorem. If $m(s_1, \ldots, s_k) = 0$, then positive relevance for the ith attribute is violated at s if and only if, for some $\alpha > 0$, the μ-measure of $\Delta(s) = \{r \in \Delta: r_j > 0 \text{ whenever } s_j > 0, j = 1, \ldots, k\}$ is concentrated in $\{r \in \Delta(s); r_i = \alpha\}$. In that case $c_i(s') = \alpha$ whenever s' is such that $s'_j > 0$ for every j for which $s_j > 0$.

(Note that, if we use (2) to extend the definition of c_i for all non-negative tuples, then, in the definition of the violation of positive relevance, we can replace $s_i + 1$ by $s_i + \epsilon$, with any $\epsilon > 0$, and the theorem remains true.)

The theorem characterizes completely the cases in which positive relevance is violated. One can construct examples of a general character. One also gets interrelations of the following kind:

Corollary. Assume that positive relevance for the ith attribute is violated both at s and at s'. If $c_i(s') = c_i(s)$ then $c_i(s'') = c_i(s)$, for every s'' such that $s''_j > 0$ for all j for which both $s_j > 0$ and $s'_j > 0$. If $c_i(s) \neq c_i(s')$ then the μ-measure of the set $\{r \in \Delta: r_j > 0 \text{ for each } j$ such that either $s_j > 0$ or $s'_j > 0\}$ is 0. This last condition is equivalent to the condition that every sample, in which every attribute that has more than zero elements either in s or in s' has more than 0 elements, is of probability 0.

Other interrelations are not difficult to find.

§3. Reichenbach's axiom of convergence roughly states that, as the total size of the sample becomes larger, the confirmation that, given the sample, the next individual will belong to the jth attribute, should approach the relative frequency of this attribute within the sample; that is, $c_j(s_1, \ldots, s_k)$ should approach s_j/S, where $S = \sum_{i=1}^{k} s_i$. One can give several precise formulations of this idea, for instance, the one given by Carnap is as follows:

Let $s^n = (s_1^n, \ldots, s_k^n)$, $n = 1, 2, \ldots$ be a sequence of distributions, with $S^n = \sum_{i=1}^{k} s_i^n$, such that $S^n \to \infty$ as $n \to \infty$, then, for each $j = 1, 2, \ldots, k$, $\lim_{n\to\infty} (c_j(s^n) - s_j^n/S^n) = 0$.

An apparently weaker formulation was suggested by Putnam:

Given $s^n = (s_1^n, \ldots, s_n^k)$ as above such that $S^n \to \infty$ as $n \to \infty$, then, the existence of a limit of s_j^n/S^n, as $n \to \infty$, implies the existence of a limit of $c_j(s^n)$, as $n \to \infty$, and the equality of both limits.

One can formulate several other versions, apparently weaker or stronger than either of these two. Using de Finetti's theorem, however, one can show the equivalence of all these versions. Our result is expressed in the following theorem which claims that the apparently weakest version one can think of implies the strongest one. The weakest version is:

(A) For every $\theta = (\theta_1, \ldots, \theta_k)$, such that the θ_i are rational, $\theta_i \geq 0$, $i = 1, \ldots, k$, and $\sum_{i=1}^{k} \theta_i = 1$, and for every j, such that $1 \leq j \leq k$, there exists a sequence of distributions $s^n = (s_1^n, \ldots, s_k^n)$ for which $\lim_{n\to\infty} s_i^n/S^n = \theta_i$, where $S^n = \sum_{i=1}^{k} s_i^n$, such that $\lim_{n\to\infty} c_j(s^n) = \theta_j$, or else, from a certain n on $c_j(s^n)$ is undefined.

(Note that the sequence s^n is allowed here to depend on the θ and on j.)

The strongest version is:

(B) For every $\epsilon > 0$ there exists N such that, for every distribution $s = (s_1, \ldots, s_k)$, if $\sum_{i=1}^{k} s_i > N$ then $\left| c_j(s) - s_j / \sum_{i=1}^{k} s_i \right| < \epsilon$, for $j = 1, \ldots, k$.

Theorem. (A) implies (B).

The theorem is proved by using a condition on the measure μ by which the probability and confirmation functions are given through (1) and (2). Using the same notation as before, we mean by "an open subset of Δ" a subset of Δ which is open in the relative topology of Δ, that is, an intersection of Δ with an open subset of the k-dimensional Euclidean space. By a subsimplex of Δ we mean a set of the form Δ_J, where $J \subseteq \{1, \ldots, k\}$ and $\Delta_J = \{r \in \Delta: r_i = 0$ for each i such that

$i \notin J\}$. Δ_J is the closed subsimplex spanned by the vertices in J. Consider the following condition

(∗) The complement, with respect to Δ, of the union of all the open subsets of Δ, whose μ-measure is 0, is a union of subsimplices of Δ.

Note that the union of all the open subsets of Δ of μ-measure 0 is also an open subset of Δ which, since it can be represented as a union of countably many sets of μ-measure 0, is also of μ-measure 0. Thus, it is the maximal open subset of measure 0. Let this set be 0_μ. Condition (∗) amounts to the following: Either every open subset of Δ has μ-measure > 0, in which case $0_\mu = \varnothing$, or else the whole interior of Δ (that is $\{r \in \Delta: r_i > 0 \text{ for } i = 1, \ldots, k\}$) has μ-measure 0 and then, taking each k-2-dimensional subsimplex, Δ_J (where J has $k - 1$ elements) such that $\mu(\Delta_J) > 0$, either every subset of Δ_J which is open in its relative topology has measure > 0, or else . . . and so on.

It can be shown that (A) implies (∗) and that (∗) implies (B). Thus (∗) is a necessary and sufficient condition for Reichenbach's axiom. The detailed proof will be presented in Volume II.

From the theorem in the preceding section it follows that if positive relevance for the ith predicate is violated at s, then $c_i(s')$ is defined and is equal to $c_i(s)$, whenever s' is such that $s'_j > 0$ whenever $s_j > 0, j = 1, \ldots, k$. Hence, if $c_i(s) = \alpha$ then

$$c_i(s_1, \ldots, s_{i-1}, s_i + n, s_{i+1}, \ldots, s_k) = \alpha$$

for all n. If $n \rightarrow \infty$ the relative frequency of the ith predicate approaches 1, and consequently, if $\alpha < 1$, we get a contradiction with Reichenbach's axiom. If $\alpha = 1$, then it is not difficult to see that $c_i(0 \ldots 1 \ldots 0) = 1$ where $(0 \ldots 1 \ldots 0)$ is the sample with 1 at the ith place and 0 everywhere else. Hence we get:

Theorem. Reichenbach's axiom implies strong instantial relevance for the ith predicate, except for the degenerate case in which $c_i(0 \ldots 1 \ldots 0) = 1$.

(Reichenbach's axiom need not imply strong instantial relevance for the degenerate case, as the following example shows. Let $k = 2$, and let $m(n, 0) = m(0, n) = \frac{1}{2}$ for all $n > 0$, and $m(n_1, n_2) = 0$ for $n_1 > 0$ and $n_2 > 0$. Then $c_1(n, 0) = c_1(n + 1, 0) = 1$, for all $n > 0$, hence positive relevance fails. Reichenbach's axiom holds, because $c_1(n_1, n_2)$ is defined only if $n_2 = 0$ and then it is always 1.)

For this corollary we do not need (∗); indeed, the argument shows that the weakest form, (A), implies directly the requirement of positive relevance. Having the condition (∗), however, and a condition on the measure μ which is equivalent to the holding of the requirement of positive instantial relevance, it is easy to construct probability functions satisfying the requirement of positive instantial relevance and violating Reichenbach's axiom.

Postscript Concerning Extension of Probability Functions

Consider a family of k attributes, $k > 2$. Let $P_{k,n}$ be the set of all propositions formed from these attributes and the first n individuals out of the infinite list $a_1, a_2, \ldots$. $P_{k,\infty}$ is the set of all propositions on which the symmetric probability functions (called also M-functions), hitherto used, were assumed to be defined. Consider now probability functions defined only for $P_{k,n}$. Each function is completely determined by its values for all the distributions $(n_1, \ldots, n_k)$ such that $n_1 + \ldots + n_k = n$. There are altogether $\binom{n+k-1}{k-1}$ such distributions. Hence, each function, m, can be correlated with a point in the $\binom{n+k-1}{k-1}$-dimensional Euclidean space, where $m(n_1, \ldots, n_k)$, the value of m for the distribution $(n_1, \ldots, n_k)$, is the $(n_1, \ldots, n_k)$ coordinate of that point. We shall identify m with that point. The value of m for distributions $(j_1, \ldots, j_k)$ for which $j_1 + \ldots + j_k \leq n$, is uniquely determined through the formula

(i) $$m(j_1, \ldots, j_k) = \sum_{\substack{n_1 \geq j_1, \ldots, n_k \geq j_k \\ n_1 + \ldots + n_k = n}} m(n_1, \ldots, n_k)$$

We shall therefore regard as meaningful all expressions "$m(j_1, \ldots, j_k)$" where $j_1 + \ldots + j_k \leq n$.

Each m satisfies the following:

(ii) $$\sum_{n_1 + \ldots + n_k = n} \frac{n!}{n_1! \cdot \ldots \cdot n_k!} m(n_1, \ldots, n_k) = 1$$

(iii) $$m(n_1, \ldots, n_k) \geq 0 \quad \text{for all} \quad (n_1, \ldots, n_k).$$

The first equation determines a $\binom{n+k-1}{k-1} - 1$ dimensional hyperplane which will be denoted by "$H_{k,n}$". All sets that will occur later will be subsets of $H_{k,n}$ and the topological terms, such as "boundary," and "interior" will, unless otherwise stated, refer to the topology of $H_{k,n}$.

The second set of inequalities determines a $\binom{n+k-1}{k-1} - 1$

dimensional closed convex polyhedron in $H_{k,n}$, which will be denoted by "$M_{k,n}$". $M_{k,n}$ has $\binom{n+k-1}{k-1}$ vertices, namely, for each $(n_1, \ldots, n_k)$ such that $n_1 + \ldots + n_k = n$, the function m such that

$$\frac{n!}{n_1! \cdot \ldots \cdot n_k!} m(n_1, \ldots, n_k) = 1$$

is a vertex of $M_{k,n}$ and these are all its vertices. It is not difficult to see that the set of inequalities together with the equation of $H_{k,n}$ is sufficient for m to be a probability function on $P_{k,n}$. Thus, $M_{k,n}$ is the set of all such functions.

Weak instantial relevance (also called "the requirement of non-negative instantial relevance") is the requirement that

$$c_i(n_1, \ldots, n_i, \ldots, n_k) \leq c_i(n_1, \ldots, n_i + 1, \ldots, n_k).$$

Since

$$c_i(j_1, \ldots, j_k) = m(j_1, \ldots, j_i + 1, \ldots, j_k)/m(j_1, \ldots, j_k),$$

the inequality is meaningful for m in $M_{k,n}$ only if $n_1 + \ldots + n_k \leq n - 2$. Moreover, the inequality is required to hold provided only that both sides are defined, that is, if $m(n_1, \ldots, n_k)$ and $m(n_1, \ldots, n_i + 1, \ldots, n_k)$ are both nonzero. Hence, weak instantial relevance amounts to the inequality:

(iv) $$m^2(n_1, \ldots, (n_i + 1), \ldots, n_k) \leq m(n_1, \ldots, n_k) \cdot m(n_1, \ldots, n_i + 2, \ldots, n_k).$$

Strong instantial relevance (also called "the requirement of positive instantial relevance") amounts to the requirement that, in (iv) equality holds only in the case in which both sides are equal to zero.

It can be shown that weak instantial relevance implies the following property:

(v) If $n_1 + \ldots + n_k = n'_1 + \ldots + n'_k = n$ and, for each i, $n_i > 0$ implies $n'_i > 0$, then $m(n_1, \ldots, n_k) = 0$ implies that $m(n'_1, \ldots, n'_k) = 0$.

This is also equivalent to:

(v*) If $m(n_1, \ldots, n_k) = 0$ then $m(j_1, \ldots, j_k) = 0$ where

$$j_i = \min(n_i, 1), \qquad i = 1, \ldots, k.$$

Let $N_{k,n}$ be the set of all m's in $M_{k,n}$ which satisfy (v). Not every m in $N_{k,n}$ satisfies weak instantial relevance, but $N_{k,n}$ is very handy in stating some of the coming results.

It is obvious that $N_{k,n}$ is a convex set. $N_{k,n}$ includes the interior of $M_{k,n}$, for m is in the interior of $M_{k,n}$ if and only if all its values are greater than zero and this implies that it is in $N_{k,n}$. $N_{k,n}$ includes part of the boundary of $M_{k,n}$. It can be shown that $m \in N_{k,n}$ if and only if there exists a family $J_1, \ldots, J_t$ of subsets of $\{1, \ldots, k\}$ each having at most n elements and none of which includes the other such that the following holds:

For every $(n_1, \ldots, n_k)$ for which m is defined, $m(n_1, \ldots, n_k) > 0$ if and only if there exists a J_p such that $n_i > 0$ implies $i \in J_p$.

This family is uniquely determined by m. If it consists of all the subsets of $\{1, \ldots, k\}$ whose number of elements is $\min(n, k)$ then m is always positive, hence it is in the interior of $M_{k,n}$ (if $n \geq k$ this means that the family consists of $\{1, \ldots, k\}$ only). Otherwise, m will be on a certain lower-dimensional face of $M_{k,n}$. This face lies in the subspace that is determined by equating some of the coordinates to zero, namely, all those coordinates in the $\binom{n+k-1}{k-1} - 1$ Euclidean space which correspond to those $(n_1, \ldots, n_k)$ for which no J_p includes $\{i: n_i > 0\}$. Since for the other coordinates m will have value >0, it follows that m will be an interior point of the face in the relative topology of this subspace. In the extreme case, where the family consists of a single set of the form $\{i\}$, m will coincide with a vertex of $M_{k,n}$, namely the vertex x such that $x(0 \ldots, n, \ldots 0) = 1$, where n occurs in the ith place. Thus $N_{k,n}$ contains altogether k vertices of $M_{k,n}$, and it does not include any face that has a vertex not among these k vertices although it might intersect it.

Let $W_{k,n}$ and $S_{k,n}$ be the sets of those m's which satisfy weak and strong instantial relevance, respectively. The following can be proved:

(I) **(a)** $S_{k,n} \subset W_{k,n} \subset N_{k,n}$ and all these sets are convex.
(b) $W_{k,n}$ is closed and it has a nonempty interior.
(c) $\mathrm{Int}(W_{k,n}) = \mathrm{Int}(S_{k,n}) = S_{k,n} \cap \mathrm{Int}(M_{k,n})$, where $\mathrm{Int}(X)$ is the interior of X.

It follows that $W_{k,n}$ and $S_{k,n}$ are $\binom{n+k-1}{k-1} - 1$ dimensional and, since $W_{k,n}$ is closed and is included but is not equal to $M_{k,n}$, the interior of $M_{k,n}$ contains part of the boundary of $W_{k,n}$. This is true whenever $n \geq 2$.

Let $E_{k,n}$ be the set of all m's in $M_{k,n}$ which can be extended to $P_{k,\infty}$. If $m \in E_{k,n}$ then, trivially, it has extensions to all $P_{k,n'}$, $n' \geq n$. By a compactness argument it can be shown that if it has extensions to all $P_{k,n'}$, $n' \geq n$, then it can be extended to $P_{k,\infty}$.

Let $R_{k,n}$ be the set of all m's in $M_{k,n}$ which have extensions to $P_{k,\infty}$ satisfying Reichenbach's axiom (hereafter R's axiom). The following was proved by the author:

(II) **(a)** $E_{k,n}$ is a closed convex subset of $N_{k,n}$.

(b) $R_{k,n}$ is a convex subset of $N_{k,n}$ intersecting the interior of $M_{k,n}$ as well as each face of $M_{k,n}$ which intersects $N_{k,n}$.

(c) $R_{k,n}$ is equal to the interior of $E_{k,n}$ with respect to $N_{k,n}$ with its induced topology, i.e., $m \in R_{k,n}$ if and only if m has a neighborhood V such that $V \cap N_{k,n} \subset E_{k,n}$.

It follows that $E_{k,n}$ and $R_{k,n}$ are $\binom{n+k-1}{k-1} - 1$ dimensional and the boundary of $E_{k,n}$, with respect to $N_{k,n}$, passes through the interior of $M_{k,n}$ as well as through each face of $M_{k,n}$ which intersects but is not included in $N_{k,n}$. This is true whenever $n \geq 2$.

The proof of this result relies on de Finetti's theorem and on the characterization (*) (in 3) of those functions on $P_{k,\infty}$ satisfying Reichenbach's axiom.

If we take a boundary point of $E_{k,n}$ which lies in the interior of $M_{k,n}$ then that point can be continued to $P_{k,\infty}$ but its continuation does not satisfy Reichenbach's axiom. The existence of such functions is not new, for we know already that, for functions on $P_{k,\infty}$ which are positive everywhere Reichenbach's axiom implies strong instantial relevance, hence if such a function violates strong instantial relevance one can take its restriction to $P_{k,n}$, where n is large enough so that the violation is at some $(n_1, \ldots, n_k)$ with $n_1 + \ldots + n_k \leq n$. That restriction can be continued to $P_{k,\infty}$ but all its continuations do not satisfy Reichenbach's axiom. It turns out, however, that there are also functions on the boundary of $E_{k,n}$ which satisfy strong instantial relevance. The following can be shown:

(III) The set of all points in $E_{k,n}$ which violate strong instantial relevance for the ith attribute at $(n_1, \ldots, n_k)$ (i.e., for which

$$c_i(n_1, \ldots, n_k) = c_i(n_1, \ldots, n_i + 1, \ldots, n_k))$$

is of dimension $\binom{n+k-1}{k-1} - \binom{n-s+k-2}{k-1}$, where s is the number of i's for which $n_i > 0$.

Since $\binom{n-s+k-2}{k-1}$ decreases as s increases, the set mentioned above will have the maximum number of dimensions if s is maximal. We have $s \leq k$ and also, since $n_1 + \ldots + n_k$ should be $\leq n-2$, $s \leq n-2$. On the other hand, if $s = \min(k, n-2)$, we can choose

$(n_1, \ldots, n_k)$ such that $n_1 + \ldots + n_k \leq n - 2$ and the number of i's for which $n_i > 0$ is s. Hence we have:

(III*) The set of all points in $E_{k,n}$ which do not satisfy strong instantial relevance is of dimension $\binom{n+k-1}{k-1} - \binom{n-s+k-2}{k-1}$, where $s = \min(k, n-2)$. Consequently, if $n - 2 \geq k$ this set has

$$\binom{n+k-1}{k-1} - \binom{n-2}{k-1}$$

dimensions and if $0 \leq n - 2 < k$ it has $\binom{n+k-1}{k-1} - k$ dimensions.

Consider now the boundary of $E_{k,n}$. Since $E_{k,n}$ is a convex $\binom{n+k-1}{k-1} - 1$ dimensional set its boundary has $\binom{n+k-1}{k-1} - 2$ dimensions. It follows, therefore, that in each case in which $\binom{n+k-1}{k-1} - \binom{n-s+k-2}{k-2} > \binom{n+k-1}{k-1} - 2$, where $s = \min(k, n-2)$, there will be boundary points of $E_{k,n}$ in the interior of $M_{k,n}$ which satisfy strong instantial relevance. For $n - 2 \geq k$ this amounts to: $\binom{n-2}{k-1} > 2$ and for $n - 2 < k$ this amounts to $k > 2$. It follows that:

(IV) If either $k = 2, n \geq 5$ or $k > 2, n \geq 2$ there are boundary points in $E_{k,n}$ in the interior of $M_{k,n}$ satisfying strong instantial relevance.

Thus, for either $k = 2, n \geq 5$, or $k > 2, n \geq 2$, we have probability functions on $P_{k,n}$ satisfying strong instantial relevance and extendible to $P_{k,\infty}$, but having no extensions to $P_{k,\infty}$ satisfying Reichenbach's axiom. Note that if $n \geq k + 2$ then each extension to $P_{k,\infty}$ of a function on $P_{k,n}$ satisfying strong instantial relevance also satisfies strong instantial relevance (by the theorem of §2).

Note that if we take a boundary point of $E_{k,n}$ in the interior of $M_{k,n}$ which is in $S_{k,n}$ then there will be a neighborhood V of that point which is in $S_{k,n}$, and $V - E_{k,n}$ will be nonempty. Now, every m in $V - E_{k,n}$ satisfies strong instantial relevance but has no extensions to $P_{k,\infty}$. Thus we get:

(V) For either $k = 2$, $n \geq 5$ or $k > 2$, $n \geq 2$ there are probability functions on $P_{k,n}$ positive everywhere and satisfying strong instantial relevance which cannot be extended to $P_{k,n'}$ for n' large enough.

This last result should not be surprising. As Humburg has shown (in Art. **4**), the requirements of instantial relevance are a special case of the Schwartz inequality, if we assume that the function is defined on $P_{k,\infty}$. Using the same method one can construct other inequalities of the form:

(vi) $$m^2(n_1 + s_1 + t_1, \ldots, n_k + s_k + t_k) \leq m(n_1 + 2s_1, \ldots, n_k + 2s_k) \cdot m(n_1 + 2t_1, \ldots, n_k + 2t_k).$$

Such an inequality is meaningful for m in $P_{k,n}$ provided that the total size of all the distributions that are involved is $\leq n$. For n large enough there are such inequalities that do not follow from (iv). This condition alone shows that the requirements of instantial relevance are not sufficient to guarantee extendibility to $P_{k,\infty}$.

Using similar methods one can show that on the boundary of $E_{k,n}$ which passes in the interior of $M_{k,n}$ there are points satisfying all the inequalities of (vi), with '$\leq$' replaced by '$<$'. This implies that (vi) is also not sufficient for the extendibility of n to $P_{k,\infty}$.

Still a wider set of inequalities consists of those implied by Hölder's inequality. They are:

(vii) $$m(n_1 + s_1 + t_1, \ldots, n_k + s_k + t_k) \leq m^{1/p}(n_1 + ps_1, \ldots, n_k + ps_k) \cdot m^{1/q}(n_1 + qt_1, \ldots, n_k + qt_k)$$

where

$$\frac{1}{p} + \frac{1}{q} = 1, \qquad p, q > 0.$$

(We have to stipulate, of course, that ps_i and qt_i are integers.)

Again, it can be shown that these too are not sufficient to guarantee extendibility.

All these, with '$\geq$' replaced by '$>$', are implied, for everywhere positive functions, by Reichenbach's axiom. But, again, there are functions with extensions to $p_{k,\infty}$ satisfying all these strict inequalities but all of whose extensions violate R's axiom.

Selected Bibliography

The contributions to these studies deal in general not with *philosophical* problems about inductive logic, but with concrete problems of the construction of a system of inductive logic. (An exception is Article **1**, because of its purpose as an introduction to the studies.) Therefore this bibliography contains only publications that concern problems of probability itself, in distinction to philosophical problems of induction. For bibliographical information on the literature of philosophical problems see the bibliographies or references given in the following books: Carnap [1950], Foster and Martin [1966], Hintikka and Suppes [1966], Kyburg [1961], Kyburg and Smokler [1964]. Most of the authors in the present bibliography accept the Bayesian interpretation of probability. The most important non-Bayesian schools of thought on probability are those represented by Popper and by Reichenbach. References to the philosophical views of Popper's school are to be found chiefly in his books (*The Logic of Scientific Discovery*, 1959; *Conjectures and Refutations*, 1962). For their (negative) views on inductive logic see the contributions by Popper and Lakatos in: Lakatos [1966*a*], which contains further references. For Reichenbach's school see his books [1949] and *Experience and Prediction* (1938); and Salmon [1966].

ACHINSTEIN, Peter

[1963*a*] Confirmation theory, order, and periodicity. *Phil. Sci.*, 30, 1–16.

[1963*b*] Variety and analogy in confirmation theory. *Phil. Sci.*, 30, 207–221. (See Carnap [1963*a*].)

ADAMS, Ernest

[1959] *Two aspects of the theory of rational betting odds.* Tech. Rep. no. 1, Univ. of California, Berkeley.

BAR-HILLEL, Yehoshua

[1951] A note on state-descriptions. *Phil. Studies*, 2, 72–75.

[1953] A note on comparative inductive logic. *Brit. J. Phil. Sci.*, 3, 308–310.

[1964] *Language and information.* Selected essays. Addison-Wesley, Reading, Mass., and London. Academic Press, Jerusalem.

BAR-HILLEL, Y. (ed.)

[1965] *Logic, methodology, and philosophy of science: Proceedings of the 1964 international congress* [in Jerusalem]. North-Holland Publ. Co., Amsterdam.

BAR-HILLEL, Y., and CARNAP, R.

[1953] Semantic information. In: Willis Jackson (ed.), *Communication theory*, Butterworth, London, 1953, pp. 503–511. [This is a lecture by Bar-Hillel, based on: Carnap and Bar-Hillel [1952]]. A slightly revised version appeared in: *Brit. J. Phil. Sci.*, 4, 147–157.

BAYES, Thomas

[1763] An essay towards solving a problem in the doctrine of chances. *Phil. Trans. Roy. Soc.*, 370–418. Repr. in: Demming [1940] and *Biometrika*, 45 (1958), 293–315.

BILLINGSLEY, Patrick

[1965] *Ergodic theory and information.* Wiley, New York.

BOCHNER, S.

[1939] Additive set functions on groups. *Ann. Math.*, 40, 769–799.

BOCHNER, S., and PHILLIPS, R. S.

[1941] Additive set functions and vector lattices. *Ann. Math.*, 42, 316–321.

BRAITHWAITE, Richard B.

[1957] On unknown probabilities. In: Körner (ed.) [1957].

CARNAP, Rudolf
[1945] On inductive logic. *Phil. Sci.*, 12, 72–97. Repr. in: Foster and Martin [1966], no. 3.
[1946] Remarks on induction and truth. *Phil. Phen. Res.*, 6, 590–602.
[1950] [Prob.] *Logical foundations of probability*. Chicago Univ. Press, Chicago. (2d ed., see [1962*b*].)
[1952*a*] [Cont.] *The continuum of inductive methods*. Chicago Univ. Press, Chicago.
[1952*b*] Meaning postulates. *Phil. Studies*, 3, 65–73. (Repr. in [1956].)
[1953*a*] On the comparative concept of confirmation. *Brit. J. Phil. Sci.*, 3, 311–318.
[1953*b*] Inductive logic and science. *Proc. Amer. Acad. of Arts and Sci.*, 80, 189–197.
[1955] I. *Statistical and inductive probability* (1–16). II. *Inductive logic and science* (repr. from [1953*b*].) Galois Institute, Brooklyn, N.Y.
[1956] *Meaning and necessity*. 2d ed. (1st, 1947). Chicago Univ. Press, Chicago. (Supplement B: repr. of [1952*b*].)
[1959] *Induktive Logik und Wahrscheinlichkeit*. (Bearbeitet von Wolfgang Stegmüller.) Springer, Wien. (Anhang B: Ein neues Axiomensystem.)
[1962*a*] The aim of inductive logic. In: Nagel, Suppes, and Tarski [1962], pp. 303–318. (A modified and expanded version appears as Art. **1** in this volume.)
[1962*b*] Preface to the second edition of [1950], pp. xiii–xxii.
[1963*a*] Variety, analogy, and periodicity in inductive logic. *Phil. Sci.*, 30, 222–227. (Reply to Achinstein [1963*a* and *b*].)
[1963*b*] Remarks on probability. *Phil. Studies*, 14, 65–75. (A modified version of [1962*b*].)
[1964*a*] Replies and systematic expositions. In: Schilpp [1964], chap. v, Probability and induction.
[1964*b*] An axiom system for inductive logic. ([1964*a*], §26.)
[1966] Probability and content measure. In: Feyerabend and Maxwell [1966], pp. 248–260.
[1968] Inductive logic and inductive intuition. In: Lakatos [1968], pp. 258–267; reply to discussion, pp. 307–314; remarks on rules of acceptance, pp. 146–149 (p. 150 should be deleted; it contains an error pointed out by Kyburg in *ibid.*, p. 165).

CARNAP, R., and BAR-HILLEL, Y.
[1952] *An outline of a theory of semantic information*. Tech. Rep. no. 247, Res. Lab. Electronics, M.I.T., Cambridge, Mass. 48 pp. (Compare: Bar-Hillel and Carnap [1953].) Repr. in Bar-Hillel [1964], pp. 221–274.

CROSSLEY, J. N. (ed.)
[1967] *Sets, models and recursion theory*. North-Holland, Amsterdam.

DAVIDSON, Donald; SUPPES, Patrick; SIEGEL, Sidney

[1957] *Decision making: An experimental approach.* Stanford Univ. Press, Stanford.

DE FINETTI. See Finetti, Bruno de.

DEMMING, W. Edward
[1940] *Facsimile of two papers of Bayes.* Graduate School, Dept. of Agriculture, Washington, D.C.

DOOB, J. L.
[1953] *Stochastic processes.* Wiley, New York.

DUBINS, L. E.
[1969] An elementary proof of Bochner's finitely additive Radon-Nikodym theorem. *Amer. Math. Monthly*, 76, 520–523.

FELLER, William
[1957–66] An introduction to probability theory and its applications. Vols. 1 (2d ed.) and 2. Wiley, New York.

FENSTAD, Jens Erik
[1967] Representations of probabilities defined on first order languages. In Crossley (ed.) [1967], pp. 186–202.
[1968] The structure of logical probabilities. *Synthese*, 18, 1–23.

FEYERABEND, Paul K., and MAXWELL, Grover.
[1966] *Mind, matter, and method: Essays in philosophy of science, in honor of Herbert Feigl.* Univ. of Minnesota Press, Minneapolis.

FINETTI, Bruno de
[1931] Sul significato soggettivo della probabilità. *Fund. Math.*, 17, 298–329.
[1937] La prévision: Ses lois logique, ses sources subjectives. *Ann. de l'Inst. Henri Poincaré*, 7, 1–68. (Engl. trans., see [1964].)
[1938] *Sur la condition d'équivalence partielle.* Colloque consacré à la théorie des probabilités, Vol. VI. Actualités Scient. et Industr., no. 739. Hermann et Cie, Paris. pp. 5–18.
[1949] *Sull' impostazione assiomatica del calcolo delle probabilità.* Univ. di Trieste. 55 pp. (Also in: *Ann. Triestini*, 19 [1949], 29–81.)
[1955] La struttura delle distribuzioni in un insieme astratto qualsiasi. *Giorn. Ist. Italiano degli Attuari*, 18, 16–28.
[1964] Foresight: Its logical laws, its subjective sources. (Engl. trans. by Kyburg of [1937].) In: Kyburg and Smokler [1964].

FINNETTI, B. de, and SAVAGE, L. J.
[1962] Sul modo di scegliere le probabilità iniziali. In: Biblioteca del "Metron", Seria C, Vol. I: *Sui fondamenti della Statistica.* Istituto di Statistica, Univ. di Roma. pp. 81–147. (Engl. summary, pp. 148–151.)

FOSTER, Marguerite H., and MARTIN, Michael L. (eds.)
[1966] *Probability, confirmation, and simplicity: Readings in the philosophy of inductive logic.* Odyssey Press, New York.

FRASER, D. A. S.
[1957] *Nonparametric methods in statistics.* Wiley, New York.

FRÉCHET, Maurice
[1915] Sur l'intégrale d'une functionelle étendue à un ensemble abstrait. *Bull. Soc. Math. France*, 43, 248–267.

GAIFMAN, Haim
[1964] Concerning measures on first-order calculi. *Israel J. Math.*, 2, 1–18.

GOOD, I. J.
[1950] *Probability and the weighing of evidence.* Hafner, New York.
[1962] Subjective probability as the measure of an unmeasurable set. In: Nagel, Suppes, and Tarski [1962], pp. 319–329.
[1965] *The estimation of probabilities: An essay in modern Bayesian methods.* Res. monogr. no. 30. M.I.T. Press, Cambridge, Mass. 109 pp.
[1967] On the principle of total evidence. *Brit. J. Phil. Sci.*, 17, 319–321.

GOODMAN, Nelson
[1955] *Fact, fiction, and forecast.* Harvard Univ. Press, Cambridge, Mass.

HACKING, Ian
[1964] On the foundations of statistics. *Brit. J. Phil. Sci.*, 15, 1–26.
[1965] *The logic of statistical inference.* Cambridge Univ. Press, London.
[1967] Slightly more realistic personal probability. In: Savage *et al.*, [1967], pp. 311–325.
[1968] On falling short of strict coherence. *Phil. Sci.*, 35, 284–286.

HALMOS, Paul R.
[1950] *Measure theory.* Van Nostrand, Princeton, N.J., New York, London.
[1962] *Algebraic logic.* Chelsea Publishing Co., New York.

HELMER, Olaf, and OPPENHEIM, Paul
[1945] A syntactical definition of probability and of degree of confirmation. *J. Symb. Logic*, 10, 25–60.

HEMPEL, Carl G.
[1945] Studies in the logic of confirmation. *Mind*, 54, 1–26, 97–120. Repr. in: Hempel [1965], no. 1, and Foster and Martin [1966], no. 14.
[1960] Inductive inconsistencies. *Synthese*, 12, 439–469. Repr. in: [1965], no. 2.

[1965] *Aspects of scientific explanation, and other essays in the philosophy of science.* Free Press, New York; Collier-Macmillan, London.

HEMPEL, C. G., and OPPENHEIM, Paul.
[1965] A definition of "degree of confirmation." *Phil. Sci.*, 12, 98–115. Repr. in: Foster and Martin (eds.) [1966], no. 16.

HERMES, Hans
[1957] Über eine logische Begründung der Wahrscheinlichkeitstheorie. *Mathematisch-Physikalische Semesterberichte*, V, 214–224.
[1958] Zum Einfachheitsprinzip in der Wahrscheinlichkeitsrechnung. *Dialectica*, 12, 317–331.

HEWITT, Edwin, and SAVAGE, Leonard J.
[1955] Symmetric measures on Cartesian products. *Trans. Amer. Math. Soc.*, 80, 470–501.

HINTIKKA, Jaakko
[1966] A two-dimensional continuum of inductive methods. In: Hintikka and Suppes (eds.) [1966], no. 7.
[1968] Induction by enumeration and induction by elimination. In: Lakatos (ed.) [1968].

HINTIKKA, J., and HILPINEN, Risto
[1966] Knowledge, acceptance, and inductive logic. In: Hintikka and Suppes (eds.) [1966], no. 1.

HINTIKKA, J., and PIETARINEN, Juhani
[1966] Semantic information and inductive logic. In: Hintikka and Suppes (eds.) [1966], no. 6.

HINTIKKA, J., and SUPPES, Patrick (eds.)
[1966] *Aspects of inductive logic.* Humanities Press, New York, and North-Holland Publ. Co., Amsterdam.

JEFFREY, Richard C.
[1956] Valuation and acceptance of scientific hypotheses. *Phil. Sci.*, 23, 237–246.
[1957] Contributions to the theory of inductive probability. Ph.D. dissertation, Princeton University.
[1965*a*] New foundations for Bayesian decision theory. In: Bar-Hillel (ed.) [1965].
[1965*b*] *The logic of decision.* McGraw-Hill, New York and London.
[1966] Goodman's query. *J. Phil.*, 63, 281–288.
[1968] Probable knowledge. In: Lakatos (ed.) [1968], pp. 166–180.

JEFFREYS, Harold
[1957] *Scientific inference.* Cambridge Univ. Press (1st ed., 1931).
[1961] *Theory of probability.* Oxford Univ. Press (1st ed., 1938).

JOHNSON, W. E.
[1921] *Logic*. Part I. Cambridge University Press, and Macmillan, New York.
[1922] *Logic*. Part II. *Ibid.*
[1926] *Logic*. Part III. *Ibid.*
All three parts were republished by Dover, New York, 1964.
[1932] Probability. *Mind*, 41, 1–16, 281–296, 408–423.

KEMENY, John G.
[1951] Review of Carnap [1950]. *J. Symb. Logic*, 16, 205–207.
[1952] Extension of the methods of inductive logic. *Phil. Studies*, 3, 38–42.
[1953*a*] A logical measure function. *J. Symb. Logic*, 18, 289–308.
[1953*b*] The use of simplicity in induction. *Phil. Review*, 62, 391–408. Repr. in: Foster and Martin (eds.) [1966], no. 22.
[1955] Fair bets and inductive probabilities. *J. Symb. Logic*, 20, 263–273.
[1964] Carnap's theory of probability and induction. In: Schilpp (ed.) [1964], no. 22, pp. 711–738.

KEMENY, J. G., and OPPENHEIM, Paul
[1952] Degree of factual support. *Phil. Sci.*, 19, 307–324.

KEMENY, J. G.; MIRKIL, Hazleton; SNELL, J. Laurie; THOMPSON, Gerald L.
[1959] *Finite mathematical structures*. Prentice-Hall, Englewood Cliffs, N.J.

KEYNES, John Maynard
[1921] *A treatise on probability*. Macmillan, London. (Repr. Harper Torchbooks, N.Y., 1962.)

KHINCHIN, A. I.
[1932] Sur les classes d'événements équivalents. *Matematičeskii Sbornik* (Moscow), 39, 40–43.

KOLMOGOROV, A. N.
[1933] *Grundbegriffe der Wahrscheinlichkeitsrechnung*. (Ergebnisse der Math., Band II, No. 3) Berlin. (Repr. Chelsea, New York, 1946.)
[1956] *Foundations of the theory of probability*. 2d ed. (1st, 1950). Chelsea, New York. (Trans. of [1933], with supplementary bibliography.)

KOLMOGOROV, A. N., and FOMIN, S. V.
[1961] *Measure, Lebesgue integrals, and Hilbert space*. Academic Press, New York and London.

KOOPMAN, B. O.
[1940*a*] The axioms and algebra of intuitive probability. *Ann. Math.*, ser. 2, 41, 269–292.
[1940*b*] The bases of probability. *Bull. Amer. Math. Soc.*, 46, 763–774. (Repr. in: Kyburg and Smokler [1964], pp. 159–172.)

KÖRNER, Stephan (ed.)
[1957] *Observation and interpretation: A symposium of philosophers and physicists.* Butterworth, London.

KRAUSS, Peter
[1969] Representation of symmetric probability models. *J. Symb. Logic*, 34, 183–193.

KYBURG, Jr., Henry E.
[1961] *Probability and the logic of rational belief.* Wesleyan Univ. Press, Middletown, Conn.
[1963] Review of: Carnap [1962*b*]. *J. Phil.*, 60, 362–364.
[1964] Recent work in inductive logic. *Amer. Phil. Quart.*, 1, 249–287.
[1965] Probability, rationality, and a rule of detachment. In: Bar-Hillel (ed.) [1965], pp. 301–310.
[1966] Probability and decision. *Phil. Sci.*, 33, 250–261.

KYBURG, H. E., and NAGEL, Ernest (eds.)
[1963] *Induction: Some current issues.* (Proc. 1961 Conference at Wesleyan University.) Wesleyan Univ. Press, Middletown, Conn.

KYBURG, H. E., and SMOKLER, Howard E. (eds.)
[1964] *Studies in subjective probability.* Wiley, New York and London.

LAKATOS, Imre (ed.)
[1968] *The problem of inductive logic: Proceedings of the Int. Colloquium in the Philos. of Science.* London, 1965, Vol. II. North-Holland Publ. Co., Amsterdam.

LEHMAN, R. Sherman
[1955] On confirmation and rational betting. *J. Symb. Logic*, 20, 251–262.

LEHMANN, E. L.
[1959] *Testing statistical hypotheses.* Wiley, New York.

LEVI, Isaac
[1967] *Gambling with truth: An essay on induction and the aims of science.* Knopf, New York; Routledge and Kegan Paul, London.

LOÈVE, Michel
[1963] *Probability theory.* 3d ed. (1st, 1955). Van Nostrand, Princeton, N.J.; New York, London.

ŁOŚ, Jerzy
[1962] *Remarks on the foundations of probability.* Proc. Intern. Congress of Mathematicians. Stockholm. pp. 225–229.

MUNROE, M. E.
[1953] *Introduction to measure and integration.* Addison-Wesley, Cambridge, Mass.

NAGEL, Ernest

[1939] *Principles of the theory of probability.* International Encyclopedia of Unified Science, Vol. I, no. 6. Univ. of Chicago Press, Chicago. (Two parts of this are repr. in: Foster and Martin (eds.) [1966]).

NAGEL, Ernest; SUPPES, Patrick; TARSKI, Alfred (eds.)

[1962] *Logic, methodology, and philosophy of science: Proceedings of the 1960 international congress.* Stanford Univ. Press, Stanford.

NAGEL, Ernest, see also: KYBURG and NAGEL (editors).

NIKODYM, O.

[1930] Sur une généralization des intégrales de M. J. Radon. *Fund. Math.*, 15, 131–179.

OPPENHEIM, Paul. See: Helmer and Oppenheim; Hempel and Oppenheim.

RAMSEY, Frank Plumpton

[1931*a*] Truth and probability. Written 1926; posthumously publ. in: [1931*c*], pp. 156–198; repr. in: Kyburg and Smokler (eds.) [1964], pp. 61–92.

[1931*b*] Further considerations. (A. Reasonable degree of belief. B. Statistics. C. Chance.) Written 1928; publ. in [1931*c*], pp. 199–211.

[1931*c*] *The foundations of mathematics and other logical* essays. (Ed. R. B. Braithwaite.) Kegan Paul, London; Harcourt Brace, New York.

REICHENBACH, Hans

[1935] *Wahrscheinlichkeitslehre.* Leiden.

[1949] *The theory of probability.* Univ. of Calif. Press, Berkeley. (Trans. of [1935].)

RÉNYI, Alfréd

[1955] On a new axiomatic theory of probability. *Acta Math. Acad. Sci. Hungaricae*, 6, fasc. 3–4, 285–335.

[1962] *Wahrscheinlichkeitsrechnung.* (Hochschulbücher für Math. Band 54.) Deutscher Verlag der Wissenschaften, Berlin (D.R.D.)

RÉVÉSZ, Pál

[1968] *The laws of large numbers.* Academic Press, New York and London.

RYLL-NARDZEWSKI, C.

[1957] On stationary sequences of random variables and the de Finetti equivalences. *Colloq. Math.*, 4, 149–156.

SAKS, Stanislaw

[1937] *Theory of the integral.* (Orig.: Monografje Matematyczne, Tom. VII, Warsaw-Lvov) Hafner, New York.

SALMON, Wesley C.
[1963] On vindicating induction. In: Kyburg and Nagel (eds.) [1963], no. II.
[1966] The foundation of scientific inference. In: *Mind and Cosmos*. Vol. III of Univ. of Pittsburgh series in the philosophy of science, pp. 135–275.

SAVAGE, Leonard J.
[1954] *The foundations of statistics*. Wiley, New York.
[1962] Subjective probability and statistical practice. In: Savage *et al.* [1962], pp. 9–35.
[1967*a*] Difficulties in the theory of personal probability. In: Savage *et al.* [1967], pp. 305–310.
[1967*b*] Implications of personal probability for induction. *J. Phil.*, 64, 593–607.

SAVAGE, L. J., *et al.*
[1962] *The foundations of statistical inference: A discussion*. Wiley, New York.
[1967] A panel discussion on personal probability. (At the Chicago meeting of Amer. Phil. Ass., May, 1967.) *Phil. Sci.*, 34, 305–332.

SAVAGE, L. J. See: Finetti and Savage; Hewitt and Savage.

SCHILPP, Paul Arthur (ed.)
[1964] *The philosophy of Rudolf Carnap*. (Library of Living Philosophers, Vol. XI.) Open Court, La Salle, Ill.; Cambridge Univ. Press, London.

SCOTT, Dana, and KRAUSS, Peter
[1966] Assigning probabilities to logical formulas. In: Hintikka and Suppes (ed.) [1966], pp. 219–264.

SHIMONY, Abner
[1955] Coherence and the axioms of confirmation. *J. Symb. Logic*, 20, 1–28.
[1967] Amplifying personal probability theory: Comments on Savage, [1967*a*]. In: Savage *et al.* [1967], pp. 326–332.

SMOKLER, H. E., see KYBURG and SMOKLER (eds.).

SMULLYAN, Raymond M.
[1968] *First-order logic*. Springer-Verlag, New York Inc.

STEGMÜLLER, Wolfgang
[1959] Carnaps Auffassung der induktiven Logik. In: Carnap [1959], pp. 1–11.

SUPPES, Patrick
[1956] The role of subjective probability and utility in decision making. In: *Proceedings of the third Berkeley symposium on mathematical*

statistics and probability (1954–55) (ed. J. Neyman). Univ. of Calif. Press, Berkeley, Vol. 5, pp. 61–73.

[1960] A comparison of the meaning and uses of models in mathematics and the empirical sciences. *Synthese*, 12, 287–301.

[1961] The philosophical relevance of decision theory. *J. Phil.*, 58. 606–614.

[1966] Probabilistic inference and the concept of total evidence. In: Hintikka and Suppes [1966], no. 3.

SUPPES, P. See: Davidson, Suppes, and Siegel; Hintikka and Suppes, NAGEL, SUPPES, and TARSKI (eds.)

TARSKI, A., see: NAGEL, E., SUPPES, P., and TARSKI, A. (eds.).

WRIGHT, Georg Henrik von

[1957] *The logical problem of induction.* Blackwell, Oxford. 2d ed. (1st, 1941).

[1962] Remarks on epistemology of subjective probability. In: Nagel, Suppes, and Tarski (eds.) [1962], pp. 330–339.